Human Anatomy

A Workbook Approach

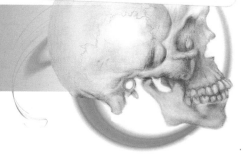

Mary Bee
University of Detroit Mercy
Oakland University William Beaumont School of Medicine

Natalie Kzirian
Contributing Author
Oakland University

Kendall Hunt
publishing company

i

Cover images
Skeleton © Jupiter Images, Inc.
Heart image © 2009 by Sebastian Kaulitzki. Used under license from Shutterstock, Inc.
Brain image © 2009 by Yakobchuck Vasyl. Used under license from Shutterstock , Inc.

Kendall Hunt
publishing company

www.kendallhunt.com
Send all inquiries to:
4050 Westmark Drive
Dubuque, IA 52004-1840

ISBN 978-0-7575-6335-5

Printed in the United States of America
10 9 8 7 6 5 4 3 2 1

Contents

Dedication   *v*

Acknowledgments   *vii*

Preface   *ix*

Unit 1   **1**
Course Introduction   3

Integumentary System   8

Skeletal System   11

Axial Skeleton   16

Appendicular Skeleton   26

Articular System   33

Muscular System   42

Muscles of the Body   46

Muscles of the Upper Extremity and Back   53

Unit 1 Study Resources   *56*

Unit 1 Practice Quizzes   *92*

Unit 2   **122**
Muscles of the Lower Extremity   123

Nervous System in General   127

Endocrine System   131

Brain   134

Spinal Cord and Meninges   137

Peripheral Nervous System (PNS)   141

Special Senses and Receptors   148

Autonomic Nervous System   153

Unit 2 Study Resources   157

Unit 2 Practice Quizzes   170

Unit 3   **214**
Heart   215

Heart Disease   223

Blood Vessels and Lymphatic System   227

Vasculature of the Body   231

Respiratory System   238

Digestive System   243

Urinary System   250

Male Reproductive System   252

Female Reproductive System   255

Unit 3 Study Resouces   258

Unit 3 Practice Quizzes   282

Dedication

This book is dedicated to my children, Evan, Ethan, and Mary Lauren Bee, and to my wonderful and incredibly supportive husband, James Bee.

I thank my family for their unconditional support and encouragement: Mary Ann Tracy, Rosemary Bee, Terry Bee, Edward G. Tracy II, Jerri Ann Buxton, and Susanne Tracy. In loving memory of Edward Tracy, who continues to be an inspiration, and Michael Tracy, who is sadly missed.

Mary Bee

I dedicate this book to my inspirational parents, Harry and Tanya Kzirian, my encouraging siblings, Rita and Andre Kzirian, and my loving fiance, Greg Brounsuzian. Thank you for being there for me every day, in every way and supporting me in every endeavor.

Natalie Kzirian

Acknowledgments

I would like to acknowledge the extraordinary efforts of Stacy Dietlin, Andrea Hulway, Carly Kmiecik, Janice Kyksa, Amanda LaBarge, Miguel Luciano, Ryan Poquette, Trisha Reckling, Dan Schlegel, and Tess Solanskey. The contributing author, Natalie Kzirian, wrote all the study resources and practice quizzes. The skull illustration was drawn by Elizabeth Grabowski. Sincere thanks are given to my publisher, Chris Trott, and my editors, Stephanie Moffett and Angela Puls.

Preface

The goal of this book is to prepare students for health professional careers by providing anatomical information that will give them a solid foundation. The workbook approach allows for an interactive approach to learning.

SPECIAL NOTES

Spellings: Spellings differ among anatomical texts and other sources. When in doubt, please follow the spelling that is in this book.

Abbreviations: Throughout this book, I have abbreviated structures where necessary. Please use the following legend for these abbreviated items.

LEGEND:		
a	=	artery
aa	=	arteries
n	=	nerve
nn	=	nerves
m	=	muscle
mm	=	muscles
v	=	vein
vv	=	veins

UNIT 1

Worksheets

1A Course Introduction .... pp. 3–7

1B Integumentary System .... pp. 8–10

1C Skeletal System .... pp. 11–15

1D Axial Skeleton .... pp. 16–25

1E Appendicular Skeleton .... pp. 26–32

1F Articular System .... pp. 33–41

1G Muscular System .... pp. 42–45

1H Muscles of the Body...................................... pp. 46–52

1I Muscles of the Upper Extremity and Back...... pp. 53–55

Study Resources

1B Integumentary System .... pp. 57–58

1C Skeletal System .... pp. 59–60

1D Axial Skeleton .... pp. 61–70

1E Appendicular Skeleton .... pp. 71–77

1F Quick Review of Articular System .... pp. 78–79

1H Muscles of the Body...................................... pp. 80–85

1I Upper Limb Musculature .... pp. 86–91

Practice Quizzes

1A Course Introduction Practice Quiz......................... p. 93

1B Integumentary System Practice Quiz.................... p. 94

1C Skeletal System Practice Quiz............................ p. 95

1D&E Axial and Appendicular Skeleton
    Practice Quiz... pp. 96–100

1F Articular System Practice Quiz.................. pp. 101–104

1I Upper Limb Musculature Practice Quiz...... pp. 105–109

1A–I Unit 1 Practice Test .... pp. 110–118

Answer Key .... pp. 119–121

WORKSHEETS

1A Course Introduction .... pp. 3–7

1B Integumentary System .... pp. 8–10

1C Skeletal System .... pp. 11–15

1D Axial Skeleton .... pp. 16–25

1E Appendicular Skeleton .... pp. 26–32

1F Articular System .... pp. 33–41

1G Muscular System .... pp. 42–45

1H Muscles of the Body .... pp. 46–52

1I Muscles of the Upper Extremity and Back ...... pp. 53–55

COURSE INTRODUCTION

I. DEFINITIONS:

A. BIOLOGY: study of living organisms.

B. _____: subdivision of biology that is concerned with the functioning of the body.

   1. It attempts to explain the physical and chemical processes that occur in the body.

C. ANATOMY: subdivision of biology that is concerned with the structure or morphology of the body.

   1. Anatomy (Greek)
     a. *Ana* = apart
     b. *Tomy* = cut

   2. Dissect (Latin)
     a. *Dis* = apart
     b. *Sectare* = cut

II. SUBDIVISIONS OF ANATOMY:

A. _____: study of cells.

   1. Greek meaning:
     a. *Kytos* = cell
     b. *Logos* = knowledge of

B. _____: study of tissues.

   1. Greek meaning:
     a. *Histo* = tissue
     b. *Logos* = knowledge of

C. _____ anatomy: study of structure visible with the naked eye.

D. Surface anatomy: study of the surface structures.

E. Developmental anatomy (_____): development of the body prior to birth.

F. _____ anatomy: comparing human structure to that of other animals.

G. Radiology: use of radiation to visualize internal body structure.

H. Anatomical _____: study of tissue that departs from the normal and thus is diseased.

III. ORGANIZATION OF THE BODY

A. Cell: smallest unit of living matter and the characteristic building block of all plant and animal tissues.

B. Tissue: collection of cells of similar structure and function.

C. Organ: consists of one or more tissues blended in such a way as to form a structure, which can perform one function or related functions.

D. Organ system: consists of one or more organs that act together in performing a major function of the body.

E. Body: composed of the 12 organ systems.

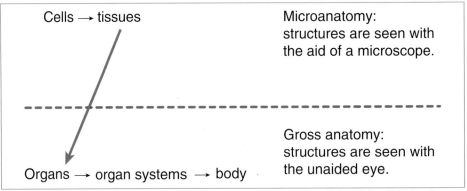

© Kendall Hunt Publishing Company

IV. METHODS OF STUDY

A. Regional: according to the natural subdivisions of the body.

1. Head: facial region, cranium

2. Neck

3. Thorax (chest)

4. Abdomen

5. Pelvis

6. Back (posterior aspect of thorax, abdomen, and pelvis)

7. Trunk (combination of thorax, abdomen, pelvis, and back)

8. Upper limb (extremity): pectoral region, arm, forearm, and hand

9. Lower limb (extremity): gluteal region, thigh, leg, and foot

B. Systemic: according to the major body systems; collections of organs that perform related functions.

Organ Systems	Structures	Function
Circulatory		Transports nutrients and oxygen to cells, removes waste molecules that are excreted from the body.
	Lymphatic vessels, nodes, supporting lymphocytes, and the lymphoid organs	Protects body from disease by purifying fluid. Involves white blood cells that produce antibodies.
Respiratory		Conducts air, brings oxygen into the lungs, and takes carbon dioxide out.
	Mouth, esophagus, stomach, small and large intestine, teeth, tongue, salivary glands, liver, gallbladder, pancreas	Receives food and digests it into nutrient molecules, which enter the cells.
Urinary		Rids the body of nitrogenous wastes and helps regulate the fluid level and chemical content of the blood.
	Skin, hair, nails, sebaceous glands, sweat glands subcutaneous tissue	Provides support and protects underlying tissues, helps regulate body temperature, contains receptors.
Skeletal	Bones of the skeleton	
Muscular	Muscles	Movement of the body.
Articular		Movement of the body.
Nervous		Conducts nerve impulses to muscles and glands and receive impulses.
Endocrine		Secretes chemicals that serve as messengers between body parts, maintains proper functioning of reproductive organs.
Reproductive	Reproductive organs	

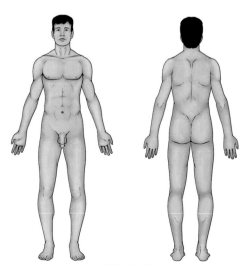

V. ANATOMICAL POSITION: REFERS TO THE POSITION THE BODY MUST BE IN WHEN USING ANATOMICAL PLANES AND TERMS OF REFERENCE.

A. It has 5 criteria.

   1. Body longitudinal

   2. Upper limbs by side

   3. Eyes directed forward

   4. Palms directed forward

   5. Toes directed forward

VI. PLANES OF REFERENCE: PLANES THAT SUBDIVIDE THE TOTAL BODY OR ORGANS. THERE ARE 4 STANDARD PLANES.

A. Median (midsagittal) plane: 1 vertical plane passing through the body dividing it into equal right and left parts.

B. Sagittal plane: any vertical plane that parallels the median plane and divides the body into unequal right and left parts.

C. Frontal (coronal) plane: any vertical plane at a right angle to the median plane that divides the body into front and back parts.

D. Horizontal (transverse) plane: any plane at a right angle to both the median and frontal planes that divides the body into upper and lower parts.

VII. TERMS OF REFERENCE: MUST ALWAYS BE USED WITH THE BODY IN THE ANATOMICAL POSITION.

A. There are 6 pairs of terms:

1. Medial: nearer the median plane.
    Lateral: farther away from the median plane.

2. Anterior (ventral): nearer the front.
    Posterior (dorsal): nearer the back.

3. Superior (cephalic): nearer the upper (head) end.
    Inferior (caudal): nearer the lower (tail) end.

4. Proximal: nearer the attached end of a limb.
    Distal: farther away from the attached end of a limb.

5. Internal: nearer the center of an organ or cavity.
    External: farther away from the center of an organ or cavity.

6. Superficial: nearer the surface of the body.
    Deep: farther away from the surface of the body.

VII. OTHER TERMS OF REFERENCE:

   A. Supine position: lying on back, belly upward.

   B. Prone position: lying on front, back upward.

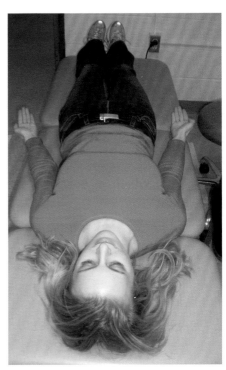

A. Supine position

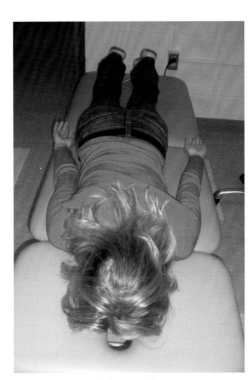

B. Prone position

I. DEFINITION: SYSTEM OF THE BODY COMPOSED OF THE _____ AND THE UNDERLYING _____ _____.

A. Skin is the largest organ in the body, comprising _____ the total weight of the body.

II. FUNCTIONS

A. _____ of underlying tissues (barrier to UV light, bacteria, radiation, water).

B. Acts as a site of _____ _____ (pain, heat, cold, touch, pressure).

C. Regulation of body _____ (erect hairs, sweat).

D. _____ excretion (sweat).

E. Formation of _____, which is essential for calcium absorbtion from the foods we eat.

III. LAYERS

A. The skin is composed of 2 layers: the _____ and the _____.

B. Both of these layers lie on an underlying layer called the _____ tissue (*sub,* below; *cutis,* skin).

C. The thickest skin is on the _____ (1/2 cm), whereas the thinnest skin is on the _____ (1/2 mm).

Integumentary system	Epidermis	Skin
	Dermis	
	Subcutaneous tissue	

IV. EPIDERMIS

A. It is the outermost layer of skin composed of stratified squamous keratinized epithelium.

B. The epidermis is _____ but does contain _____ and nerve endings.

C. The deepest layers of epidermis have cells that undergo _____ and _____ to the outermost layers, where they become desiccated, convert to keratin, and eventually slough off.

D. It takes about _____ days for a cell to go from birth to slough.

   1. Thus, the epithelium (not total skin) is constantly

      _____.

E. Deeper layers also contain _____ that produce the dark pigment _____.

   1. This pigment is responsible for skin _____
      and also protects the individual from the harmful effects of

      _____.

F. The keratin is very thick on the palms and soles and forms
   _____ that occur
   in characteristic patterns (fingerprints; toe prints).

V. DERMIS

A. It is the layer deep to the epidermis composed of a dense irregular _____, which
   does contain both _____
   and _____.

B. It is _____ of the thickness of the skin (epidermis is _____).

C. It has many collagen fibers, _____, and
   _____.

VI. SUBCUTANEOUS TISSUE

A. It lies deep to the dermis and is made of loose connective tissue
   with an abundance of _____ cells.

B. _____ and _____ course
   through it on their way to the dermis.

C. The adipose tissue is more abundant in females than in males
   and provides _____, conserves body
   _____, and acts as a _____.

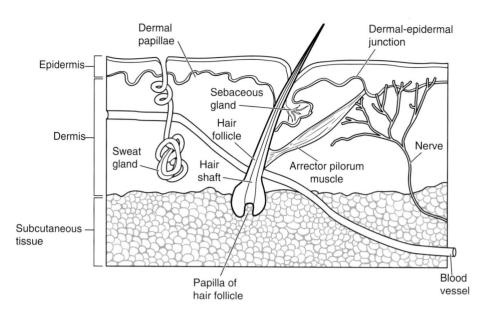

VII. ASSOCIATED STRUCTURES

A. Associated structures: structures that are part of the integument that have specific functions.

B. _____: derived from the epidermis and growing down into the dermis and subcutaneous tissue.

   1. They contain hairs, which form by _____ undergoing mitosis.

   2. When a follicle becomes inactive, the hair it produces becomes lost.

C. _____: oil-producing glands that result from disintegration of some gland cells.

   1. A duct passes the oily secretion, called _____, into the neck of the hair follicle.

D. _____ MUSCLES: smooth muscles attached to the hair follicle and the _____ _____ junction.

   1. Contraction due to cold weather causes the hairs to stand erect and traps a layer of air within the hairs, which acts as an insulator to keep _____ inside the body.

E. _____: have their secretion part in the dermis and their ducts passing through the epidermis to open at PORES on the skin surface.

   1. Sweat is _____ and _____ and cools the body as it evaporates.

F. _____: protective structures of hard _____ located at the tips of fingers and toes.

SKELETAL SYSTEM

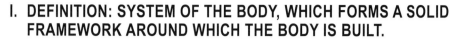

I. **DEFINITION: SYSTEM OF THE BODY, WHICH FORMS A SOLID FRAMEWORK AROUND WHICH THE BODY IS BUILT.**

   A. It is composed of bones and cartilage.

II. **FUNCTIONS OF THE SKELETON**

   A. _____ of the body.

   B. Attachment for skeletal muscles (origin, insertion).

   C. Protection of certain vital organs.

      1. Example: brain by skull and _____ by thoracic cage.

   D. Manufacture certain _____ cells: hemopoiesis (bone marrow).

   E. Storage of certain chemical substances.

      1. Example: calcium, phosphate

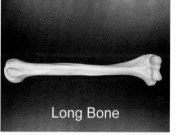

Long Bone

III. **BONE**

   A. Types of bones:

      1. _____ bone: a bone in which the length exceeds the width, and is characterized by having a medullary (marrow) canal.

         a. Example: humerus

      2. Short bone: a bone in which the length equals the width.

         a. Example: carpal bones

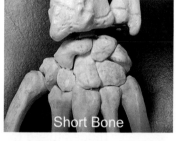

Short Bone

      3. _____ bone: a bone expanded into 1 plane.

         a. Example: scapula

      4. Irregular bone: a bone that does not fit into any of the other 3 categories.

         a. Example: _____

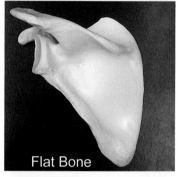

Flat Bone

IV. **DIVISIONS OF THE SKELETON:**

   A. AXIAL SKELETON: part of the skeleton that occupies the central axis of the body.

      1. Skull and hyoid (23)

      2. Vertebral column (7 cervical, 12 thoracic, 5 lumbar, _____ coccyx = 26)

      3. Ribs and sternum (12 pairs of ribs + sternum = 25)

      4. Bones of middle _____ (6)

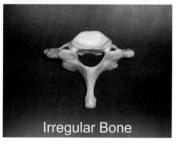

Irregular Bone

Skeletal
Framework

AXIAL SKELETON   APPENDICULAR SKELETON

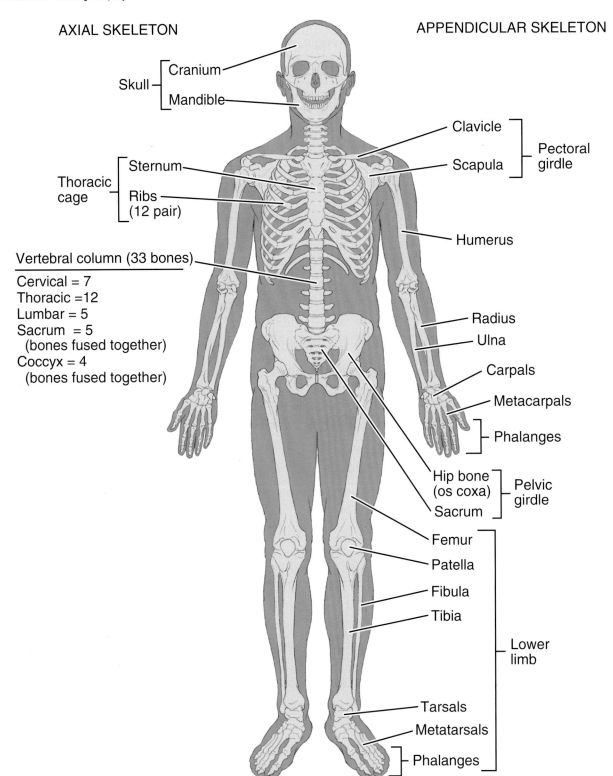

Skull —⎡— Cranium
        ⎣— Mandible

Thoracic —⎡— Sternum
cage   ⎣— Ribs
             (12 pair)

Vertebral column (33 bones)
Cervical = 7
Thoracic =12
Lumbar = 5
Sacrum = 5
  (bones fused together)
Coccyx = 4
  (bones fused together)

Clavicle ⎤
         ⎥ Pectoral
Scapula ⎦ girdle

Humerus

Radius
Ulna
Carpals
Metacarpals
Phalanges

Hip bone ⎤
(os coxa) ⎥ Pelvic
Sacrum   ⎦ girdle

Femur
Patella
Fibula
Tibia

Lower
limb

Tarsals
Metatarsals
Phalanges

B. APPENDICULAR SKELETON: part of the skeleton that comprises the appendages.

    1. Bones of the upper limb (64)

        a. Clavicle: collar bone

        b. Scapula: shoulder blade

        c. _____: arm

        d. Ulna and radius: forearm

        e. Eight carpal bones: wrist

        f. Five metacarpal bones: _____

        g. Fourteen phalanges: fingers

    2. Bones of the lower limb (____)

        a. Hip bone

        b. _____: thigh

        c. Patella

        d. Tibia and fibula: leg

        e. Seven tarsal bones: ankle

        f. Five _____ bones: foot

        g. Fourteen phalanges: toes

C. TOTAL NUMBER OF BONES = 206

D. Aside from 206 named bones:

    1. _____ bone: bone located in tendons.

    2. Ectopic bone: pathological bone formation

V. DIAGRAM OF A LONG BONE

A. Epiphysis

B. Diaphysis

C. Compact bone

D. Spongy bone

E. Periosteum

F. Endosteum

G. Medullary cavity

H. Articular cartilage

I. Articular capsule

J. Epiphyseal disc

K. Metaphysis

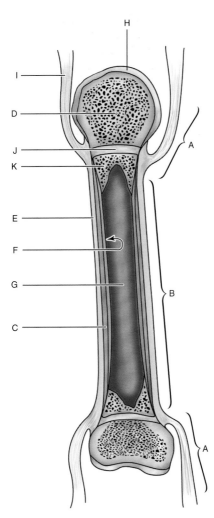

VI. DEFINITIONS

A. _____: the two ends of a long bone, which are wider than the shaft and take part in the formation of a joint.

B. _____: shaft of a long bone.

C. _____ bone: bone laid down in concentric layers making it appear solid.

  1. This type of bone forms the outer surface of all bones.

  2. It is thicker in the diaphysis and thinner at the epiphysis.

D. _____ bone: composed of very thin plates of bone that meet other plates of bone at various angles, leaving spaces between them.

  1. Spongy bone is found in the epiphysis.

E. _____: connective tissue sheath composed of 2 layers:

  1. Outer layer: tough fibrous layer that serves as a place of insertion for muscle tendons.

  2. Inner layer: delicate cellular layer responsible for producing growth in the diameter of the bone.

F. _____: thin, cellular layer found lining the medullary cavity and the cavities of spongy bone.

  1. Its primary function is to destroy bone, thus allowing for growth in the diameter of the marrow cavity, which prevents bone from becoming too solid and heavy as it increases in size.

G. _____ (marrow) cavity: cavity running the length of the diaphysis that contains either red marrow (which actively forms blood cells), yellow marrow (does not form blood cells but develops numerous fat cells), or combinations of the two.

H. _____ cartilage: thin layer of hyaline cartilage covering the articular surface of each epiphysis.

  1. Resiliency of this material cushions the joint during movement.

I. _____ capsule: connects together the 2 bones and completely encircles the joint, thus enclosing a cavity that is called the joint cavity or synovial cavity.

  1. The capsule itself is composed of 2 layers:

    a. Outer fibrous layer: continuous with the periosteum of bone.

    b. An inner layer: lines the inside of the fibrous layer.

      i. The inner layer is also called the _____ membrane.

      ii. It is quite vascular and produces synovial fluid that fills the joint cavity, lubricates the joint, and nourishes the articular cartilage.

J. Epiphyseal disc: in _____ of a growing child, it is a cartilaginous plate located at the junction of epiphysis and diaphysis that allows for growth in the length of bone.

   1. This disc is not present when growth is complete.

K. _____: spongy bone tissue located at the junction of the diaphysis and the epiphyseal disc.

   1. In the adult, the bony tissue of the metaphysis is continuous with the epiphysis.

VII. CARTILAGE

A. Definition: cartilage is a tough connective tissue, which is composed of cells embedded in a firm, gel-like intercellular substance.

   1. It is not as hard as bone, and exhibits some degree of flexibility.

   2. It is called gristle by laymen.

   3. It lacks nerves.

   4. It lacks blood vessels.

      a. Nutrients diffuse through the intercellular substance.

   5. The entire embryo skeleton is initially cartilage, but it is replaced by bone during growth (ossification).

   6. The classification of cartilage is via the histologic appearance of the intercellular matrix.

B. Three types of cartilage are described

   1. HYALINE CARTILAGE: so named because it has a _____, translucent appearance.

      a. _____

      b. Epiphyseal discs

      c. Articular cartilages

      d. Costal cartilages (between ribs and _____)

      e. Larynx, trachea, and bronchi (respiratory system)

      f. Nasal cartilages

   2. FIBROCARTILAGE

      a. Interpubic disc (symphysis pubis)

      b. Intervertebral discs (between adjacent _____)

   3. ELASTIC CARTILAGE

      a. Auricle (part of external _____)

      b. Auditory tube (connects ear and pharynx)

      c. _____ (flap that keeps food from entering lungs)

AXIAL SKELETON

Color and label specified numbered structures

1 _____

2 _____

3 _____

4 _____

5 _____

6 _____

7 _____

8 _____

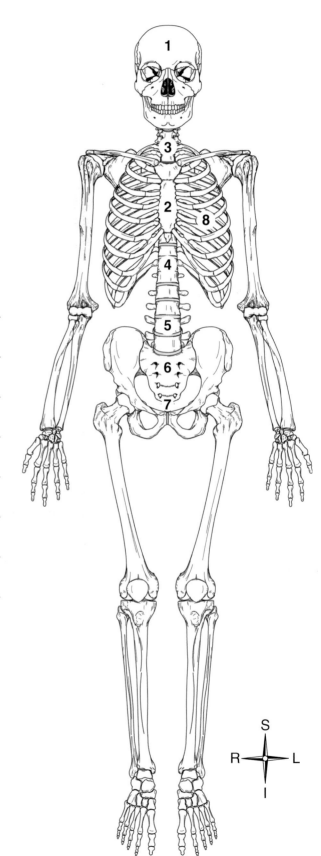

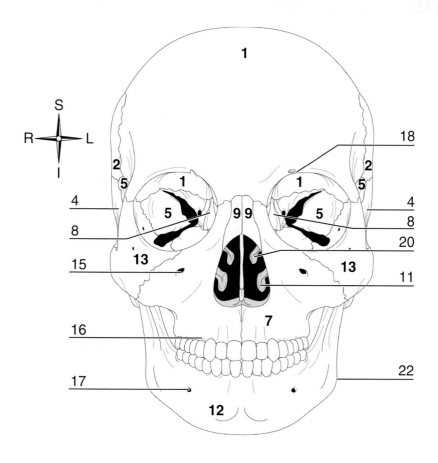

Frontal =

Parietal =

Temporal =

Sphenoid =

Maxilla =

Lacrimal =

Nasal =

Inferior Nasal Concha =

Mandible =

Zygomatic =

Infraorbital Foramen =

Alveolar Processes of Maxilla =

Mental Foramen =

Middle Nasal Conchae =

Supraorbital Notch =

Angle of Mandible =

Top, left Lateral
View of the Skull

Bottom, Skull viewed from below

© Kendall Hunt Publishing Company

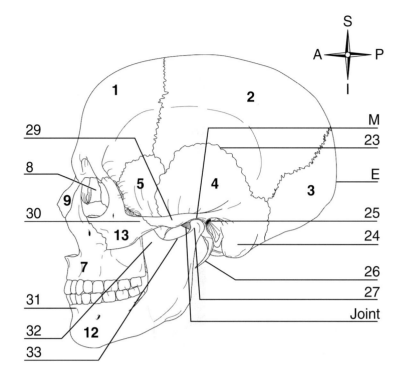

External Occipital Protuberence =

Temporomandibular Joint (TMJ) =

Occipital Bone =

Squamous Suture =

Mastoid Process =

External Acoustic Meatus =

Styloid Process of Temporal Bone =

Condyloid Process =

Zygomatic Arch (with the Zygomatic Bone) =

Zygomatic Arch (with the Temporal Bone) =

Alveolar Processes of Mandible =

Coronoid Process of Mandible =

Coronoid Notch =

**Inferior View
of the Skull**

© Kendall Hunt Publishing Company

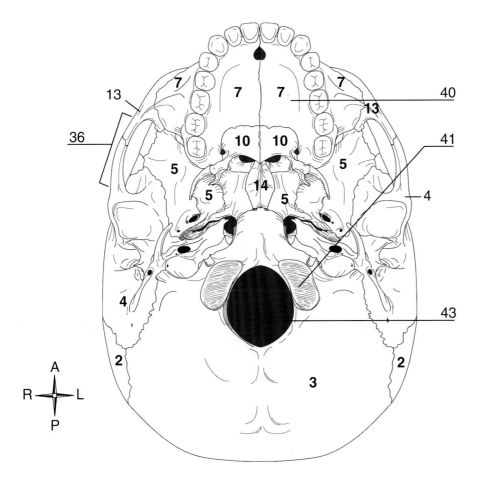

Palatine Bone =

Vomer =

Zygomatic Arch =

Palatine Process of Maxilla =

Occipital Condyle =

Foramen Magnum =

Floor of the
Cranial Cavity

© Kendall Hunt Publishing Company

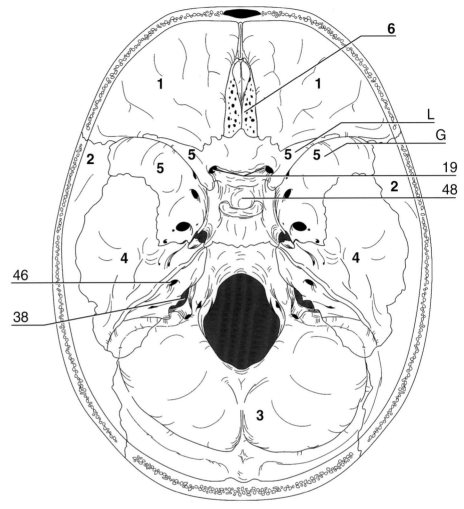

Lesser Wing of Sphenoid =

Greater Wing of Sphenoid =

Optic Canal (contains CN II) =

Jugular Foramen (contains CN IX, X, XI) =

Internal Acoustic Meatus (contains CN VII, VIII) =

Cribriform Plate =

Sella Turcica =

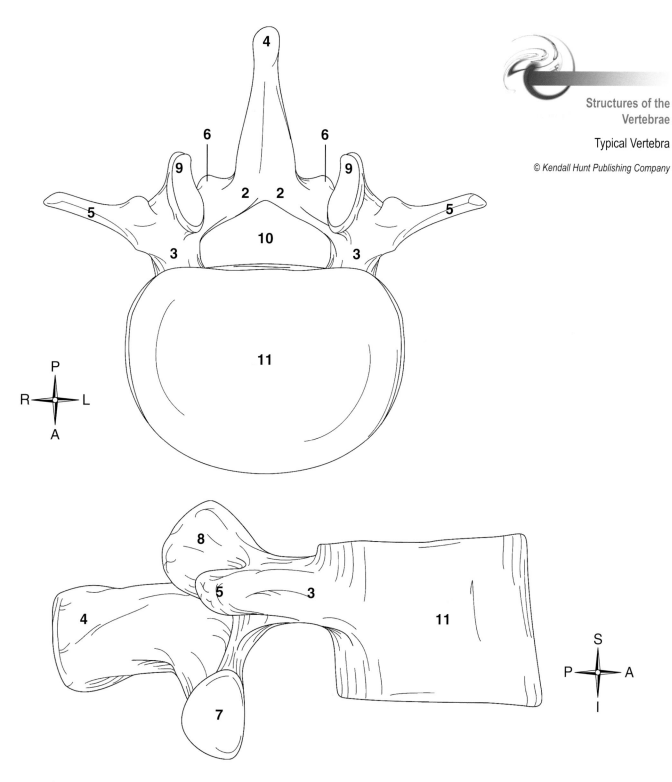

Lamina =

Pedicle =

Vertebral Arch =

Spinous Process =

Transverse Process =

Inferior Articular Process =

Inferior Articular Facet =

Superior Articular Process =

Superior Articular Facet =

Vertebral Foramen =

Body of Vertebra =

Cervical Vertebrae

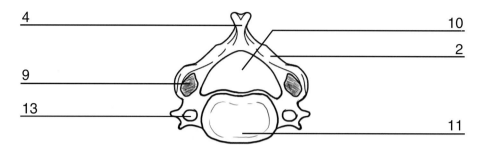

4

10

2

9

13

11

Thoracic Vertebrae

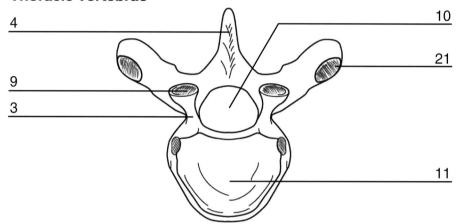

4

10

21

9

3

11

Lumbar Vertebrae

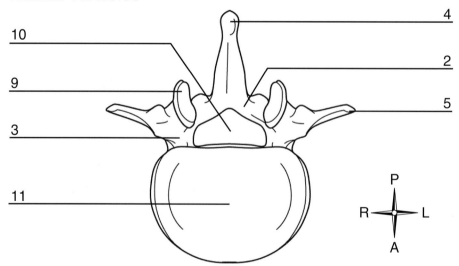

4

10

2

9

5

3

11

P

R — L

A

Types of Vertebrae

The Vertebral Column

Vertebral Column

© *Kendall Hunt Publishing Company*

Cervical Vertebrae =

Cervical Curve =

Thoracic Vertebrae =

Thoracic Curve =

Lumbar Vertebrae =

Lumbar Curve =

Intervertebral Discs =

Sacrum =

Sacral Curve =

Coccyx =

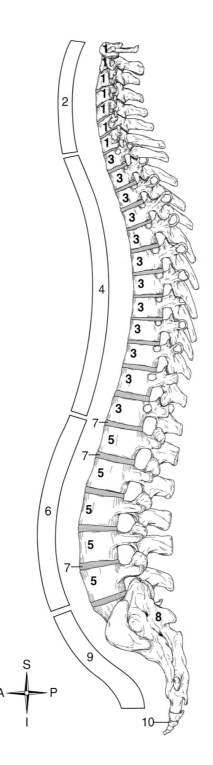

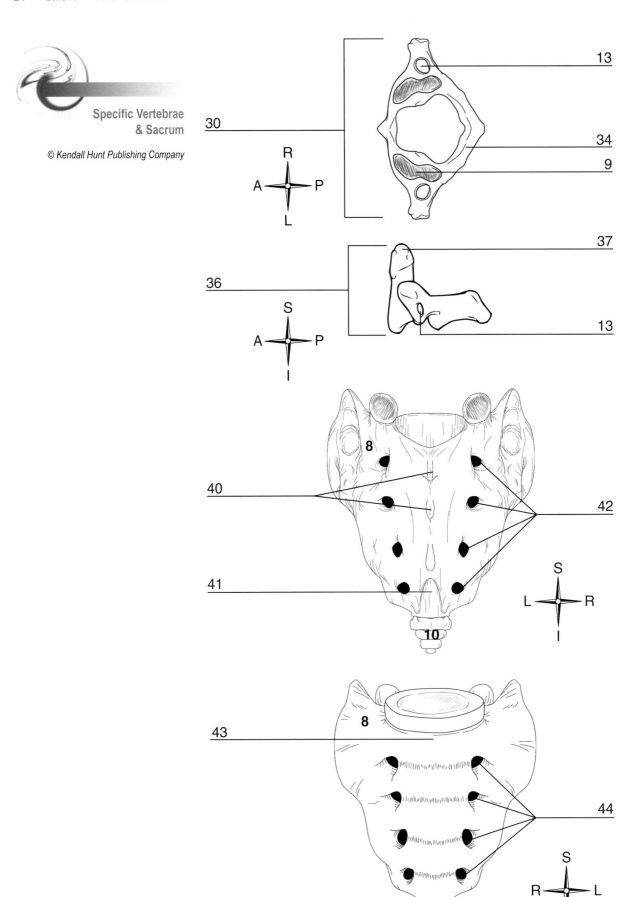

Specific Vertebrae
& Sacrum

© Kendall Hunt Publishing Company

30

36

40

41

42

43

44

13

34

9

37

13

8

10

8

10

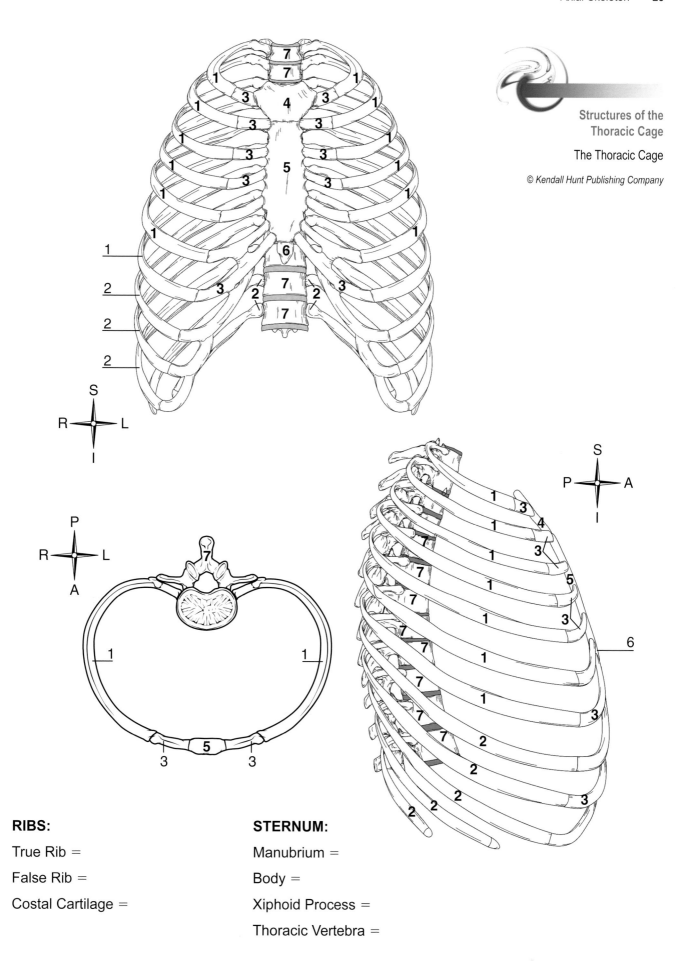

RIBS:

True Rib =

False Rib =

Costal Cartilage =

STERNUM:

Manubrium =

Body =

Xiphoid Process =

Thoracic Vertebra =

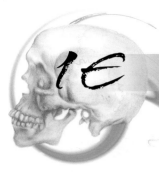

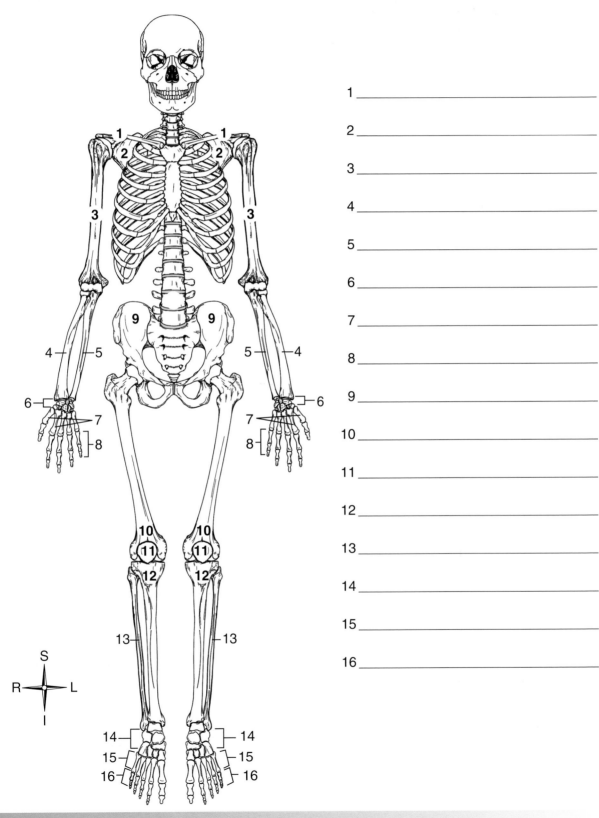

1 _____

2 _____

3 _____

4 _____

5 _____

6 _____

7 _____

8 _____

9 _____

10 _____

11 _____

12 _____

13 _____

14 _____

15 _____

16 _____

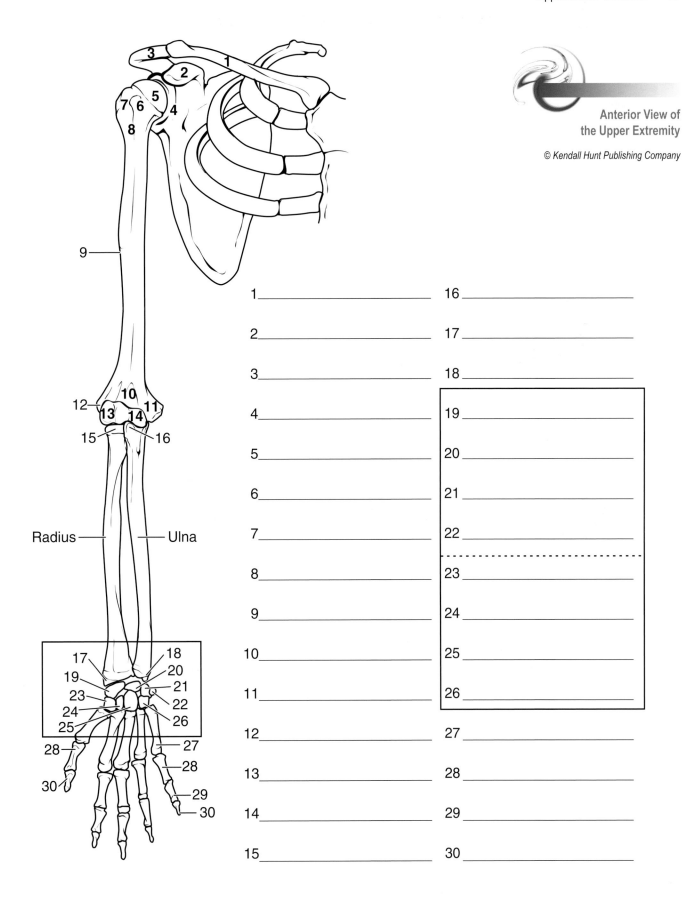

Anterior View of
the Upper Extremity

© Kendall Hunt Publishing Company

Radius —   — Ulna

1_____   16_____

2_____   17_____

3_____   18_____

4_____   19_____

5_____   20_____

6_____   21_____

7_____   22_____

8_____   23_____

9_____   24_____

10_____   25_____

11_____   26_____

12_____   27_____

13_____   28_____

14_____   29_____

15_____   30_____

**Posterior View of
the Upper Extremity**

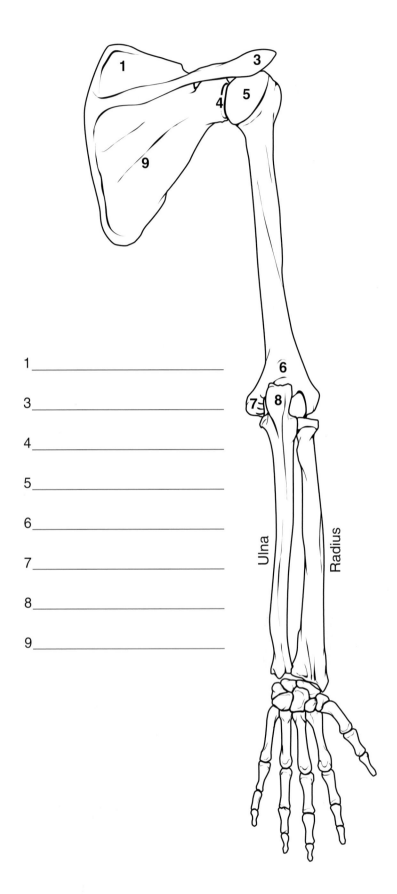

1_____

3_____

4_____

5_____

6_____

7_____

8_____

9_____

Ulna

Radius

**Proximal
Structures of the
Upper Extremity**

The Upper Extremity

© *Kendall Hunt Publishing Company*

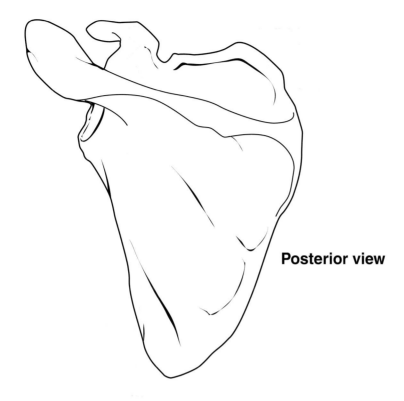

Posterior view

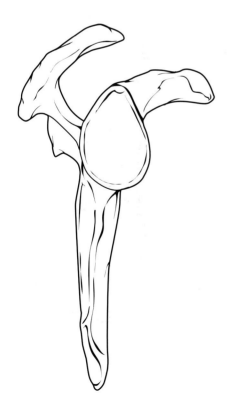

Lateral view

Scapula

supraspinous fossa = 1

coracoid process = 2

acromion = 3

glenoid cavity = 4

spine of scapula = 5

infraspinous fossa = 9

subscapular fossa = 10

supraglenoid tubercle = 11

infraglenoid tubercle = 12

medial border = 13

lateral border = 14

superior border = 15

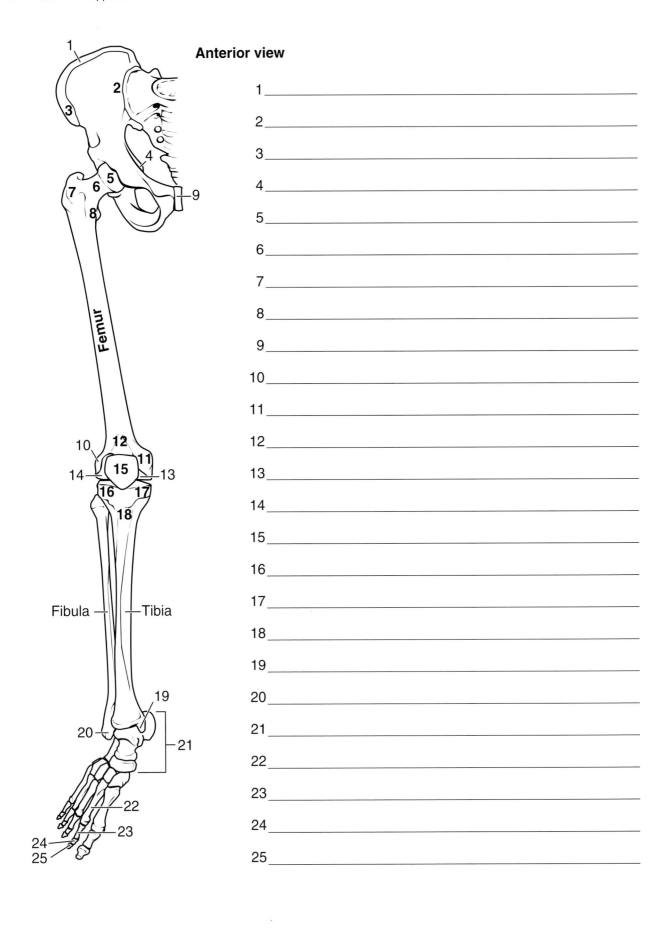

Anterior view

1 _____

2 _____

3 _____

4 _____

5 _____

6 _____

7 _____

8 _____

9 _____

10 _____

11 _____

12 _____

13 _____

14 _____

15 _____

16 _____

17 _____

18 _____

19 _____

20 _____

21 _____

22 _____

23 _____

24 _____

25 _____

Posterior view

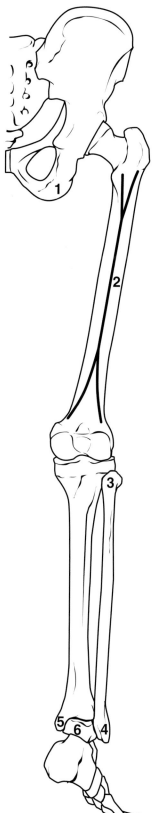

1 _____

2 _____

3 _____

4 _____

5 _____

6 _____

Posterior view

Structures of the
Lower Extremity

The Lower Extremity

© Kendall Hunt Publishing Company

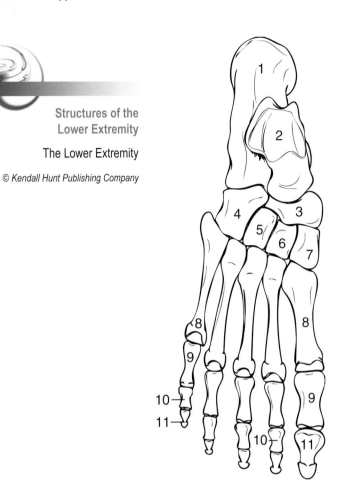

Calcaneus =

Talus =

Navicular =

Cuboid =

Lateral Cuneiform =

Intermediate Cuneiform =

Medial Cuneiform =

Metatarsal =

Proximal Phalanx =

Middle Phalanx =

Distal Phalanx =

Os Coxa

1 _____

2 _____

3 _____

4 _____

5 _____

6 _____

7 _____

8 _____

9 _____

Ilium

Pubis

Ischium

ARTICULAR SYSTEM

I. MEANING

  A. JOINT or ARTICULATION

    1. Origin: ARTICULUS (Latin = joint)

    2. Definition: refers to connections between components of the skeletal system.

II. RELATED TERMS

  A. ARTHROLOGY

    1. Origin: ARTHRON (Greek = joint)

    2. Definition: study of _____.

  B. ARTHRITIS

    1. Origin: ARTHRON (Greek = joint)

    2. Definition: _____ of joints.

III. CLASSIFICATION OF JOINTS

  A. Criteria for classification: the nature of the intervening tissue

    1. For example, the tissue between the 2 articulating ends of the bones.

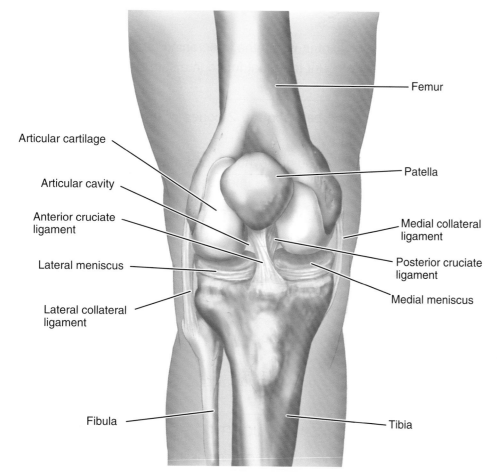

Right Knee Joint

© Kendall Hunt Publishing Company

B. Classification: there are 3 major types of joints:

1. _____ (synarthroses): intervening tissue is merely fibrous connective tissue.

2. CARTILAGINOUS (amphiarthroses): intervening tissue is cartilage.

3. _____ (diarthroses): intervening tissue is synovial fluid.

IV. FIBROUS: A JOINT THAT IS UNITED BY FIBROUS CONNECTIVE TISSUE.

A. SUTURE

1. Formed by two bones whose articulating surfaces are serrated.

a. For example, in the form of interdigitations.

b. These interdigitating borders are held together by fibrous connective tissue.

2. It is _____.

3. It is located only in the _____.

4. Example: sagittal suture

B. SYNDESMOSES

1. A fibrous joint in which the intervening connective tissue is of greater amount than that found in a suture.

2. It is slightly _____.

3. It is located between the 2 bones of the forearm and the 2 bones of the leg.

4. Example: radioulnar syndesmosis (in which the intervening connective tissue is the interosseous membrane).

V. CARTILAGINOUS: A JOINT UNITED BY CARTILAGE.

A. HYALINE CARTILAGE JOINT

1. A joint in which the intervening tissue is _____ cartilage.

2. It is immovable.

3. Located between the epiphysis and diaphysis of growing bone.

a. It is a temporary condition that will later ossify.

4. Example: _____ disc

B. FIBROCARTILAGINOUS JOINT

1. A joint in which the intervening tissue is _____.

2. It is slightly movable.

3. Locations:

   a. Examples:

      i. Between adjacent vertebral bodies: _____ discs.

      ii. Between the right and left pubic bones: interpubic disc

Synovial Joint

© Kendall Hunt Publishing Company

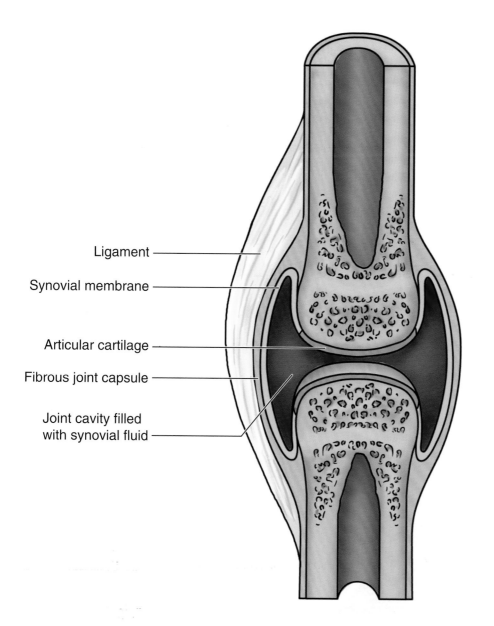

Ligament

Synovial membrane

Articular cartilage

Fibrous joint capsule

Joint cavity filled with synovial fluid

VI. SYNOVIAL JOINT: Joint characterized by the possession of a cavity and specialized to permit free movement.

A. A joint in which the intervening tissue is synovial fluid.

B. The ends of the articulating bones are covered by ARTICULAR CARTILAGE.

   1. It is a layer of _____ cartilage.

   2. It is _____.

3. It lacks nerves.

4. It is radiolucent (cannot be seen on radiographs).

C. The ARTICULAR CAPSULE encapsulates the joint.

1. The articular capsule connects together the 2 bones and completely encircles the joint, thus enclosing the synovial

_____.

2. It is composed of 2 layers:

a. An outer fibrous layer that is continuous with the _____ of bone.

b. An inner layer that is called the SYNOVIAL MEMBRANE that lines the inside of the fibrous layer.

i. It is quite vascular and produces the synovial fluid that fills the synovial cavity.

ii. It _____ the joint and nourishes the articular cartilage.

D. The synovial fluid is derived from _____.

VII. MOVEMENTS AT SYNOVIAL JOINTS

A. Types of movement

1. GLIDING MOVEMENTS

a. Involve a slight slipping of 1 bone over another, usually flat surfaces.

b. Little actual movement occurs.

abduct thigh   adduct thigh

2. ANGULAR MOVEMENTS

   a. _____: bending of a joint so that the angle becomes more acute.

   b. EXTENSION: straightening of a flexed joint.

   c. ABDUCTION: movement in a frontal plane away from the median plane.

   d. ADDUCTION: movement in a frontal plane toward the median plane.

   e. _____: combination of the above 4 movements.

   f. Angular movements of the foot at the ankle joint:

      i. dorsiflexion—moving the dorsum of the foot toward the anterior leg

      ii. plantar flexion—moving the dorsum of the foot away from the anterior leg

     plantar flex the foot   dorsiflex the foot

      iii. eversion—moving the lateral surface of the foot superiorly

      iv. inversion—moving the medial surface of the foot superiorly

 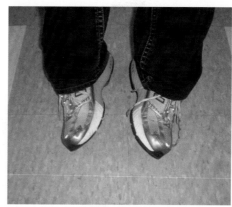

     everting the foot   inverting the foot

3. ROTATION

    a. MEDIAL ROTATION: anterior aspect of the limb rotates medially.

    b. LATERAL ROTATION: anterior aspect of the limb rotates laterally.

    c. _____: medial rotation of the forearm.

    d. SUPINATION: lateral rotation of the forearm.

medial rotation
of arm   lateral rotation
of arm

B. Limitations of movement

    1. Shape of the _____ surfaces.

    2. _____ and capsule at the joint.

    3. Muscles that act on the joint.

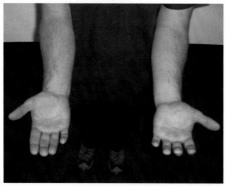
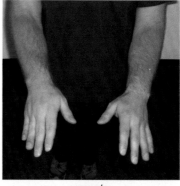

supinate   pronate

Remember:
It's best to be supinated when
holding a bowl of soup!

VIII. TYPES OF SYNOVIAL JOINTS

A. How synovial joints are classified:

1. Synovial joints are classified according to the shapes of the articular surfaces of the constituent bones.

2. The shape is responsible for the type of movement allowed at the joint and the range of movement.

Types of Synovial Joint

Synovial joints are classified according to the shape of the articulating surfaces and/or the type of movement they permit. In this type of joint the articulating bones move freely on one another

© Kendall Hunt Publishing Company

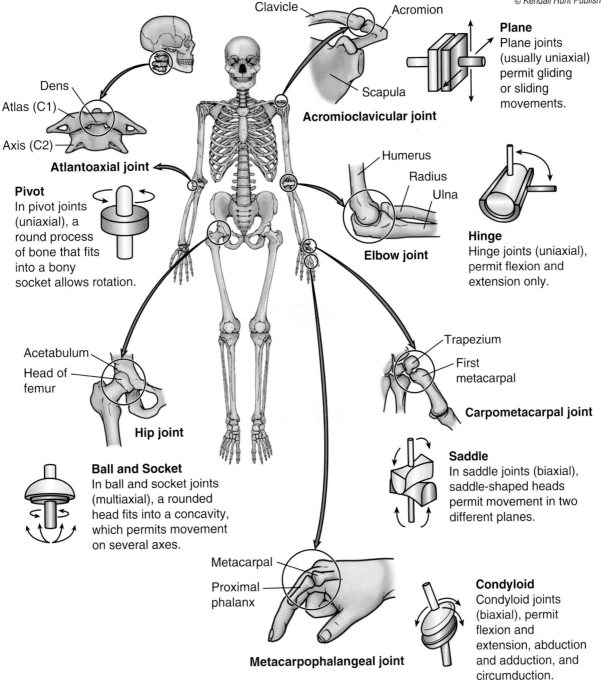

Clavicle

Acromion

Scapula

Acromioclavicular joint

Plane
Plane joints (usually uniaxial) permit gliding or sliding movements.

Dens

Atlas (C1)

Axis (C2)

Atlantoaxial joint

Pivot
In pivot joints (uniaxial), a round process of bone that fits into a bony socket allows rotation.

Humerus

Radius

Ulna

Elbow joint

Hinge
Hinge joints (uniaxial), permit flexion and extension only.

Acetabulum

Head of femur

Hip joint

Ball and Socket
In ball and socket joints (multiaxial), a rounded head fits into a concavity, which permits movement on several axes.

Trapezium

First metacarpal

Carpometacarpal joint

Saddle
In saddle joints (biaxial), saddle-shaped heads permit movement in two different planes.

Metacarpal

Proximal phalanx

Metacarpophalangeal joint

Condyloid
Condyloid joints (biaxial), permit flexion and extension, abduction and adduction, and circumduction.

B. There are 6 types of synovial joints:

1. PLANE

    a. Articular surfaces almost _____.

    b. Allows sliding or gliding movements.

    c. Example: between _____ and tarsal bones.

2. HINGE (*GINGYLMUS*)

    a. Articular surfaces present 1 or more convex projections fitting into a concave surface or surfaces.

    b. Allows movements of flexion and extension in 1 plane (_____ plane).

    c. Example: elbow, interphalangeal, knee, and ankle joints

3. PIVOT (*TROCHOID*)

    a. Articular surfaces present a rounded projection rotating within a _____ depression.

    b. Allows movements of medial and lateral rotation around a longitudinal axis.

    c. Example: between radius and _____ (radioulnar joint)

4. CONDYLOID (*ELLIPSOIDAL*)

    a. Articular surfaces present a condyloid projection fitting into a concave depression.

    b. Allows movements of _____, extension, abduction, and adduction in 2 planes (frontal and sagittal planes).

    c. Example: _____ joint

5. SADDLE (*SELLAR*)

    a. Articular surfaces are _____ concave-convex.

        i. Each articular surface presents both a concave surface and a convex surface.

        ii. When the articular surfaces of these 2 bones are joined, the concave and convex surfaces of the first bone simultaneously fit into the respective convex and concave surfaces of the second bone.

    b. Allows movements of flexion, extension, abduction, and adduction in 2 planes (same as condyloid), plus

        _____.

    c. Example: carpometacarpal joint of the _____

6. BALL AND SOCKET (*SPHEROIDEA*)

    a. Articular surfaces present a spherical surface of 1 bone moving within a _____ of the other bone.

    b. Allows movements of flexion, extension, abduction, adduction, circumduction, and rotation in an _____ number of planes.

    c. Example: shoulder and hip

IX. RULE OF STABILITY OF A JOINT

A. As the degree of freedom of movement _____, the stability of the joint decreases.

X. BURSA

A. Definition

    1. From Greek: *bursa* = a _____

    2. A bursa is a small connective tissue sac lined with a synovial membrane. It contains a synovial-like fluid.

B. BURSITIS: inflammation of a bursa.

C. Function

    1. Facilitates movement by minimizing friction between 2 moving structures.

D. Structure

    1. It is a small closed connective tissue sac lined with a secretory synovial membrane.

    2. It is filled with a clear viscous fluid, which is secreted by the synovial membrane.

        a. The fluid is responsible for the cushioning effect of the bursa.

    3. An elongated bursa, which encloses a tendon, is called a SYNOVIAL SHEATH, which is often located between the tendons of the wrist and ankle and the retinacula (connective tissue structures that _____ tendons) of the wrist and ankle.

E. Location

    1. Found between 2 structures, which move on 1 another, in which friction needs to be decreased.

        a. Between _____ and bone.
            i. Example: elbow and knee

        b. Between tendons and _____.
            i. Example: ankle

        c. Between muscle and bone.
            i. Example: shoulder

        d. Between tendon and _____.
            i. Example: wrist and ankle

MUSCULAR SYSTEM

I. **DEFINITION: SYSTEM COMPOSED OF ALL THE MUSCLES OF THE BODY AND CONCERNED WITH MOVEMENTS OF THE TOTAL BODY AS WELL AS MOVEMENTS WITHIN THE BODY.**

II. **PROPERTIES OF MUSCLE TISSUE:**

   A. _____: ability of muscle tissue to shorten or contract.

   B. _____: ability of muscle tissue to be extended or stretched within limits.

   C. _____: ability of muscle tissue to return to its original state after being stretched.

   D. _____: the susceptibility of muscle tissue to react to external stimuli.

   E. _____: state in which muscle is partially contracted allowing it to react instantly when stimulated.

III. **CLASSIFICATION OF MUSCLE BASED ON NERVOUS CONTROL:**

   A. _____: muscle **not** subject to the control of the will.

   1. _____ and _____ muscle are of this type.

   B. _____: muscle subject to the control of the will.

   1. _____ muscle is of this type.

IV. **SMOOTH MUSCLE**

   A. It is located comprising the walls of the _____ as well as the _____ of the body.

   1. It does not appear striated.

   B. Long spindles thick in the center and _____ at the ends.

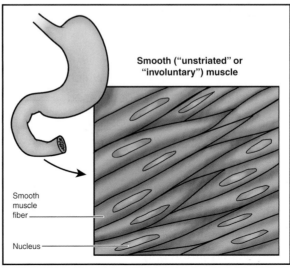

Smooth ("unstriated" or "involuntary") muscle

Smooth muscle fiber

Nucleus

C. ___ nuclei per cell.

D. May be circularly arranged; when muscles contract, obliterate cavity or _____ of organ.

V. CARDIAC MUSCLE

A. It is located in the _____.

B. It appears striated.

C. _____ nuclei per cell.

VI. SKELETAL MUSCLE

A. Composed of very long cells (up to _____ cm in length).

B. Because these cells are very long, more than 1 nucleus is needed to carry out cellular functions, and thus the cells are _____.

C. It is attached to the skeleton and affords movement of skeletal elements when they contract.

D. Have special terms for cellular parts,

1. *Sarco*- refers to "muscle."

2. _____: cell membrane

3. _____: cytoplasm

E. A special type of organelle known as a _____ _____ is found within skeletal muscle cells.

1. There are 2 different types of myofilaments found within the myofibril.

a. They are called _____ and _____ and are arranged in a patterns that appears as alternating light and dark _____.

Cardiac muscle
Intercalated disc
Nucleus
Muscle fiber
© Kendall Hunt Publishing Company

Skeletal ("striated" or "voluntary") muscle
Nucleus
Muscle fiber
© Kendall Hunt Publishing Company

VII. FASCIA

A. DEFINITION: connective tissue layer located _____ muscles and _____ adjacent muscles.

B. FUNCTIONS

1. Permits _____ of 1 muscle over another.

2. Provides _____ for passage of vessels and nerves.

VIII. NOMENCLATURE OF MUSCLES: CRITERIA FOR CLASSIFICATION

   A. FUNCTION

     1. Example: _____

   B. SHAPE

     1. Example: _____

   C. LOCATION

     1. Example: _____

   D. NUMBER OF HEADS OF ORIGIN

     1. Example: _____

   E. STRUCTURE (direction of fibers)

     1. Example: _____

IX. INDIVIDUAL MUSCLE CAN ONLY BE PROPERLY DESCRIBED BY INDICATING ITS 4 CRITERIA:

   A. _____: nonmovable point of attachment.

   B. _____: moveable point of attachment.

   C. _____: movement a particular muscle produces.

   D. _____: nerve supply to a muscle.

X. MUSCLE ATTACHMENTS

   A. Bone

   B. Cartilage

   C. Skin

   D. Fascia

   E. Tendons (attach muscle to bone)

   F. Aponeurosis (flattened tendon)

XI. BLOOD SUPPLY OF MUSCLE

   A. Skeletal muscles are involved in _____ and are very active organs.

     1. Thus, they require a _____ amount of blood.

XII. NERVE SUPPLY OF MUSCLE

   A. Skeletal muscles are innervated by 2 types of nerve fibers.

     1. _____: nerve fibers carry nerve impulses from receptors (muscle spindles) in the muscle to the central nervous system (brain and spinal cord).

     2. _____: nerve fibers carry nerve impulses from the central nervous system to muscle.

XIII. FUNCTIONAL CLASSIFICATION OF MUSCLES

   A. Keep in mind that muscles work in opposing pairs.

   B. _____: a muscle that directly pro-
       duces the desired movement.

      1. For example, when the extensor digitorum muscle _____
          the digits, it is acting as a prime mover.

   C. _____: a muscle that produces a movement
       _____ to that of a prime mover.

      1. For example, the flexor digitorum profundus, which flexes the
          digits, is antagonist to the extensor digitorum.

   D. _____: a muscle that adds a little extra force to
       help the prime mover perform the desirable movements.

      1. An example of this includes the flexor digitorum profundus
          muscle, which is assisted by the flexor digitorum superficialis
          when flexing the digits.

   E. _____: muscles that maintain body position while
       a part is moving.

      1. This occurs in the shoulder, when a muscle (serratus ante-
          rior) holds the scapula at an angle, so that the humerus can
          move.

      2. The muscle that fixes the scapula is acting as fixator.

XIV. LEVER SYSTEMS

What is a lever system?

How is this applied to the human body?

Muscular System

Muscles of the face and head.

© Kendall Hunt Publishing Company

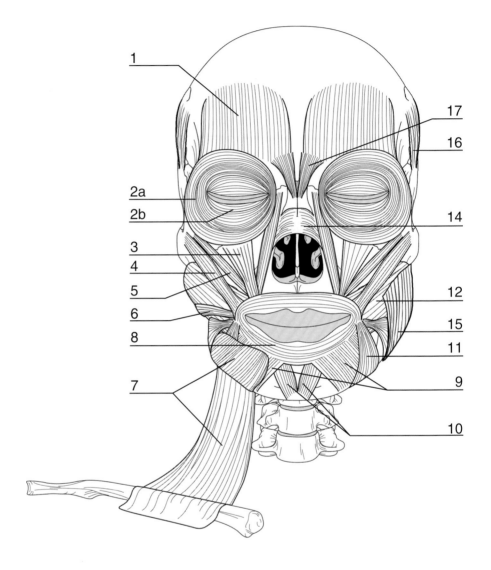

1 =

2 =

2a =

2b =

3 =

4 =

5 =

6 =

7 =

8 =

9 =

10 =

11 =

12 =

13 =

14 =

15 =

Orbicularis oculi, orbital part

Orbicularis oculi, palpebral part

Frontalis

Depressor anguli oris

Risorius

Zygomaticus major & minor

Orbicularis oris

Nasalis

Corrugator supercilli

Mentalis

Procerus

Muscular System

Superficial and deep muscles of
the neck, shoulder, thorax,
and abdomen

© Kendall Hunt Publishing Company

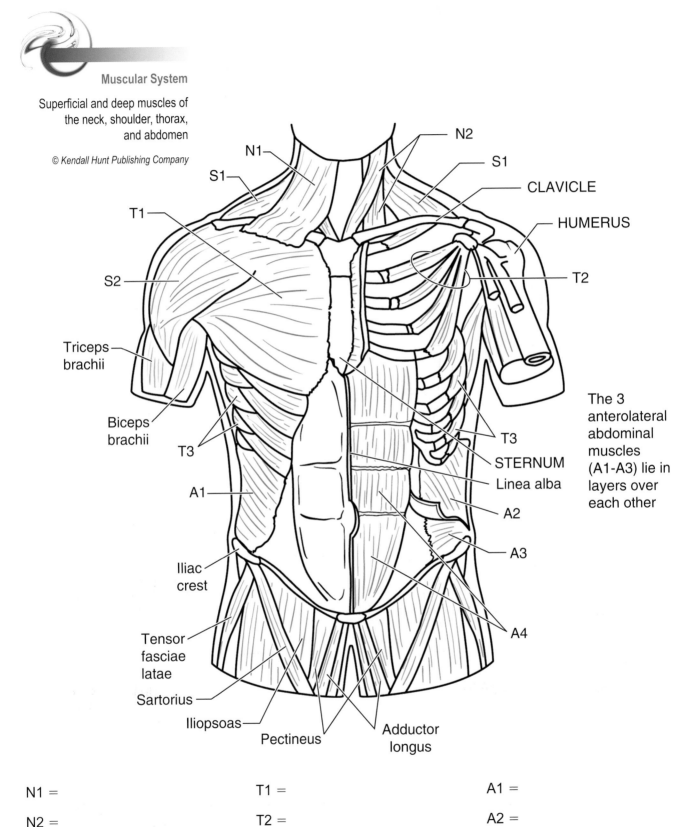

The 3
anterolateral
abdominal
muscles
(A1-A3) lie in
layers over
each other

N1 =

N2 =

S1 =

S2 =

T1 =

T2 =

T3 =

A1 =

A2 =

A3 =

A4 =

1 =   3c =   8 =

2a =   4 =   9 =

2b =   5 =   10 =

3a =   6 =   11 =

3b =   7 =

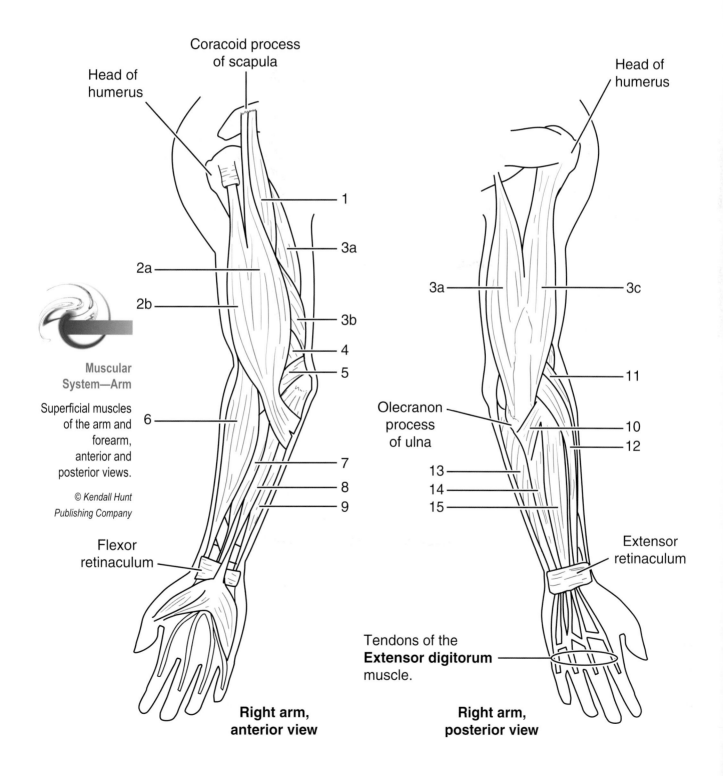

Coracoid process
of scapula

Head of
humerus

Head of
humerus

**Muscular
System—Arm**

Superficial muscles
of the arm and
forearm,
anterior and
posterior views.

© Kendall Hunt
Publishing Company

1

3a

2a

2b

3b

4

5

6

7

8

9

3a

3c

11

Olecranon
process
of ulna

10

12

13

14

15

Flexor
retinaculum

Extensor
retinaculum

Tendons of the
Extensor digitorum
muscle.

**Right arm,
anterior view**

**Right arm,
posterior view**

1 =   7 =   13 =

2 =   8 =   14 =

3 =   9 =   16 =

4 =   10 =   17 =

5 =   11 =   18 =

6 =   12 =

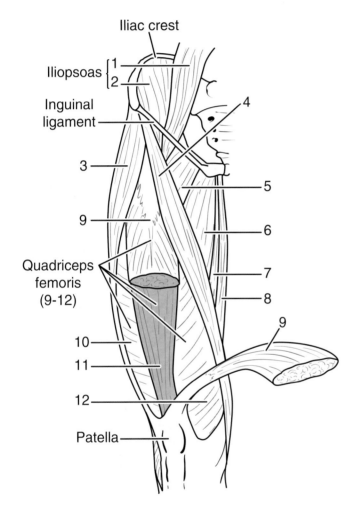

Iliac crest

Iliopsoas { 1
            2

Inguinal
ligament

4

3

5

9

6

Quadriceps
femoris
(9-12)

7

8

10

9

11

12

Patella

**Muscles of right thigh,
Anterior view**

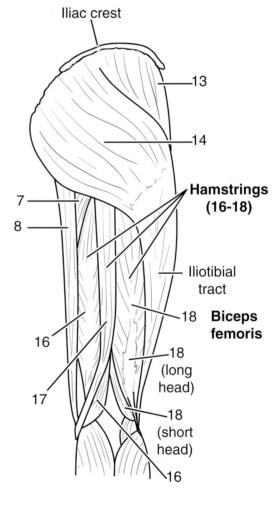

Iliac crest

13

14

Hamstrings
(16-18)

7

8

Iliotibial
tract

16

18   Biceps
      femoris

18
(long
head)

17

18
(short
head)

16

**Muscles of right thigh,
Posterior view**

Muscular
System—Leg

Muscles of the thigh, anterior and
posterior views.

1 =

2 =

3 =

4 =

5 =

6 =

7 =

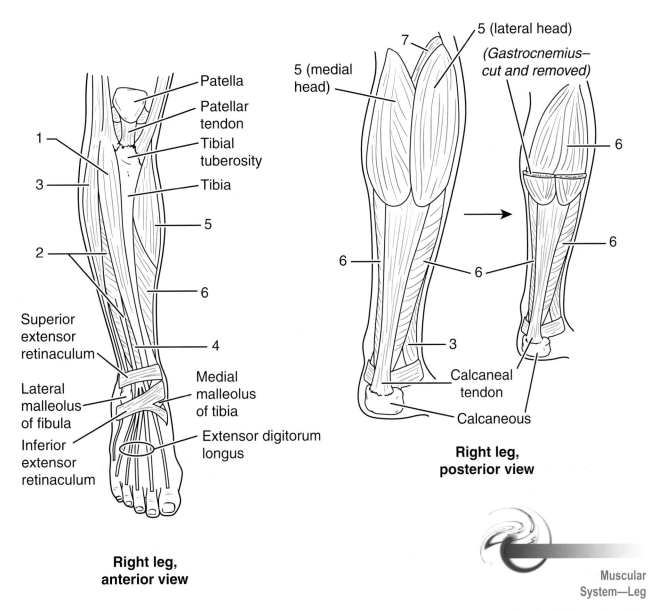

**Right leg,
anterior view**

**Right leg,
posterior view**

Muscular
System—Leg

Muscles that move the ankle,
foot, and toes, anterior
and posterior views.

Muscular
System

Superficial and deep muscles
of the neck, shoulder, back,
and gluteal region.

© Kendall Hunt Publishing Company

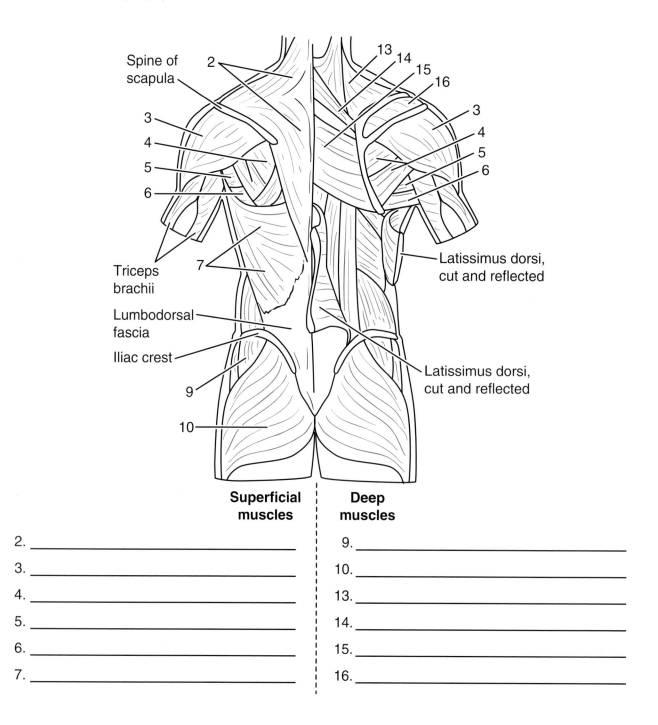

Spine of
scapula
2
13 14
15
16
3
4
5
6
3
4
5
6
Triceps
brachii
7
Latissimus dorsi,
cut and reflected
Lumbodorsal
fascia
Iliac crest
9
Latissimus dorsi,
cut and reflected
10

**Superficial
muscles**

**Deep
muscles**

2. _____
3. _____
4. _____
5. _____
6. _____
7. _____

9. _____
10. _____
13. _____
14. _____
15. _____
16. _____

MUSCLES OF THE UPPER EXTREMITY AND BACK

Back (407)

Muscle	Origin	Insertion	Action	Innervation
Trapezius m.	Skull, cervical, and thoracic vertebrae	Spine of scapula Acromion Clavicle	Elevation, depression, and adduction of scapula	Cranial nerve XI, Accessory n.
Latissimus dorsi m.	Thoracic and lumbar vertebrae, sacrum, iliac crest	Intertubercular sulcus of humerus	Adduction, extension, medial rotation of arm	Thoracodorsal n.
Levator scapulae m.	Vertebrae C1–C4	Medial border of scapula above spine	Elevation of scapula	C3–C4
Rhomboid minor m.	Vertebrae C7 and T1	Medial border of scapula at spine	Adduction of scapula	Dorsal scapular n.
Rhomboid major m.	Vertebrae T2–T5	Medial border of scapula below spine	Adduction of scapula	Dorsal scapular n.

Chest (407)

Muscle	Origin	Insertion	Action	Innervation
Pectoralis major m.	Clavicle, sternum, costal cartilages 1–6	Crest of greater tubercle of humerus	Adduct, medially rotate, and flex arm	Medial and lateral pectoral nn.
Pectoralis minor m.	Ribs 2–5	Coracoid process	Depress scapula	Medial pectoral n.
Serratus anterior m.	Ribs 1–8	Medial border of scapula	Upwardly rotate scapula	Long thoracic n.

Shoulder (407–410)

Muscle	Origin	Insertion	Action	Innervation
Deltoid m.	Spine of scapula Acromion Clavicle	Deltoid tuberosity of humerus	Flex, extend, med and laterally rotate, and abduct arm	Axillary n.
Supraspinatus m.*	Supraspinous fossa	Greater tubercle of humerus	Abduct arm	Suprascapular n.
Infraspinatus m.*	Infraspinous fossa	Greater tubercle of humerus	Laterally rotate arm	Suprascapular n.
Teres minor m.*	Lateral border of infraspinous fossa	Greater tubercle of humerus	Laterally rotate arm	Axillary n.
Subscapularis m.*	Subscapular fossa	Lesser tubercle of humerus	Medially rotate arm	Upper and Lower subscapular nn.
Teres major m.	Inferior angle of infraspinous fossa	Crest of lesser tubercle of humerus	Adduct, medially rotate arm	Lower subscapular n.

*Rotator cuff muscles.

53

Arm (414, 415)

Muscle	Origin	Insertion	Action	Innervation
Triceps Brachii m.				
Long head	Infraglenoid tubercle			
Lateral head	Humerus above radial n.	Olecranon process	Extend forearm	Radial n.
Medial head	Humerus below radial n.			
Biceps brachii m.				
Long head	Supraglenoid tubercle	Radial tuberosity	Flex and supinate forearm	Musculocutaneous n.
Short head	Coracoid process			Musculocutaneous n.
Coracobrachialis m.	Coracoid process	Middle medial of humerus	Flex arm	Musculocutaneous n.
Brachialis m.	Lower humerus	Coronoid process of ulna	Flex forearm	Musculocutaneous n.

Anterior Superficial Forearm Muscles (425, 429)

Muscle	Action	Innervation
Pronator teres m.	Pronate forearm	Median n.
Flexor carpi radialis m.	Flex and abduct wrist	Median n.
Palmaris longus m.	Flex wrist	Median n.
Flexor carpi ulnaris m.	Flex and adduct wrist	Ulnar n.

Anterior Intermediate Forearm Muscles (426, 430)

Muscle	Action	Innervation
Flexor digitorum superficialis m.	Flex digits	Median n.

Anterior Deep Forearm Muscles (423, 426, 431)

Muscle	Action	Innervation
Flexor digitorum profundus m.	Flex digits	Median n., Ulnar n.
Flexor pollicis longus m.	Flex thumb	Median n.
Pronator quadratus m.	Pronate wrist	Median n.

Posterior Superficial Forearm Muscles (424, 427)

Muscle	Action	Innervation
Brachioradialis m.	Flex forearm	Radial n.
Extensor carpi radialis longus m.	Extend and abduct wrist	Radial n.
Extensor carpi radialis brevis m.	Extend and abduct wrist	Radial n.
Extensor digitorum m.	Extend digits 2–5	Radial n.
Extensor digiti minimi m.	Extend digit 5	Radial n.
Extensor carpi ulnaris m.	Extend and adduct wrist	Radial n.
Anconeus m. (aka fourth head of triceps brachii)	Extend forearm	Radial n.

Posterior Deep Forearm Muscles (423, 424, 428)

Muscle	Action	Innervation
Supinator m.	Supinate forearm	Radial n.
Abductor pollicis longus m.	Abduct thumb	Radial n.
Extensor pollicis brevis m.	Extend thumb	Radial n.
Extensor pollicis longus m.	Extend thumb	Radial n.
Extensor indicis m.	Extend index finger	Radial n.

41375 Zip Code of the Forearm

Hand (442–444, 446, 448)

Muscle	Action	Innervation
Thenar Muscles		
Abductor pollicis brevis m.	Abduct thumb	Median n.
Flexor pollicis brevis m.	Flex thumb	Median n., Ulnar n.
Opponens pollicis m.	Oppose thumb	Median n.
Adductor pollicis m.	Adduct thumb	Ulnar n.
Hypothenar Muscles		
Abductor digiti minimi m.	Abduct digit 5	Ulnar n.
Flexor digiti minimi brevis m.	Flex digit 5	Ulnar n.
Opponens digiti minimi m.	Oppose digit 5	Ulnar n.
Palmaris brevis	Pull skin	Ulnar n.
Small Hand Muscles		
Lumbricals 1–4	Move digits (Z position)	Median n., Ulnar n.
Dorsal interossei 1–4	Abduct digits	Ulnar n.
Palmar interossei 1–3	Adduct digits	Ulnar n.

STUDY RESOURCES

1B Integumentary System .... pp. 57–58

1C Skeletal System .... pp. 59–60

1D Axial Skeleton .... pp. 61–70

1E Appendicular Skeleton .... pp. 71–77

1F Articular System .... pp. 78–79

1H Muscles of the Body..................................... pp. 80–85

1I Upper Limb Musculature .... pp. 86–91

Label and define all structures.

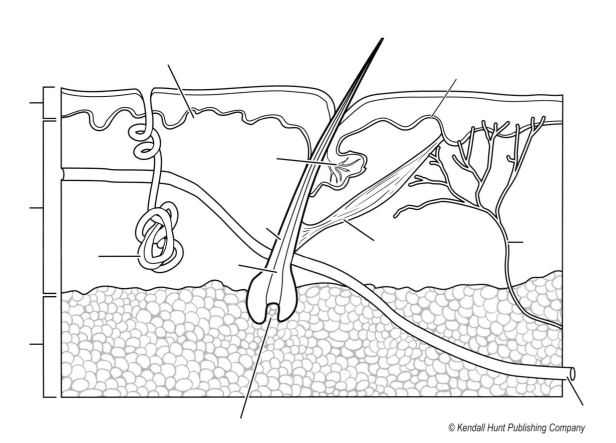

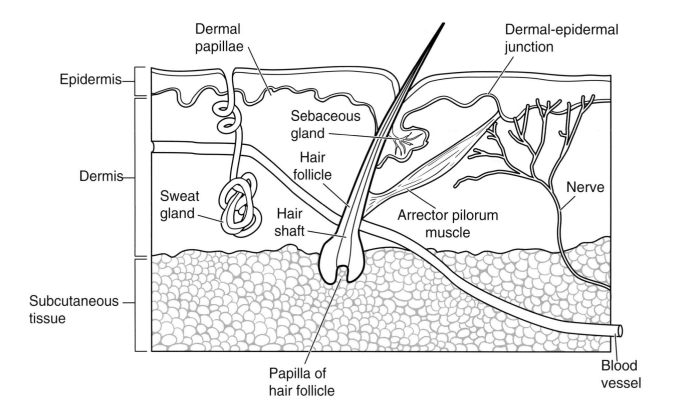

Hair follicles: derived from epidermis; goes down to subcutaneous tissue; contain follicle cells →
mitosis occurs.

Arrector pilorum m.: SMOOTH muscle; attached to hair at DERMAL-EPIDERMAL

JXN; pulls hair up to trap body heat near skin sweat gland: secreation part in dermis; duct opens at
epidermis = PORE; secrete sweat (water & NaCl) to cool body

Nail: hard keratin

Label and define this diagram.

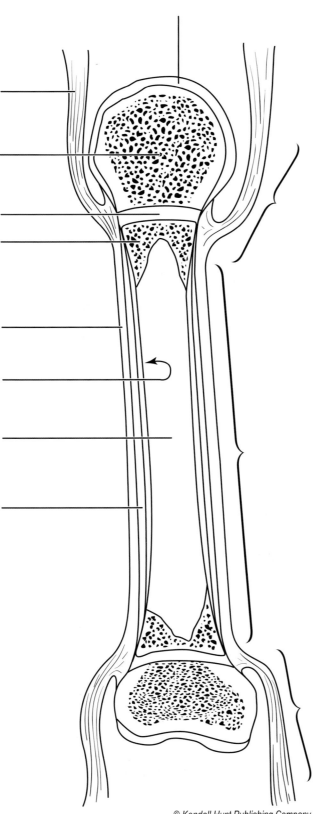

Articular capsule: connects 2 bones together; encircles full joint → enclosing joint cavity = joint cavity/synovial cavity
- outer layer: fibrous; continuous w/ periosteum
- inner layer: SYNOVIAL MEMBRANE; lines inside fibrous layer, vascular, produces synovial fluid (fills joint cavity); lubricates & nourishes joint & articular cartilage

Spongy bone: very thin plates of bone at various angles, spaces between them

Epiphyseal disc: cartilagenous plate in embyro/child; allows for bone growth in length: becomes metaphysis when growth complete; mitosis occurs

Metaphysis: spongy bone tissue; in adult, metaphysis is continuous with epiphysis

Periosteum: CT sheath (2 layers)
- outer layer: tough fibrous (insertion place)
- inner layer: delicate cellular (produce growth in diameter of bone

Endosteum: thin, cellular layer, found in spongy bone cavities
- 1 fxn: destroys bone
- growth in diameter of marrow cavity
- prevents bone from being too solid & heavy

Medullary (marrow) cavity: contains either red marrow, yellow marrow or both
- red: forms blood cells
- yellow: develops and stores fat cells

Compact bone: bone in concentric layers (looks solid)
- forms outer surface of ALL bones
- thicker in diaphysis

Articular cartilage: thin layer of hyaline cartilage covering articular surface; cushions joint

Epiphysis: take part in formation of a joint

Diaphysis: shaft of long bone

Epiphysis: take part in formation of a joint

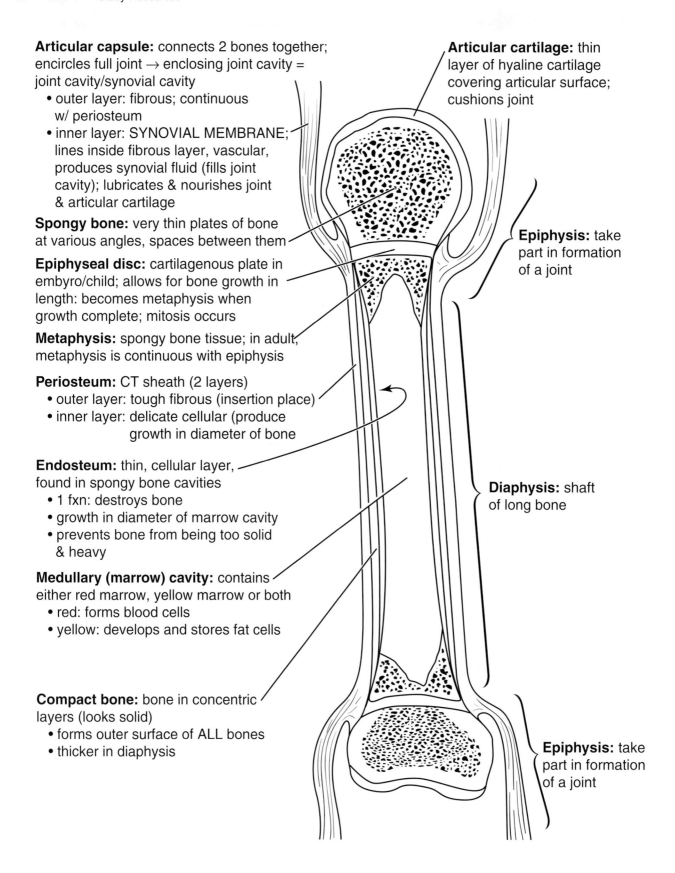

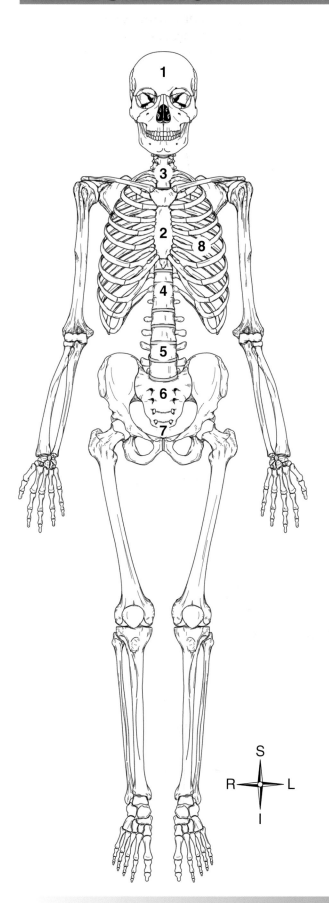

Color and label specified numbered structures

1 _____

2 _____

3 _____

4 _____

5 _____

6 _____

7 _____

8 _____

S

R ✛ L

I

The Skull

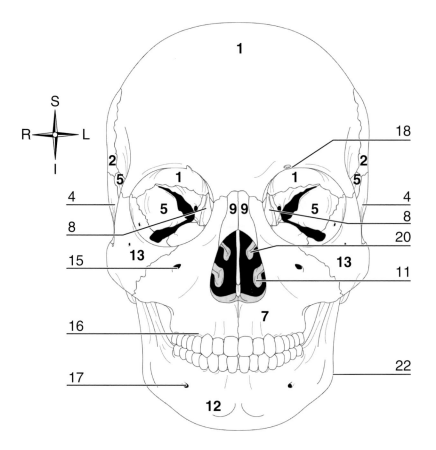

Frontal =   Mandible =

Parietal =   Zygomatic =

Temporal =   Infraorbital Foramen =

Sphenoid =   Alveolar Processes of Maxilla =

Maxilla =   Mental Foramen =

Lacrimal =   Middle Nasal Conchae =

Nasal =   Supraorbital Notch =

Inferior Nasal Concha =   Angle of Mandible =

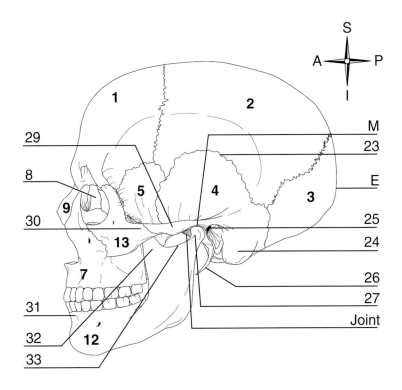

Top, left Lateral
View of the Skull

Bottom, Skull viewed from below

© Kendall Hunt Publishing Company

External Occipital Protuberence =

Temporomandibular Joint (TMJ) =

Occipital Bone =

Squamous Suture =

Mastoid Process =

External Acoustic Meatus =

Styloid Process of Temporal Bone =

Condyloid Process =

Zygomatic Arch (with the Zygomatic Bone) =

Zygomatic Arch (with the Temporal Bone) =

Alveolar Processes of Mandible =

Coronoid Process of Mandible =

Coronoid Notch =

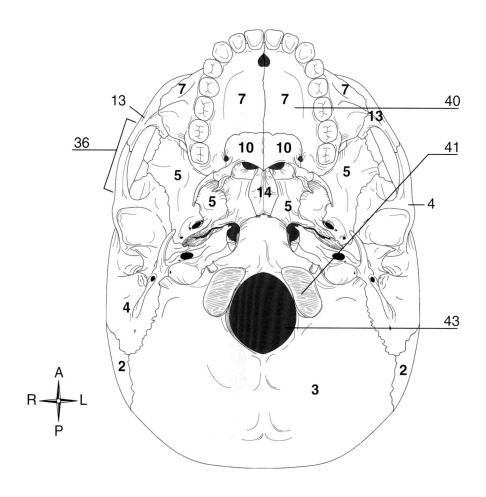

Palatine Bone =   Palatine Process of Maxilla =

Vomer =   Occipital Condyle =

Zygomatic Arch =   Foramen Magnum =

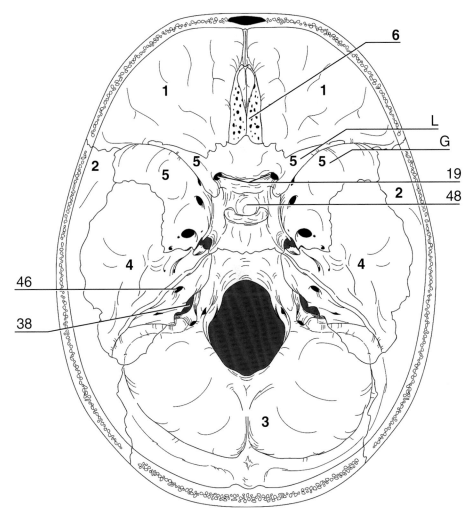

Floor of the Cranial Cavity

© *Kendall Hunt Publishing Company*

Lesser Wing of Sphenoid =

Greater Wing of Sphenoid =

Optic Canal (contains CN II) =

Jugular Foramen (contains CN IX, X, XI) =

Internal Acoustic Meatus (contains CN VII, VIII) =

Cribriform Plate =

Sella Turcica =

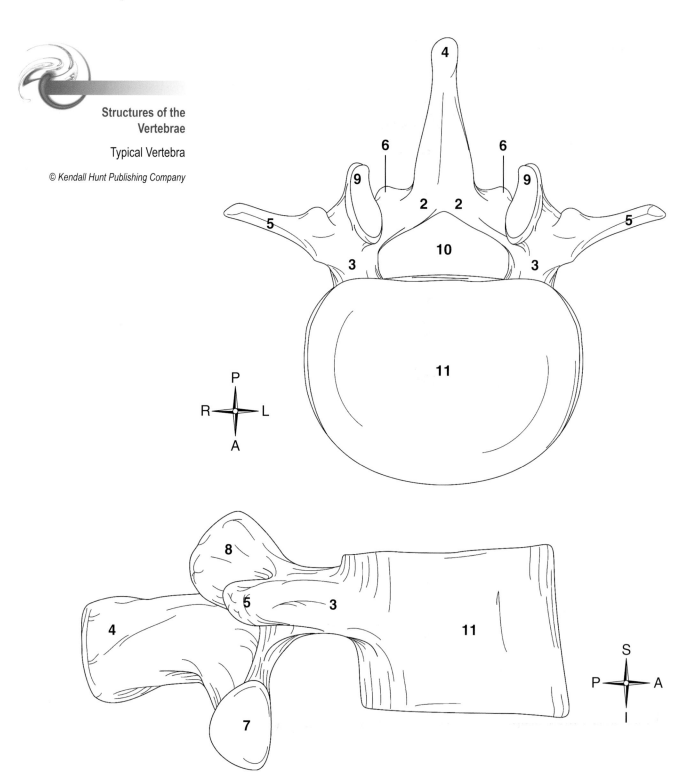

Structures of the
Vertebrae

Typical Vertebra

© Kendall Hunt Publishing Company

Vertebral Arch =

Lamina =

Pedicle =

Spinous Process =

Transverse Process =

Inferior Articular Process =

Inferior Articular Facet =

Superior Articular Process =

Superior Articular Facet =

Vertebral Foramen =

Body of Vertebra =

Cervical Vertebrae

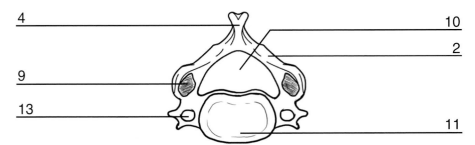

4 _____ 10
  2
9 _____
13 _____
  11

Thoracic Vertebrae

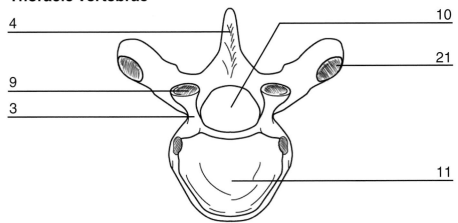

4 _____ 10
  21
9 _____
3 _____
  11

Lumbar Vertebrae

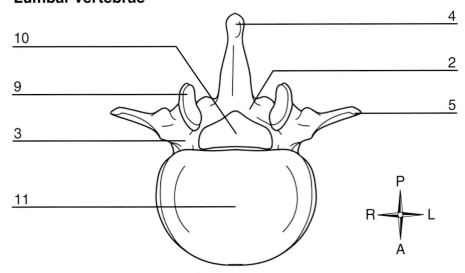

10 _____ 4
  2
9 _____ 5
3 _____
11 _____

P
R —✦— L
A

Cervical Vertebra =   Lumbar Curve =

Cervical Curve =   Intervertebral Discs =

Thoracic Vertebra =   Sacrum =

Thoracic Curve =   Sacral Curve =

Lumbar Vertebra =   Coccyx =

Types of Vertebrae

The Vertebral Column

© Kendall Hunt Publishing Company

Vertebral Column

© Kendall Hunt Publishing Company

Cervical Vertebrae =

Cervical Curve =

Thoracic Vertebrae =

Thoracic Curve =

Lumbar Vertebrae =

Lumbar Curve =

Intervertebral Discs =

Sacrum =

Sacral Curve =

Coccyx =

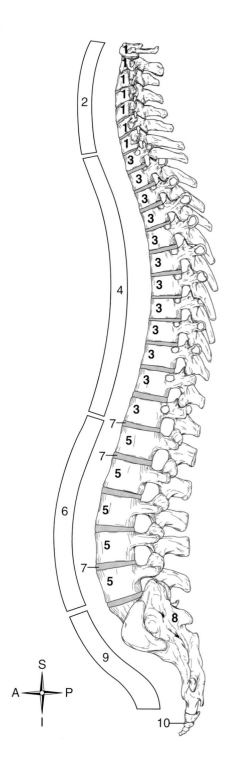

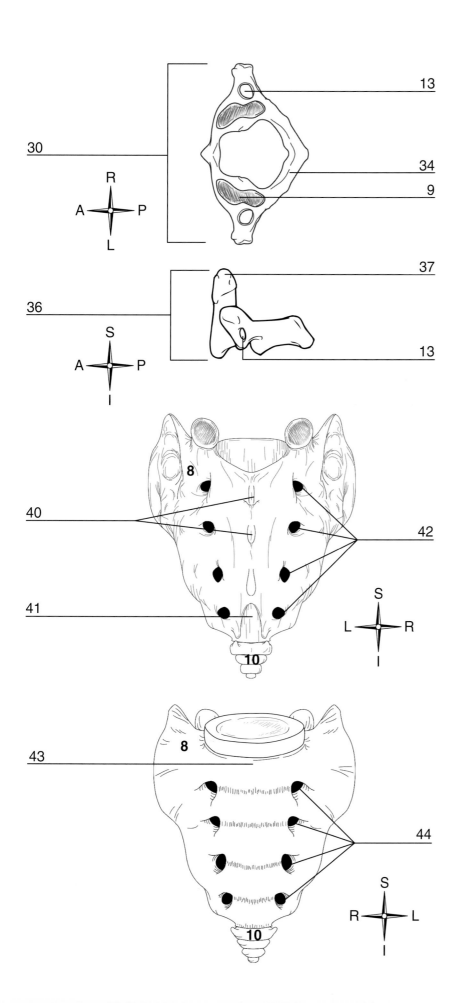

Specific Vetebrae & Sacrum

© *Kendall Hunt Publishing Company*

30

13

34

9

R
A — P
L

36

37

13

S
A — P
I

40

8

42

41

10

S
L — R
I

43

8

44

10

S
R — L
I

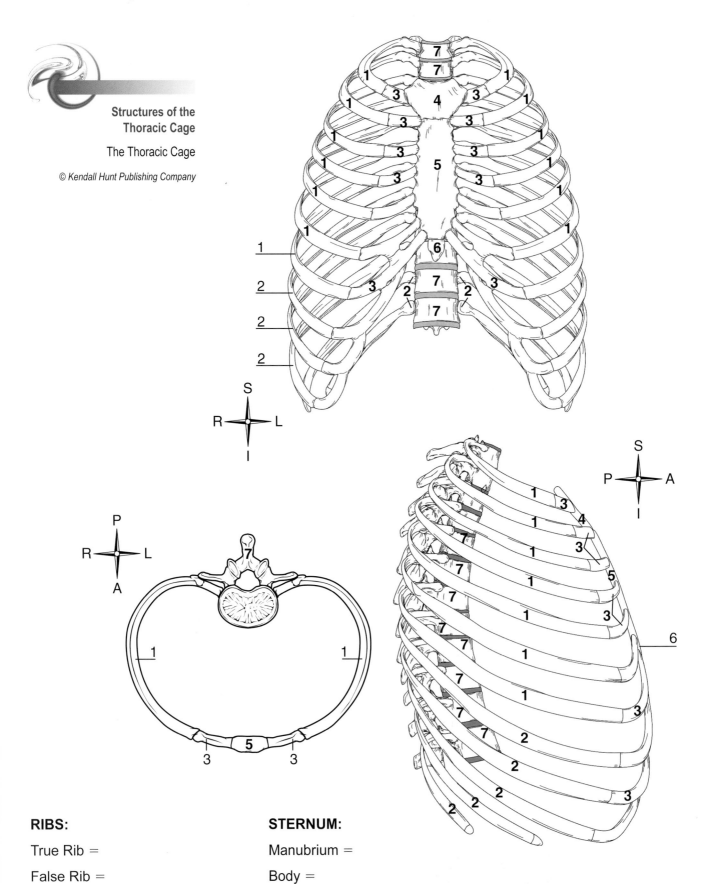

Structures of the
Thoracic Cage

The Thoracic Cage

© Kendall Hunt Publishing Company

RIBS:

True Rib =

False Rib =

Costal Cartilage =

STERNUM:

Manubrium =

Body =

Xiphoid Process =

Thoracic Vertebra =

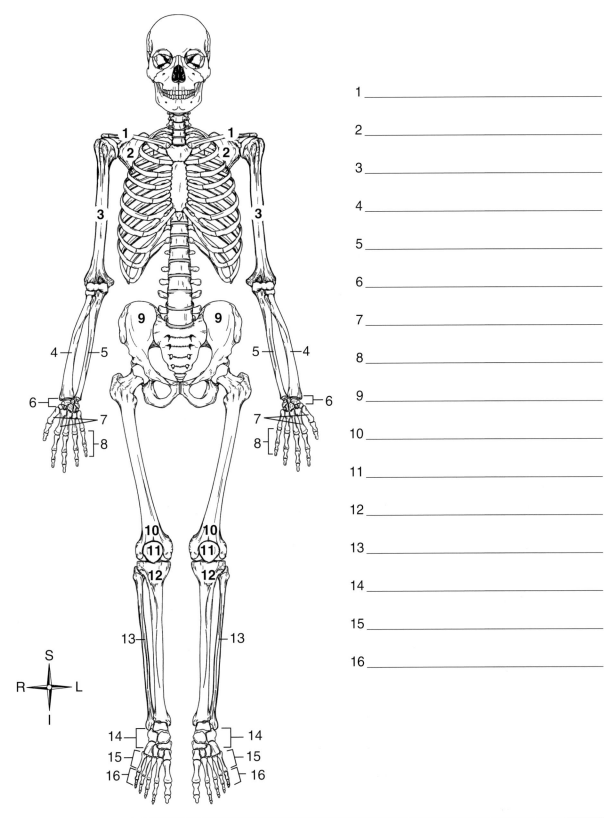

1 _____

2 _____

3 _____

4 _____

5 _____

6 _____

7 _____

8 _____

9 _____

10 _____

11 _____

12 _____

13 _____

14 _____

15 _____

16 _____

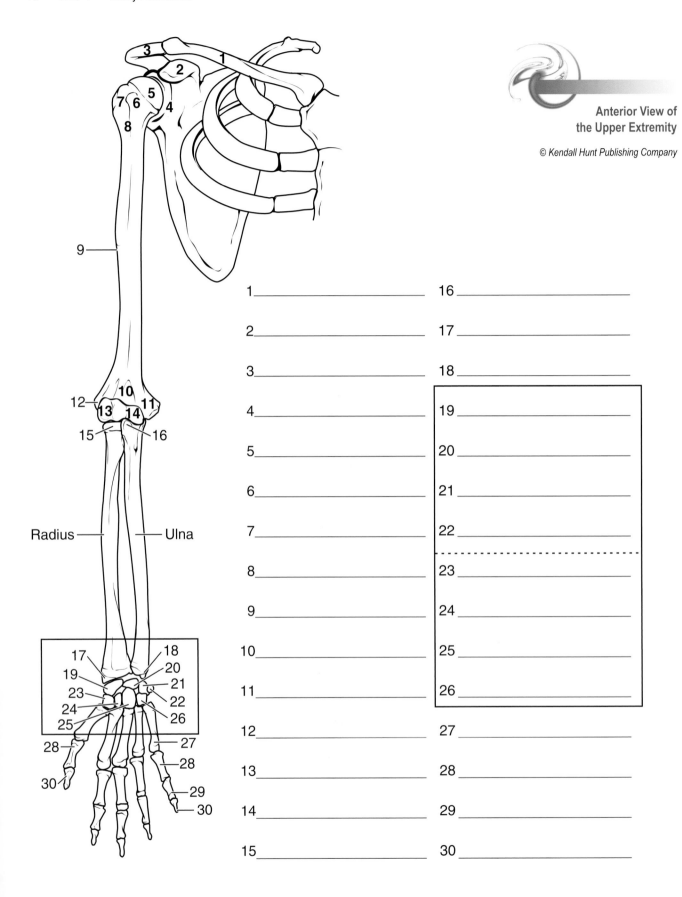

Anterior View of
the Upper Extremity

© Kendall Hunt Publishing Company

Radius———   ———Ulna

1 _____   16 _____

2 _____   17 _____

3 _____   18 _____

4 _____   19 _____

5 _____   20 _____

6 _____   21 _____

7 _____   22 _____

8 _____   23 _____

9 _____   24 _____

10 _____   25 _____

11 _____   26 _____

12 _____   27 _____

13 _____   28 _____

14 _____   29 _____

15 _____   30 _____

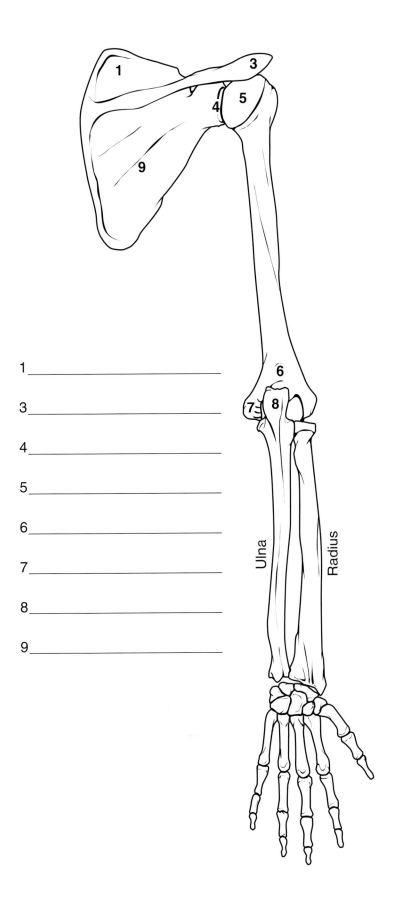

Ulna

Radius

1 _____

3 _____

4 _____

5 _____

6 _____

7 _____

8 _____

9 _____

**Proximal
Structures of the
Upper Extremity**

The Upper Extremity

© *Kendall Hunt Publishing Company*

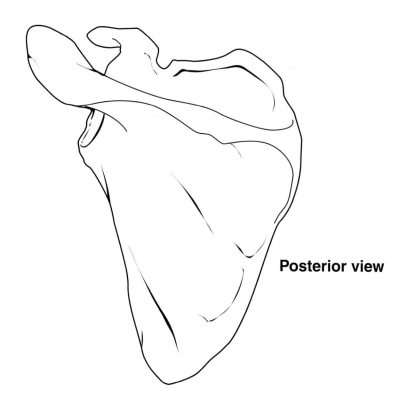

Posterior view

Lateral view

Scapula

supraspinous fossa = 1

coracoid process = 2

acromion = 3

glenoid cavity = 4

spine of scapula = 5

infraspinous fossa = 9

subscapular fossa = 10

supraglenoid tubercle = 11

infraglenoid tubercle = 12

medial border = 13

lateral border = 14

superior border = 15

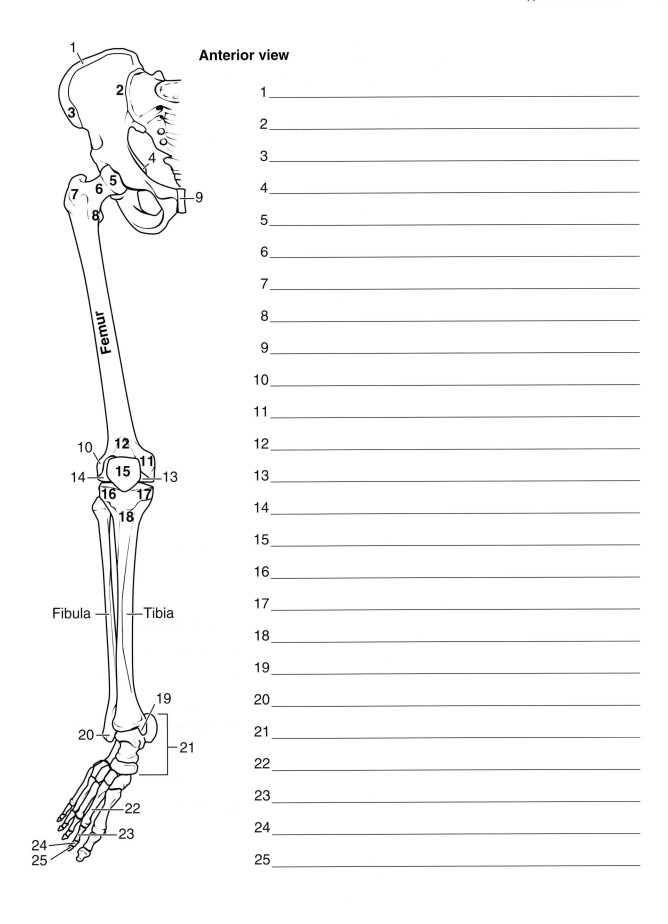

Anterior view

1 _____

2 _____

3 _____

4 _____

5 _____

6 _____

7 _____

8 _____

9 _____

10 _____

11 _____

12 _____

13 _____

14 _____

15 _____

16 _____

17 _____

18 _____

19 _____

20 _____

21 _____

22 _____

23 _____

24 _____

25 _____

**Posterior View of
the Left Lower Extremity**

© Kendall Hunt Publishing Company

Posterior view

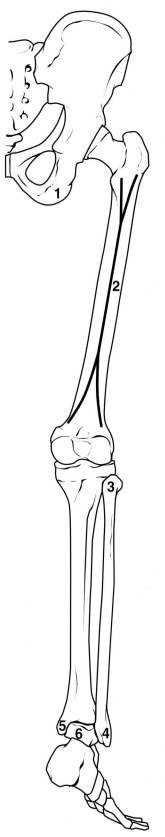

1 _____

2 _____

3 _____

4 _____

5 _____

6 _____

Posterior view

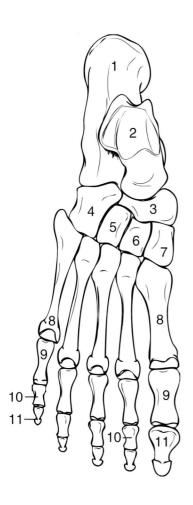

Structures of the Lower Extremity

The Lower Extremity

© Kendall Hunt Publishing Company

Calcaneus =
Talus =
Navicular =
Cuboid =
Lateral Cuneiform =
Intermediate Cuneiform =
Medial Cuneiform =
Metatarsal =
Proximal Phalanx =
Middle Phalanx =
Distal Phalanx =

Os Coxa

1 _____

2 _____

3 _____

4 _____

5 _____

6 _____

7 _____

8 _____

9 _____

Ilium

Pubis

Ischium

ARTICULAR SYSTEM

Classification of Joints

Fibrous (synarthroses)	Cartilaginous (amphiarthroses)	Synovial (diarthroses)
• Suture	• Hyaline cartilage	• Plane
• Syndesmoses	• Fibrocartilaginous	• Hinge (gingylmus)
		• Pivot (trochoid)
		• Saddle (sellar)
		• Condyloid (ellipsoidal)
		• Ball and socket (spheroidea)

Movements of Joints

Immovable Joints	Slightly Movable Joints
• Suture	• Syndesmoses
• Hyaline	• Fibrocartilaginous

Synovial Joint Movements

Gliding	Medial and Lateral Rotation	Flex and Extend	Abduct and Adduct	Circumduction	Rotation
• Plane	• Pivot • Saddle • Ball and socket	• Hinge • Condyloid • Saddle • Ball and socket	• Condyloid • Saddle • Ball and socket	• Condyloid • Saddle • Ball and socket	• Saddle • Ball and socket

Examples of Joints

- Sagittal suture = suture
- Radioulnar joint (syndesmosis) (interosseous membrane) = syndesmoses
- Epiphyseal disc = hyaline cartilage
- Intervertebral and interpubic disc = fibrocartilaginous joint
- Between carpal and tarsal bones = plane
- Elbow, interphalangeal, knee, and ankle joints = hinge
- Radioulnar joint (between ulna and radius; not interosseous membrane) = pivot
- Wrist joint = condyloid
- Carpometacarpal joint of the thumb = saddle
- Shoulder and hip = ball and socket

Note: Synovial joints share a relationship from your skeletal system worksheet regarding the articular cartilage and capsule. New things to remember: synovial membrane is vascular and produces synovial fluid (which is derived from blood) that fills synovial cavity to lubricate the joint and nourish articular cartilage.

Movements at Synovial Joints

These are the same actions you may have learned in anatomy lab.

Examples for Rule of Stability

* Shoulder has great range of movement so the stability of the joint is decreased.
* The knee joint can only flex and extend, so it is relatively stable, especially compared with the shoulder joint (ball and socket).

Bursa

* Sac containing synovial-LIKE (viscid) fluid
* Helps minimize friction; helps to cushion joints

Synovial Sheath

Elongated bursa enclosing tendon found where friction needs to be decreased
* Found between:
  * Bone and skin
  * Bone and muscle
  * Bone and tendon
  * Retinacula and tendon

Muscular System

Muscles of the face and head.

© Kendall Hunt Publishing Company

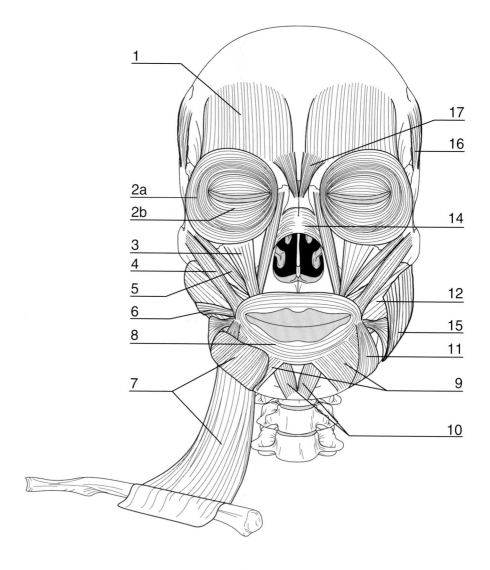

1 =

2 =

2a =

2b =

3 =

4 =

5 =

6 =

7 =

8 =

9 =

10 =

11 =

12 =

13 =

14 =

15 =

Muscular System

Superficial and deep muscles of the neck, shoulder, thorax, and abdomen

© Kendall Hunt Publishing Company

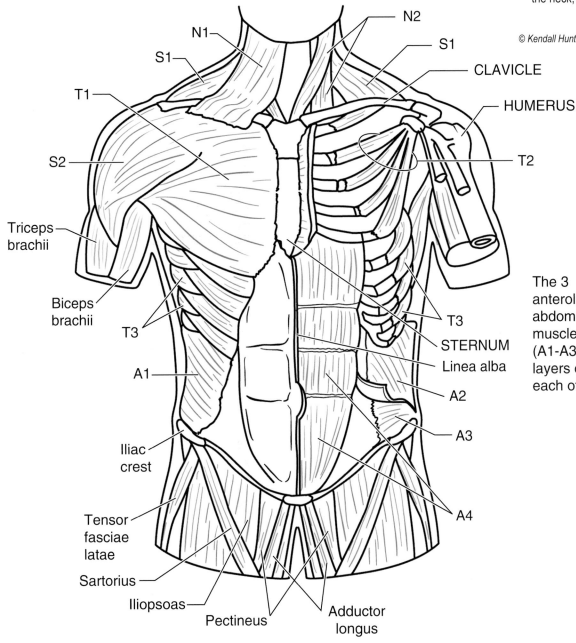

N2

N1

S1

S1

T1

CLAVICLE

HUMERUS

S2

T2

Triceps brachii

Biceps brachii

T3

A1

T3

STERNUM

Linea alba

A2

A3

The 3 anterolateral abdominal muscles (A1-A3) lie in layers over each other

Iliac crest

A4

Tensor fasciae latae

Sartorius

Iliopsoas

Pectineus

Adductor longus

N1 =

N2 =

S1 =

S2 =

T1 =

T2 =

T3 =

A1 =

A2 =

A3 =

A4 =

1 =   3c =   8 =

2a =   4 =   9 =

2b =   5 =   10 =

3a =   6 =   11 =

3b =   7 =

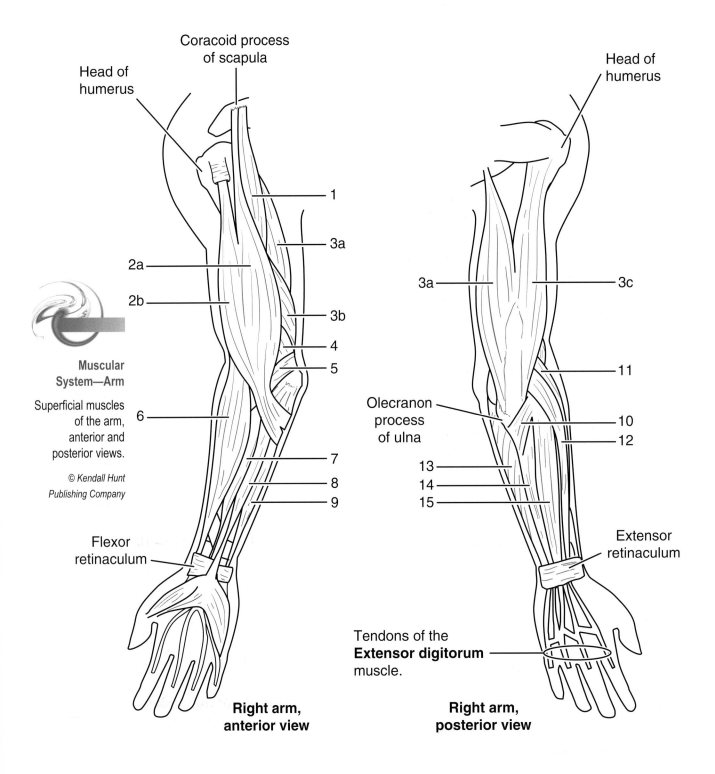

Coracoid process
of scapula

Head of
humerus

Head of
humerus

1

3a

2a

2b

3b

4

5

3a

3c

11

**Muscular
System—Arm**

Superficial muscles
of the arm,
anterior and
posterior views.

© *Kendall Hunt
Publishing Company*

6

Olecranon
process
of ulna

10

12

7

8

9

13

14

15

Flexor
retinaculum

Extensor
retinaculum

Tendons of the
Extensor digitorum
muscle.

**Right arm,
anterior view**

**Right arm,
posterior view**

1 =   7 =   13 =

2 =   8 =   14 =

3 =   9 =   16 =

4 =   10 =   17 =

5 =   11 =   18 =

6 =   12 =

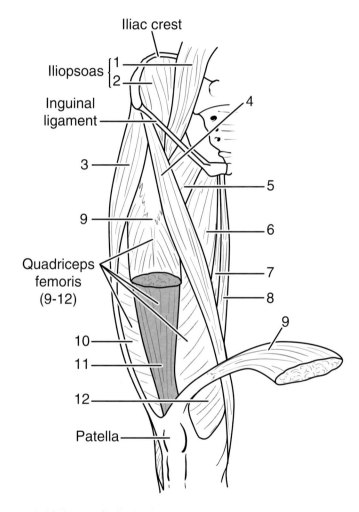

**Muscles of right thigh,
Anterior view**

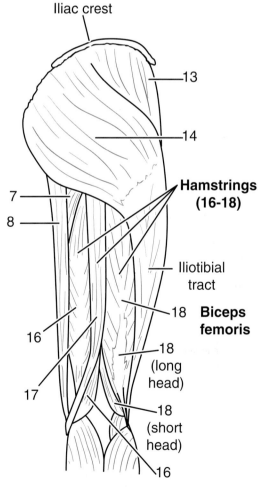

**Muscles of right thigh,
Posterior view**

**Muscular
System—Leg**

Muscles of the thigh, anterior and
posterior views.

1 =   5 =

2 =   6 =

3 =   7 =

4 =

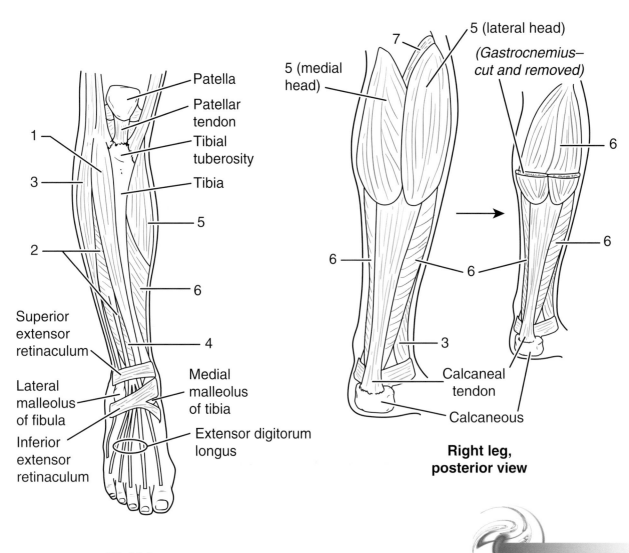

Patella

Patellar
tendon

Tibial
tuberosity

Tibia

1

3

5

2

6

Superior
extensor
retinaculum

4

Lateral
malleolus
of fibula

Medial
malleolus
of tibia

Inferior
extensor
retinaculum

Extensor digitorum
longus

**Right leg,
anterior view**

7

5 (medial
head)

5 (lateral head)

*(Gastrocnemius–
cut and removed)*

6

6

6

6

6

3

Calcaneal
tendon

Calcaneous

**Right leg,
posterior view**

**Muscular
System—Leg**

Muscles that move the ankle,
foot, and toes, anterior
and posterior views.

**Muscular
System**

Superficial and deep muscles
of the neck, shoulder, back,
and gluteal region.

© Kendall Hunt Publishing Company

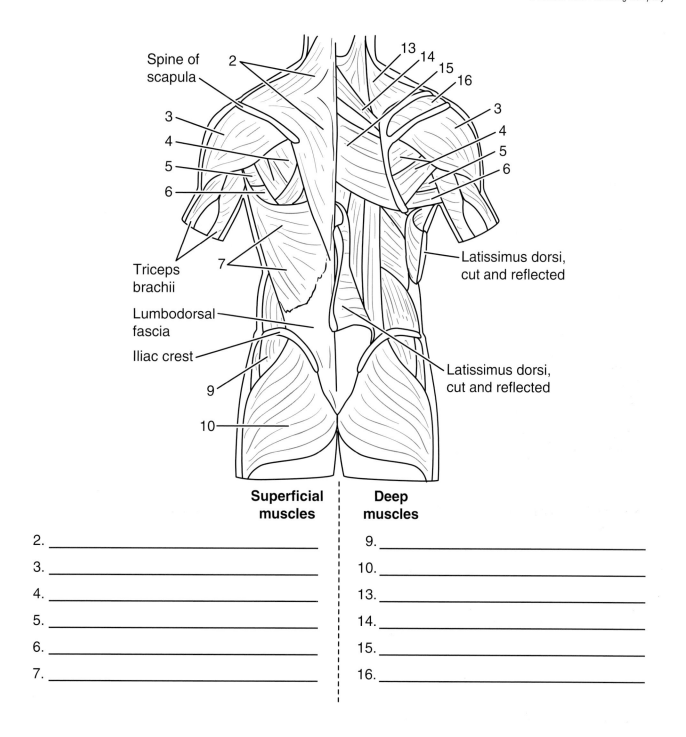

Spine of
scapula

Triceps
brachii

Lumbodorsal
fascia

Iliac crest

Latissimus dorsi,
cut and reflected

Latissimus dorsi,
cut and reflected

**Superficial
muscles**

**Deep
muscles**

2. _____

3. _____

4. _____

5. _____

6. _____

7. _____

9. _____

10. _____

13. _____

14. _____

15. _____

16. _____

Muscle Associations of the Upper Limb—Origins and Insertions

Bone Structure	Muscle	Origin or Insertion	No. of Muscles That Attach
Skull	Trapezius	Origin	1
Cervical vertebrae	Trapezius	Origin	3
	Levator scapulae	Origin	
	Rhomboid minor	Origin	
Thoracic vertebrae	Trapezius	Origin	4
	Latissimus dorsi	Origin	
	Rhomboid minor	Origin	
	Rhomboid major	Origin	
Lumbar vertebrae	Latissimus dorsi	Origin	1
Spine of scapula	Trapezius	Insertion	2
	Deltoid	Origin	
Acromion	Trapezius	Insertion	2
	Deltoid	Origin	
Clavicle	Trapezius	Insertion	3
	Pectoralis major	Origin	
	Deltoid	Origin	
Sacrum	Latissimus dorsi	Origin	1
Costal cartilage 1–6	Pectoralis major	Origin	1
Crest of the greater tubercle	Pectoralis major	Insertion	1
Ribs 2–5	Pectoralis minor	Origin	1
Ribs 1–8	Serratus anterior	Origin	1
Coracoid process	Pectoralis minor	Insertion	3
	Short head of biceps brachii	Origin	
	Coracobrachialis	Origin	
Medial border of scapula	Serratus anterior	Insertion	4
Above spine	Levator scapulae	Insertion	
At the spine	Rhomboid minor	Insertion	
Below the spine	Rhomboid major	Insertion	

Bone Structure	Muscle	Origin or Insertion	No. of Muscles That Attach
Deltoid tuberosity	Deltoid	Insertion	1
Greater tubercle	Supraspinatus	Insertion	3
	Infraspinatus	Insertion	
	Teres minor	Insertion	
Infraspinous fossa	Infraspinatus	Origin	1
Lateral border of infraspinous fossa	Teres minor	Origin	1
Inferior angle of infraspinous fossa	Teres major	Origin	1
Supraspinous fossa	Supraspinatus	Origin	1
Subscapular fossa	Subscapularis	Origin	1
Lesser tubercle	Subscapularis	Insertion	1
Crest of lesser tubercle	Teres major	Insertion	1
Glenoid tubercle			2
Infraglenoid tubercle	Long head of triceps brachii	Origin	1
Supraglenoid tubercle	Long head of biceps brachii	Origin	1
Humerus			4
Above radial nerve	Lateral head of triceps brachii	Origin	1
Below radial nerve	Medial head of triceps brachii	Origin	1
Lower	Brachialis	Origin	1
Middle medial	Coracobrachialis	Insertion	1
Olecranon process of ulna	Triceps brachii	Insertion	1
Radial tuberosity	Biceps brachii	Insertion	1
Coronoid process of ulna	Brachialis	Insertion	1

Muscle Associations of the Upper Limb—Actions

Actions	No. of Muscle	Muscle Name
Adduction of scapula	3	Trapezius Rhomboid minor Rhomboid major
Elevate the scapula	2	Trapezius Levator scapulae
Depress the scapula	2	Trapezius Pectoralis minor
Extend arm	2	Latissimus dorsi Deltoid
Adduct arm	3	Latissimus dorsi Teres major Pectoralis major
Medially rotate arm	5	Latissimus dorsi Teres major Pectoralis major Subscapularis Deltoid
Flex arm	3	Pectoralis major Deltoid Coracobrachialis
Upward rotation of scapula	1	Serratus anterior
Laterally rotate arm	3	Deltoid Infraspinatus Teres minor
Abduct arm	2	Supraspinatus Deltoid
Extend forearm	2	Triceps brachii Anconeus
Flex forearm	3	Biceps brachii Brachialis Brachioradialis

Actions	No. of Muscle	Muscle Name
Supinate forearm	2	Biceps brachii
		Supinator
Pronate forearm	1	Pronator teres
Pronate hand	1	Pronator quadratus
Flex hand	3	Flexor carpi radialis
		Flexor carpi ulnaris
		Palmaris longus
Adduct hand	2	Flexor carpi ulnaris
		Extensor carpi ulnaris
Abduct hand	3	Flexor carpi radialis
		Extensor carpi radialis longus
		Extensor carpi radialis brevis
Flex digits 2-5	2	Flexor digitorum superficialis
		Flexor digitorum profundus
Flex thumb	1	Flexor pollicis longus
Extend hand	3	Extensor carpi radialis longus
		Extensor carpi radialis brevis
		Extensor carpi ulnaris
Extend digit 5	1	Extensor digiti minimi
Extend digits 2-5	1	Extensor digitorum
Abduct thumb	1	Abductor pollicis longus
Extend thumb	2	Extensor pollicis longus
		Extensor pollicis brevis
Extend index finger	1	Extensor indicis

Muscles Associated of the Upper Limb—Innervations

Nerve	Number of Muscles it Innervates	Names of Muscles
Cranial nerve XI–accessory nerve	1	Trapezius
Long thoracic nerve	1	Serratus anterior
Thoracodorsal nerve	1	Latissimus dorsi
C3 and C4	1	Levator scapulae
Dorsal scapular nerve	2	Rhomboid minor Rhomboid major
Medial and lateral pectoral nerves	1	Pectoralis major
Medial pectoral nerve	1	Pectoralis minor
Axillary nerve	2	Deltoid Teres minor
Suprascapular nerve	2	Supraspinatus Infraspinatus
Upper and lower subscapular nerve	1	Subscapularis
Lower subscapular nerve	1	Teres major
Musculocutaneous nerve	3	Coracobrachialis Biceps brachii Brachialis
Radial nerve	13	Triceps brachii Brachioradialis Extensor carpi radialis longus Extensor carpi radialis brevis Extensor digitorum Extensor digiti minimi Extensor carpi ulnaris Anconeus Supinator Abductor pollicis longus Extensor pollicis brevis Extensor pollicis longus Extensor indicis

Nerve	Number of Muscles it Innervates	Names of Muscles
Median nerve	6.5	Pronator teres
		Flexor carpi radialis
		Palmaris longus
		Flexor digitorum superficialis
		Flexor digitorum profundus (1/2)
		Flexor pollicis longus
		Pronator quadratus
Ulnar nerve	1.5	Flexor carpi ulnaris
		Flexor digitorum profundus (1/2)

PRACTICE QUIZZES

1A Course Introduction Practice Quiz........................ p. 93

1B Integumentary System Practice Quiz................... p. 94

1C Skeletal System Practice Quiz............................ p. 95

1D&E Axial and Appendicular Skeleton
    Practice Quiz.. pp. 96–100

1F Articular System Practice Quiz.................. pp. 101–105

1I Upper Limb Musculature Practice Quiz...... pp. 106–109

1A–I Unit 1 Practice Test ....pp. 110–118

Answer Key .... pp. 119–121

Course Introduction Practice Quiz

1. The word *sectare* means:
   a. "Cut" in Spanish
   b. "Apart" in Greek
   c. "Cut" in Greek
   d. "Apart" in Latin
   e. None of the above

2. Gross anatomy is the study of:
   a. Animal anatomy
   b. Cells
   c. Tissues
   d. Tissues that depart from normal
   e. Structures visible to the naked eye

3. Tissues are structures studied in the field of:
   a. Gross anatomy
   b. Developmental anatomy
   c. Comparative anatomy
   d. Microanatomy
   e. All of the above

4. The function: movement of the body belongs to all of the following systems EXCEPT: (Choose all that apply.)
   a. Integumentary system
   b. Muscular system
   c. Articular system
   d. Reproductive system
   e. Skeletal system

5. All of the following are criteria for anatomical position EXCEPT:
   a. Eyes directed forward
   b. Body erect
   c. Palms at side
   d. Upper limbs by side
   e. Toes directed forward

6. Abduction occurs in the _____ plane.
   a. Frontal plane
   b. Horizontal plane
   c. Transverse plane
   d. Midsagittal plane
   e. Sagittal plane

7. The heart is _____ to the intestines.
   a. Cephalic
   b. Superficial
   c. External
   d. Proximal
   e. None of the above

Integumentary System Practice Quiz

1. The structure indicated by the letter A courses through what layers of the integumentary system? (Choose all that apply.)
   a. Dermis
   b. Epidermis
   c. Subcutaneous tissue
   d. All of the above
   e. None of the above

2. The structure indicated by the letter B is found in what layers of the integumentary system? (Choose all that apply.)
   a. Dermis
   b. Epidermis
   c. Subcutaneous tissue
   d. None of the above
   e. All of the above

3. The structure indicated by the letter C is derived from:
   a. Dermis
   b. Subcutaneous tissue
   c. Epidermis
   d. Follicle shaft
   e. Hair cells

4. The structure indicated by the letter D is made up of:
   a. Nerves
   b. Blood vessels
   c. Skeletal muscle
   d. Smooth muscle
   e. Keratin

5. The structure indicated by the letter E is named the:
   a. Epidermis
   b. Dermis
   c. Papillary ridges
   d. Dermal papillae
   e. Fingerprint

6. F is made up of:
   a. Sebaceous glands
   b. Adipose cells
   c. Cubodial cells
   d. Collagen fibers
   e. None of the above

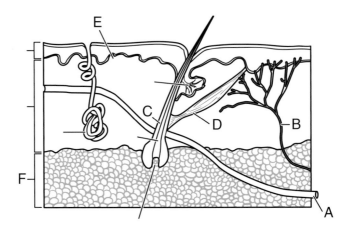

Skeletal System Practice Quiz

1. All of the following are functions of the skeleton EXCEPT: (Choose all that apply.)
   a. Manufacture blue blood cells
   b. Framework of the body
   c. Protection of the integumentary system
   d. Storage of certain chemical substances
   e. Attachment for skeletal muscles

2. All of the following describes a long bone: (Choose all that apply.)
   a. A bone in which the length equals the width
   b. A bone in which the length exceeds the width
   c. A bone in which the width exceeds the length
   d. A bone expanded into one plane
   e. Has a medullary canal

3. All of the following are bones found in the axial skeleton EXCEPT: (Choose all that apply.)
   a. Femur
   b. Sternum
   c. Sacrum
   d. Hyoid
   e. Clavicle

4. All of the following are true statements EXCEPT: (Choose all that apply.)
   a. E is composed of 2 layers
   b. C can be found in adults
   c. D is spongy bone tissue that can be found between the diaphysis and epiphysis
   d. BD is hyaline cartilage and helps to cushion the joint
   e. AD is bone laid in concentric layers

5. All of the following are false regarding cartilage EXCEPT: (Choose all that apply.)
   a. It is vascular
   b. It contains nerves
   c. The embryo is initially cartilage
   d. There are 3 types of cartilage
   e. Cartilage is described as a firm, gel-like intercellular substance

6. Choose the incorrect pair(s): (Choose all that apply.)
   a. Embryo—elastic
   b. Interpubic disc—fibrocartilage
   c. Hyaline—epiphyseal disc
   d. Nasal cartilage—elastic
   e. Auricle—hyaline

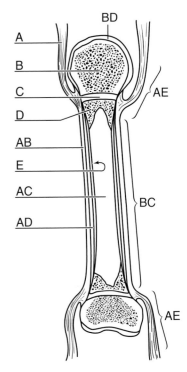

ID&E Axial and Appendicular Skeleton
Practice Quiz

1. Identify the supraorbital notch or foramen.
2. Identify the mental foramen.

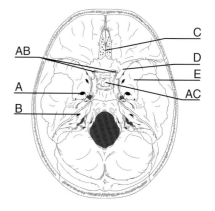

3. Identify the structure that cranial nerve II passes through.
4. Identify the sella turcica.

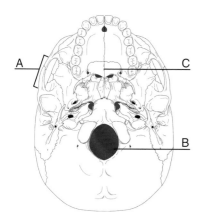

5. Identify the palatine process of the maxilla.
6. Identify the zygomatic arch.

7. Identify the nasal bone.
8. Identify the coronoid notch.
9. Identify the alveolar processes.
10. Identify the condyloid process.

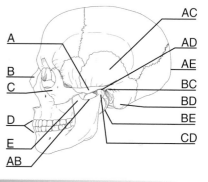

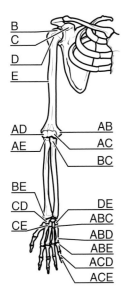

11. Identify the coracoid process.
12. Identify the head of the humerus.
13. Identify the trochlea.
14. Identify the pisiform.
15. Identify the distal phalange.

16. Identify the infraspinous fossa.
17. Identify the anatomical neck of the humerus.
18. Identify the olecranon fossa.
19. Identify the groove for the ulnar nerve.
20. Identify the olecranon process.
21. Identify the styloid process of the ulna.

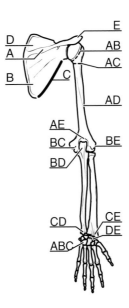

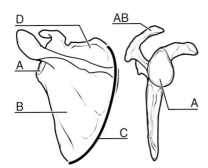

22. Identify the glenoid fossa.
23. Identify the vertebral border.
24. Identify the acromion.

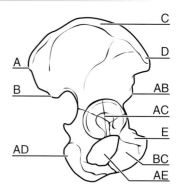

25. Identify the iliac crest.
26. Identify the inferior ramus.
27. Identify the ischial tuberosity.
28. Identify the acetabulum.

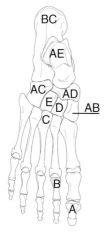

29. Identify the talus.
30. Identify the calcaneous.
31. Identify the medial cuneiform.
32. Identify the proximal phalanx.

33. Identify the transverse process.
34. Identify the pedicle.
35. Identify the inferior articular process/facet.
36. Identify the vertebral arch.
37. Identify the vertebral foramen.

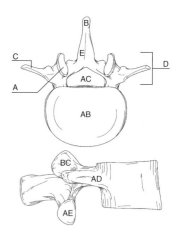

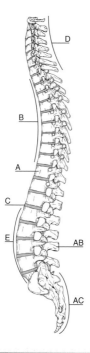

38. Identify the secondary curvatures.
39. Identify the intervertebral disc.

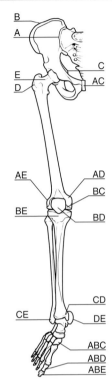

40. Identify the greater trochanter.
41. Identify the iliosacral joint.
42. Identify the adductor tubercle.
43. Identify the patella.
44. Identify the ischial spine.
45. Identify the tibial tuberosity.
46. Identify the medial malleolus.

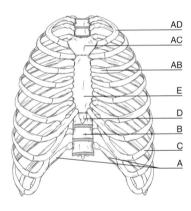

47. Identify the costal cartilage.
48. Identify the xiphoid process.
49. Identify a false and floating rib (choose just one).
50. Identify the thoracic vertebrae.

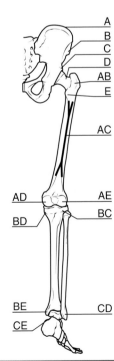

51. Identify the linea aspera.
52. Identify the ASIS.
53. Identify the lesser trochanter.
54. Identify the medial condyle of the femur.
55. Identify the lateral condyle of the tibia.
56. Identify the lateral malleolus.

57. Identify the superior articular facet.
58. Identify the bifid spinous process.
59. Identify the transverse costal facet.
60. Identify the body of a lumbar vertebra.

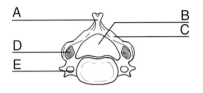

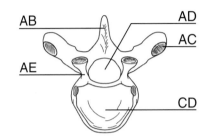

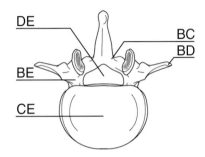

61. Identify the atlas.
62. Identify the dens.

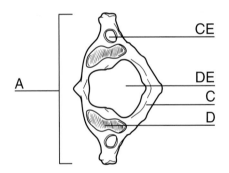

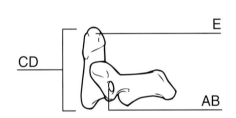

63. Identify the promontory.
64. Identify the anterior sacral foramina.

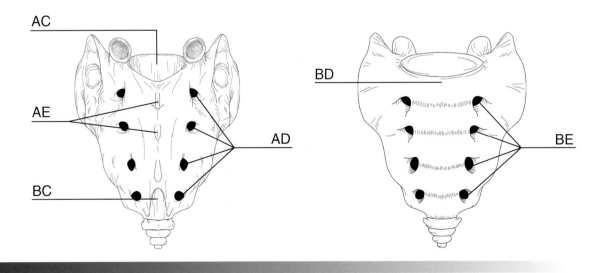

ARTICULAR SYSTEM PRACTICE QUIZ

1. The word *arthron* means:
   a. "Author" in Greek
   b. "Joint" in Latin
   c. "Joint" in Greek
   d. "Study of joints" in Greek
   e. None of the above

Match the following:

2. Synarthroses   a. Cartilaginous

3. Amphiarthroses   b. Synovial

4. Diarthroses   c. Fibrous

5. All of the following are true regarding fibrous joints EXCEPT: (Choose all that apply.)
   a. Can be immovable or slightly moveable.
   b. Articulating surfaces can be serrated (interdigitations).
   c. Located only in the skull.
   d. Can be found in between the radioulnar syndesmosis (interosseous membrane).
   e. Can be found in between vertebral bodies.

6. The following pairs are true EXCEPT:
   a. Suture joint and sagittal suture
   b. Syndesmosis joint and joint between two bones of the leg
   c. Hyaline cartilage joint and interpubic disc
   d. Fibrocartilaginous joint and intervertebral disc
   e. Synovial joint and tarsals

7. Syndesmosis:
   a. Has connective tissue in a greater amount than that found in a suture.
   b. Is immovable.
   c. Contains epithelial tissue.
   d. Has an epiphyseal plate.
   e. Is hollow.

8. The _____ joint(s) are immovable. (Choose all that apply.)
   a. Syndesmosis
   b. Suture
   c. Hyaline
   d. Fibrocartilaginous
   e. Synovial

9. Hyaline cartilage can be found: (Choose all that apply.)
   a. In the epiphyseal disc
   b. In the interpubic disc
   c. Sagittal suture
   d. Between the epiphysis and diaphysis of a growing bone
   e. Between carpal bones

10. The _____ joint(s) are slightly movable. (Choose all that apply.)
    a. Suture
    b. Syndesmosis
    c. Hyaline cartilage
    d. Fibrocartilaginous
    e. All of the above

11. All of the following are true of synovial joints EXCEPT: (Choose all that apply.)
    a. Possess a cavity
    b. Have an articular capsule that is a layer of hyaline cartilage
    c. Are avascular in the articular cartilage
    d. Lack nerves
    e. The articular capsule has one layer

12. Choose the statement that is FALSE regarding the articular capsule. (Choose all that apply.)
    a. Articular capsule encloses the synovial cavity
    b. The outer fibrous layer is continuous with the endosteum of bone
    c. Inner layer is called the synovial membrane
    d. It is avascular
    e. It produces synovial fluid

13. Movement of a synovial joint includes all of the following EXCEPT:
    a. Flexion
    b. Rotation
    c. Abduction
    d. Gliding
    e. None of the above

Match the following:

14. Pronation   a. Bending of a joint so the angle is acute

15. Medial rotation   b. Movement in the frontal plane away from medial plane

16. Abduction   c. Medial rotation of the forearm

17. Circumduction   d. Anterior aspect of the limb rotating medially

18. Flexion   e. Combination of flexion, extension, abduction, and adduction

19. All of the following are limitations of movement EXCEPT:
    a. Shape of the joint
    b. Ligaments and capsule at the joint
    c. Muscles that act on a joint
    d. Shape of the articulating surfaces

20. There are _____ types of synovial joints.
    a. 7
    b. 4
    c. 5
    d. 8
    e. None of the above

21. Synovial joints: (Choose all that apply.)
   a. Are hard to move around
   b. Are classified according to shapes of bones
   c. Contain fluid derived from blood
   d. Eventually ossify
   e. All of the above

22. Choose the statement(s) that is/are FALSE regarding a plane joint.
   a. The plane joint is flat
   b. The plane joint has a sliding movement
   c. The plane join can flex and extend
   d. The plane joint is reciprocally concave-convex

23. An example of the hinge joint is/are all of the following EXCEPT: (Choose all that apply.)
   a. Elbow
   b. Knee
   c. Ankle
   d. Interphalangeal
   e. Wrist joint

24. The _____ joint presents a rounded projection that rotates within a concave depression.
   a. Condyloid
   b. Saddle
   c. Ball and socket
   d. Pivot
   e. Hinge

25. Choose the joint(s) that allows medial and lateral rotation: (Choose all that apply.)
   a. Pivot
   b. Hinge
   c. Condyloid
   d. Ball and socket
   e. Saddle

26. Choose the joint(s) that allows adduction: (Choose all that apply.)
   a. Condyloid
   b. Saddle
   c. Ball and socket
   d. Plane
   e. Pivot

27. The following is an example of a saddle joint:
   a. Carpometacarpal joint of the thumb
   b. Hip joint
   c. Wrist joint
   d. Radioulnar joint
   e. Interphalangeal joint

28. The following statements are true regarding the rule of stability of a joint. (Choose all that apply.)
   a. As the degree of freedom of movement decreases, the stability of the joint increases
   b. As the degree of freedom of movement increases, the stability of the joint decreases

c. As the degree of freedom of movement decreases, the stability of the joint decreases

d. As the degree of freedom of movement increases, the stability of the joint increases

29. Bursitis is: (Choose all that apply.)
   a. Inflammation of a bursa
   b. Inflammation of a joint
   c. Inflammation of a purse
   d. Inflammation of a connective tissue sac lined with a synovial membrane
   e. Contains synovial fluid

30. All of the following statements are true regarding a synovial sheath EXCEPT:
   a. Elongated bursa
   b. Encloses a tendon
   c. Found between the radius and ulna
   d. Found between retinacula and wrist
   e. Found between tendons of wrist and ankle

31. Bursa can be found between all of the following EXCEPT: (Choose all that apply.)
   a. Skin and bone
   b. Muscle and bone
   c. Adipose tissue and bone
   d. Tendon and bone
   e. Tendon and muscle

Upper Limb Musculature Practice Quiz

Note: This practice quiz may include questions regarding nerves you may not have to know for your exam.

1. What is the insertion of the muscle that originates where the muscle indicated by the letter A inserts?
2. What is the muscle that shares the same action as the muscle indicated by the letter B?
3. What is/are the action(s) of the muscle indicated by the letter C?
4. What is the origin of the muscle that shares the same action as the muscle indicated by the letter D?
5. What is/are the common action(s) shared by the muscle indicated by the letter E? The muscle also inserts into the crest of the lesser tubercle.
6. What is the action(s) of the muscle indicated by the letter G?
7. What is the innervation of the muscle indicated by the letter F?
8. Name one muscle that shares a similar origin of the muscle indicated by the letter F.
9. Name a muscle of the shoulder that shares a common action(s) with the muscle indicated by the letter A.
10. What other muscle has the same action(s) as the muscle indicated by the letter b?
11. Name the muscle(s) that share the same insertion as the muscle indicated by the letter c.
12. Name all of the shoulder rotators.
13. Name the muscle(s) that originates where the muscle indicated by the letter A inserts.

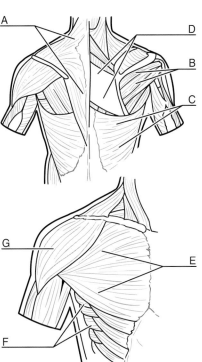

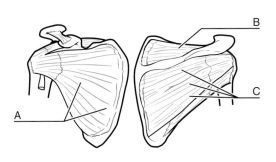

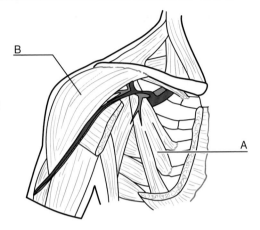

14. What is the innervation of the muscle indicated by the letter B?
15. What other muscle(s) share(s) the same action(s) as the muscle indicated by the letter A?
16. What is the action(s) of the muscle indicated by the letter A?

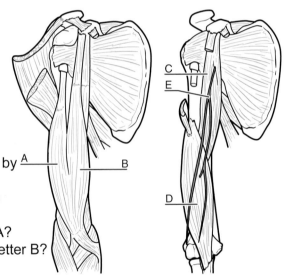

17. What is the origin of the muscle indicated by the letter B?
18. What is the insertion of the muscle indicated by the letter C?
19. What other muscle shares the same origin as the muscle indicated by the letter C?
20. What is the origin and insertion of the muscle indicated by the letter D?
21. What group of muscles does the nerve indicated by the letter E innervate?
22. What is the origin of the muscle indicated by the letter A?
23. What is the innervation of the muscle indicated by the letter B?

Superficial layer   **Deep layer**

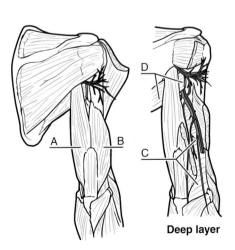

24. What is the insertion of the muscle indicated by the letter C?
25. What is the origin of the muscle indicated by the letter D?
26. What do the muscles indicated by the letters A, B and C have in common?
27. What is the action of the muscle indicated by the letter A?

Deep layer

Supinated position   **Pronated position**

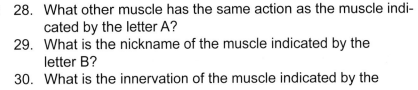

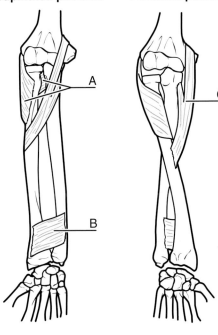

28. What other muscle has the same action as the muscle indicated by the letter A?
29. What is the nickname of the muscle indicated by the letter B?
30. What is the innervation of the muscle indicated by the letter B?
31. What is the innervation of the muscle indicated by the letter A?
32. What layer is the muscle indicated by the letter C in?
33. What is the action of the muscle indicated by the letter C?
34. What layer is the muscle indicated by the letter B in?

35. What other muscle shares the same action as the muscle indicated by the letter A?
36. What is the innervation of the muscle indicated by the letter B?
37. What is the name of the muscle indicated by the letter B?
38. What is the action of the muscle indicated by the letter C?
39. What is the action of the muscle indicated by the letter D?
40. What is the name of the muscle indicated by the letter G?
41. What is the action of the muscle indicated by the letter E?
42. What is the action of the muscle indicated by the letter F?

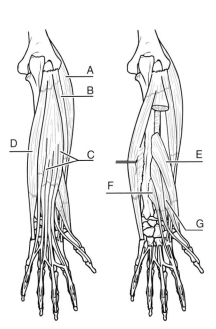

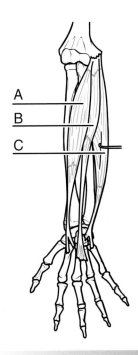

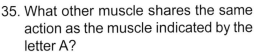
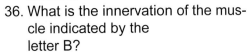

43. What is the action of the muscle indicated by the letter A?
44. What is the name of the muscle indicated in the letter B?
45. What is the action of the muscle indicated by the letter B?
46. What layer are all these muscles located in?
47. What is the innervation of the muscle indicated by the letter C?

48. What is the action of the muscle indicated by the letter B?
49. What is the action of the muscle indicated by the letter C?
50. What is the innervation of the muscle indicated by the letter A?
51. What is the innervation of the muscle indicated by the letter C?
52. What layer is the muscle indicated by the letter B in?

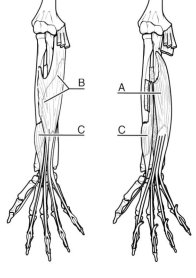

53. What is the action of the muscle indicated by the letter A?
54. What muscle shares the same action(s) as the muscle indicated by the letter B?
55. What is the innervation of the muscle indicated by the letter E?
56. What is the action of the muscle indicated by the letter E?
57. What is the action of the muscle indicated by the letter C?
58. What is the innervation of the muscle indicated by the letter D?
59. What is the name of the muscle indicated by the letter A?

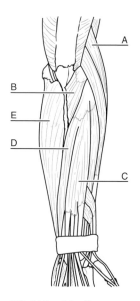

60. What is the nerve indicated by the letter A?
61. What are the 3 cords indicated by the letter E?
62. What are the ventral rami of the brachial plexus?
63. How many total nerves does the brachial plexus give off?
64. Name the muscle(s) that are innervated by the letter D in the forearm.
65. Name the nerve indicated by the letter B?
66. Name the muscle(s) that are supplied in the arm by the nerve indicated by the letter C.

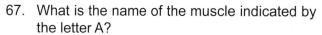

67. What is the name of the muscle indicated by the letter A?
68. What is the muscle that shares the same action as the muscle indicated by the letter C?
69. What is the nickname of the muscle indicated by the letter C?
70. What is the actual name of the muscle indicated by the letter B?
71. What layer is the muscle indicated by the letter D located in?

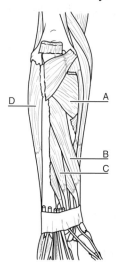

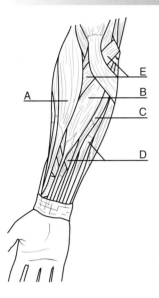

72. What is the innervation of the muscle indicated by the letter A?
73. What is the action of the muscle indicated by the letter B?
74. What percentage of the population is missing the muscle indicated by the letter C?
75. What is the innervation of the muscle indicated by the letter D?
76. What is the action of the muscle indicated by the letter E?

77. What percentage of the time does the nerve indicated by the letter A pierce the muscle indicated by the letter C?
78. What area(s) of the upper limb does the nerve indicated by the B innervate?
79. What is the action of the muscle indicated by the letter C?
80. What other muscle(s) has the same action as the muscle indicated by the letter C?
81. What is the name of the nerve indicated by the letter D?
82. What is the action of the muscle indicated by the letter E?
83. What other muscle(s) has the same action as the muscle indicated by the letter E?

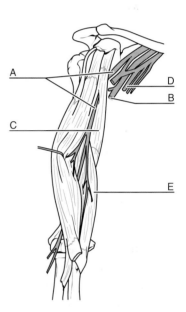

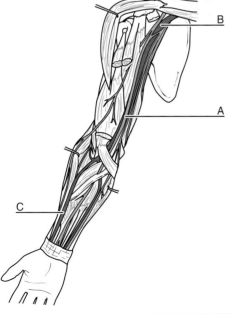

84. What is the structure the vessel must pass to become the vessel indicated by the letter A?
85. What is the name of the vessel indicated by the letter B?
86. What structure must the vessel pass to become the vessel indicated by the letter C?
87. What is the structure the vessel must pass to become the right subclavian artery?
88. What is the name of the vessel found before the vessel indicated by the letter B?
89. What is the name of the vessel indicated by the letter B?
90. What structure does the vessel indicated by the letter C form when it enters the palm of the hand?
91. How many muscles flex at the shoulder?
92. How many muscles are innervated by the ulnar nerve?
93. How many muscles abduct the shoulder?
94. How many muscles attach to the medial border of the scapula
95. How many muscles medially rotate at shoulder?

UNIT 1   PRACTICE TEST

1. All of the following are matching pairs EXCEPT: (Choose all that apply.)
   a. Histology and study of tissues
   b. Embryology and development of the body prior to birth
   c. Gross anatomy and structures seen with the aid of a microscope
   d. Comparative anatomy and comparing human structure to other humans

2. Which of the following systems functions to transport nutrient and oxygen to cells and removes waste molecules that are excreted from the body?
   a. Lymphatic system
   b. Circulatory system
   c. Respiratory system
   d. Digestive system
   e. Endocrine system

3. All of the following structures belong to the respiratory system EXCEPT: (Choose all that apply.)
   a. Trachea
   b. Pharynx
   c. Nasal cavity
   d. Oral cavity
   e. None of the above

4. The following plane is at a right angle to both the median and frontal planes:
   a. Median plane
   b. Frontal plane
   c. Sagittal plane
   d. Midsagittal plane
   e. Horizontal plane

5. Choose the statement that is FALSE regarding the skeletal system's function: (Choose all that apply.)
   a. Hemopoiesis occurs
   b. It provides the framework of the body
   c. It stores chemical substances
   d. It protects vital organs
   e. None of the above

6. An example of an irregular bone is: (Choose all that apply.)
   a. Scapula
   b. Scaphoid
   c. Humerus
   d. Vertebrae
   e. Metacarpal

7. The following bone(s) are part of the axial skeleton EXCEPT: (Choose all that apply.)
   a. Os coxa
   b. Bones of the middle ear
   c. Clavicle
   d. Scapula
   e. Sacrum

8. The following is/are false regarding cartilage: (Choose all that apply.)
   a. Lacks nerves
   b. Vascular
   c. Composed of cells embedded in a watery liquid intercellular substance
   d. Exhibits flexibility to some degree
   e. Entire embryo skeleton initially cartilage

9. All of the following are examples of hyaline cartilage EXCEPT: (Choose all that apply.)
   a. Epiglottis   d. Trachea
   b. Epiphyseal disc   e. Auditory tube
   c. Interpubic disc

For questions 10–13, use the figure on the left and use the letters on the diagram to match the correct statement

10. This structure is not found in an adult.

11. Contains blood cells and fat cells.

12. Can produce growth in diameter of the bone (choose all that apply).

13. Produces synovial fluid.

Use the diagrams to the right to answer questions 14–22.

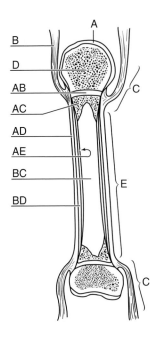

14. All of the following structures are associated with the structure indicated by the letter A EXCEPT: (Choose all that apply.)
    a. Zygomatic arch
    b. Infraorbital foramen
    c. Mandibular fossa
    d. Mastoid process

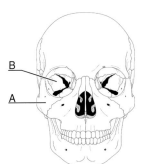

15. All of the following structures are associated with the structure indicated by the letter B EXCEPT:
    a. Supraorbital notch   d. Lesser wing
    b. Sella turcica   e. Greater wing
    c. Optic canal

16. The structure indicated by the letter C articulates with: (Choose all that apply.)
    a. Temporal bone   d. Coronoid notch
    b. External acoustic meatus e. Condyloid process
    c. Mandibular fossa

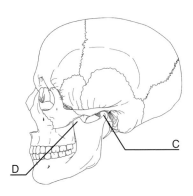

17. The structure indicated by the letter D is the:
    a. Alveolar process   d. Condyloid process
    b. Temporomandibular joint e. Coracoid process
    c. Coronoid process

18. Choose the structure(s) that make up the hard palate using the diagram below.

19. Choose the structure(s) that articulate with cervical vertebrae 1 (atlas) using the diagram below.

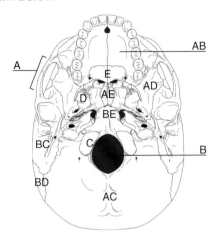

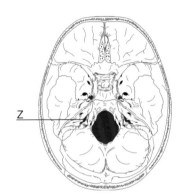

20. The cranial nerves that go through the exit indicated by the letter Z is/are:
    a. VI and VII
    b. IX, X, and XI
    c. XII, and XIII
    d. XI
    e. VII and VIII

21. Using the diagram on the right, identify this bone:
    a. Cervical vertebrae
    b. Sacrum vertebrae
    c. Lumbar vertebrae
    d. Thoracic vertebrae
    e. Coccyx vertebrae

22. Choose the false statement(s) using the answer from question 21. (Choose all that apply.)
    a. This structure gives a primary curvature
    b. This structure gives a secondary curvature
    c. This structure gives a curvature that is concave anteriorly
    d. This structure gives a curvature that is concave posteriorly
    e. This structure possess transverse foramen

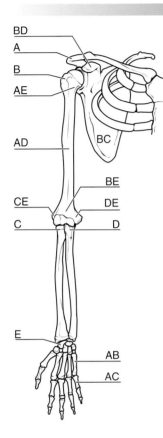

Use the diagram on the left for questions 23–25.

23. What does the structure indicated by the letter D articulate with?
    a. Head of the radius
    b. Coracoid fossa
    c. Capitulim
    d. Coronoid process
    e. Coronoid fossa

24. Choose the letter that indicates the acromion.

25. Choose the structure that contains the groove for ulnar nerve on its posterior aspect.

Use the diagram on the right for questions 26–27.

26. The structure indicated by the letters AC articulate with:
    a. Obturator foramen
    b. Iliosacral joint
    c. Acetabulum
    d. Ischial tuberosity
    e. Pelvic sacral foramina

27. Choose the structure(s) that make up the ankle.

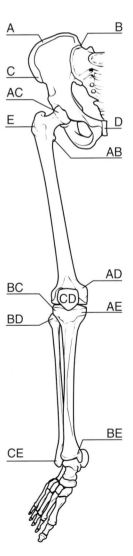

28. Which statement is/are false regarding the integumentary system? (Choose all that apply.)
    a. The skin is the largest organ in the body
    b. Formation of vitamin D takes place
    c. Protects underlying tissues from radiation
    d. Helps to move the body
    e. It is solely made up from the epidermis and dermis

29. All of the following match EXCEPT: (Choose all that apply.)
    a. Epidermis—avascular
    b. Dermis—stratified squamous keratinized epithelium
    c. Epidermis—dense irregular connective tissue
    d. Subcutaneous tissue—adipose cells
    e. Dermis—vascular and contains nerves

Use the diagram below to answer questions 30–33.

30. Choose the letter(s) that indicate(s) the structure(s) that produce oil.

31. Choose the structure that (indirectly) helps to keep body heat inside the body.

32. Choose the letter(s) that indicate(s) the structure that has mitosis occur in its deepest layers.

33. Choose the letter(s) that indicate(s) where the pores of sweat glands are found.

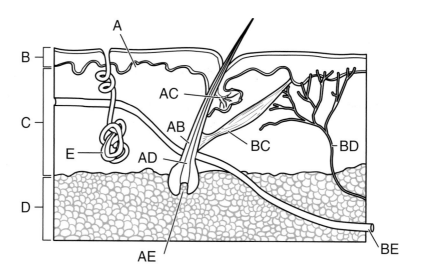

Using the choices below, answer questions 34–39.
   A. 1   B. 2   C. 3   E. 4   AB. 5   AC. 13
   AD. 12   AE. 11   BC. 7   BD. 6   D. 6.5

34. How many muscles flex the wrist?

35. How many muscles are innervated by the radial nerve in the arm and forearm?

36. How many muscles abduct at the shoulder?

37. How many muscles abduct the wrist?

38. How many muscles insert into the medial border of the scapula?

39. How many muscles are innervated by the median nerve in the forearm?

40. All of the following muscles laterally rotate the shoulder EXCEPT: (Choose all that apply.)
   a. Deltoid   d. Infraspinatus
   b. Supraspinatus   e. Teres minor
   c. Teres major

41. All of the following muscles originate at the thoracic vertebrae EXCEPT: (Choose all that apply.)
    a. Latissimus dorsi
    b. Rhomboid major and minor
    c. Levator scapulae
    d. Trapezius
    e. Deltoid

42. All of the following is/are origins of the triceps brachii EXCEPT: (Choose all that apply.)
    a. Supraglenoid tubercle
    b. Humerus above radial nerve
    c. Coracoid process
    d. Lower humerus
    e. Olecranon process

43. The greater tubercle serves as an attachment for all of the following muscles EXCEPT: (Choose all that apply.)
    a. Supraspinatus
    b. Subscapularis
    c. Teres major
    d. Teres minor
    e. Infraspinatus

44. All of the following are included in the hypothenar muscles EXCEPT: (Choose all that apply.)
    a. Abductor digiti minimi
    b. Flexor digiti minimi brevis
    c. Opponens digiti minimi
    d. Palmaris brevis
    e. None of the above

45. How many muscles medially rotate the shoulder?
    a. 5
    b. 4
    c. 3
    d. 6
    e. 44

46. The following muscles extend the elbow: (Choose all that apply.)
    a. Triceps brachii
    b. Extensor carpi radialis longus and brevis
    c. Extensor carpi ulnaris
    d. Anconeus
    e. Latissimus dorsi

47. Using the diagram on the right, choose the letter(s) that indicate(s) the muscle named transverse abdominis: (Choose all that apply.)

48. Using the diagram on the right, choose the letter(s) that indicate(s) the muscle named serratus anterior (choose all that apply).

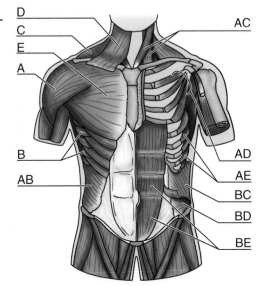

49. Using the diagram below, choose the letter(s) that indicate(s) the muscle named semimembranosus.

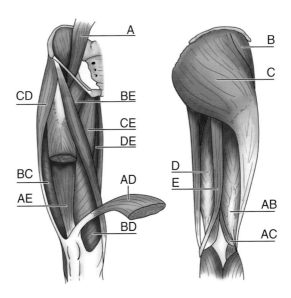

50. Using the diagram above, choose the letter(s) that indicate(s) the muscle named rectus femoris.

51. Choose the false statement: (Choose all that apply.)
    a. Smooth muscle can be found in internal organs and blood vessels
    b. Only cardiac and skeletal muscles are striated
    c. The muscle fiber is the special type of organelle that contains actin and myosin
    d. Irritability is a property of muscle tissue
    e. Fascia is named by classification according to function, shape, location, and structure

52. The following pair helps carry nerve impulses from receptors to the central nervous system:
    a. Motor/efferent
    b. Motor/afferent
    c. Sensory/efferent
    d. Sensory/afferent
    e. Afferent/efferent

53. Choose the false statement(s): (Choose all that apply.)
    a. Synergist muscles maintain body position while a part is moving
    b. The arrangement of elements as load-fulcrum-effort refers to a second-class lever
    c. Supination or flexing with biceps brachii is an example of a first-class lever
    d. The arrangement of elements as load-effort-fulcrum refers to a third-class lever
    e. The extensor digitorum muscle extending the digits is acting as a prime mover

54. The following are all types of amphiarthroses joints EXCEPT: (Choose all that apply.)
    a. Epiphyseal disc
    b. Floppy disc
    c. Intervertebral disc
    d. Interpubic disc
    e. Compact disc

55. Choose the false statement(s): (Choose all that apply.)
    a. Synovial joints can be seen on radiograph
    b. Fibrocartilaginous joints are slightly movable
    c. Hyaline cartilage and some fibrous joints are immovable
    d. The outer fibrous layer of the articular capsule is continuous with the periosteum
    e. Interdigitations can be found in syndesmosis joints

56. *Articulus* means:
    a. "Arthritis" in Greek
    b. "Joint" in Greek
    c. "Joint" in Latin
    d. "Arthritis" in Latin
    e. "Study of joints" in Greek

57. *Pronation* is defined as:
    a. Anterior aspect of the limb rotates medially
    b. Anterior aspect of the limb rotates laterally
    c. Medial rotation of the forearm
    d. Lateral rotation of the forearm
    e. Movement in the frontal plane away from the median plane

58. Choose the false statement(s): (Choose all that apply.)
    a. A plane joint allows movements of flexion and extension in one plane
    b. A condyloid projection fits into a concave depression in a condyloid joint
    c. An example of a pivot is the radioulnar joint
    d. The joints with the most movement allowed is the saddle and ball and socket joint
    e. A bursa is a purse lined with a synovial membrane

59. All of the following are true statements EXCEPT:
    a. Bursa are filled with clear, viscid fluid
    b. The synovial sheath can be found between retinacula of the wrist
    c. Bursa can be found between muscle and bone
    d. Hyaline cartilage is a type of fibrous joint
    e. Synovial joints specialize in free movement

60. All of the following are true regarding the hinge joint EXCEPT:
    a. It allows movement of flexion, extension, and medial and lateral rotation
    b. Movements occur in the sagittal plane
    c. Interphalangeal joint is an example
    d. One articular surface is more convex projections fitting into a concave surface
    e. It is a synovial joint

61. All of the following are true regarding the saddle joint EXCEPT:
    a. Carpometacarpal joint of the thumb is an example
    b. The joint is reciprocally concave-convex
    c. Movements are flexion, extension, abduction, and adduction and rotation
    d. None of the above

62. Choose the correct statement: (Choose all that apply.)
    a. Bursa aid in minimizing friction
    b. Synarthroses is made up of fibrous connective tissue
    c. Sutures are slightly movable
    d. Syndesmoses has a smaller amount of connective tissue than a suture
    e. All of the above are true statements

63. All of the following are true regarding synovial joints EXCEPT:
    a. Synovial fluid is derived from blood
    b. The articular capsule of a synovial joint has an inner layer that is avascular
    c. The synovial membrane nourishes the articular cartilage
    d. Muscles act to limit the movement of a joint
    e. They allow gliding movements

64. Choose the false statement.
    a. A short bone can be used in a plane joint
    b. There are 6 types of synovial joints and 3 major classification groups for joints
    c. Hyaline cartilage will later ossify
    d. Synovial joint is encapsulated by articular cartilage
    e. The synovial joint lacks nerves

65. All of the following function in the frontal plane EXCEPT: (Choose all that apply.)
    a. Circumduction
    b. Flexion
    c. Extension
    d. Abduction
    e. Adduction

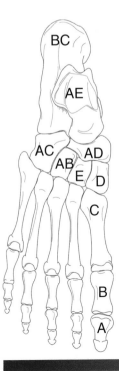

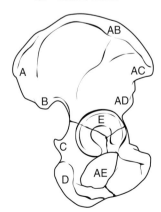

66. Using the diagram on the left, choose the letter(s) that indicate(s) the posterior inferior iliac spine.

67. Using the diagram on the right, choose the letter(s) that indicate(s) the cuneiform bones.

68. Using the diagram on the right, choose the letter(s) that indicate(s) your proximal phalange.

ANSWER KEY

For Unit 1 Practice Quizzes and Tests

1A Course Introduction Practice Quiz
1. e
2. e
3. d
4. a, d
5. c
6. a
7. a

1B Integumentary System Practice Quiz
1. a, c
2. e
3. c
4. d
5. d
6. b

1C Skeletal System Practice Quiz
1. a, c
2. b, e
3. a, e
4. a, b
5. c, d, e
6. a, d, e

1D&E Axial and Appendicular Skeleton Practice Quiz
1. d
2. c
3. ab
4. ac
5. c
6. a
7. b

8. ab
9. d
10. cd
11. c
12. b
13. ac
14. abc
15. ace
16. b
17. ab
18. ae
19. bc
20. bd
21. cd
22. a
23. c
24. ab
25. c
26. bc
27. ad
28. ac
29. ae
30. bc
31. ab
32. b
33. c
34. ad
35. ae
36. d
37. ac
38. d, e
39. c
40. d
41. a
42. ad
43. bd
44. c
45. be

46. cd
47. ab
48. d
49. a
50. b
51. ac
52. b
53. e
54. ad
55. bc
56. cd
57. d
58. a
59. ac
60. ce
61. a
62. e
63. bd
64. be

1F Articular System Practice Quiz
1. c
2. c
3. a
4. b
5. e, c
6. c
7. a
8. b, c
9. a, d
10. b, d
11. b, e
12. b, d
13. e
14. c
15. d
16. b

17. e
18. a
19. a
20. e
21. b, c
22. c, d
23. e
24. d
25. a, d, e
26. a, b, c
27. a
28. a, b
29. a, d
30. c
31. c, e

1I Upper Limb Musculature Practice Quiz

1. Deltoid tuberosity
2. Teres minor muscle
3. Extend, adduct, and medially rotate at shoulder
4. C7 and T1
5. Adduct and medially rotate at the shoulder
6. Flex, extend, medially and laterally rotate, and abduct at shoulder
7. Branch of brachial plexus – long thoracic nerve
8. Pectoralis minor
9. Pectoralis major, teres major, deltoid, or latissimus dorsi
10. Deltoid
11. Supraspinatus and teres minor
12. Supraspinatus, infraspinatus, subscapularis, and teres minor
13. Coracobrachialis and short head of biceps brachii
14. Branch of brachial plexus—axillary nerve
15. Trapezius
16. Flex and supinate the forearm
17. Coracoid process
18. Middle medial humerus
19. Short head of biceps brachii
20. Lower humerus and coronoid process
21. Anterior arm muscles
22. Infraglenoid tubercle
23. Radial nerve
24. Olecranon process
25. Inferior angle of infraspinous fossa
26. Insertion, action, and innervation
27. Supinates forearm
28. biceps brachii
29. Sweat band muscle/ wrist band muscle
30. Median nerve
31. Radial nerve
32. Superficial anterior forearm
33. Pronates forearm
34. deep anterior forearm
35. extensor carpi radialis brevis
36. Radial nerve
37. Extensor carpi radialis brevis
38. Extend digits 2–5
39. Adduct and extend the wrist
40. Extensor pollicis brevis
41. Abduct thumb
42. Extend digit 2 or index finger
43. Flex and abduct wrist
44. Palmaris longus
45. Flex wrist
46. Superficial anterior forearm
47. Ulnar nerve
48. Flex digits 2–5
49. Flex thumb
50. Ulnar and median nerve
51. Median nerve
52. Intermediate layer of anterior forearm
53. Flex forearm
54. Triceps brachii
55. Ulnar nerve
56. Flex and adduct the wrist
57. Extend digit 5
58. Radial nerve
59. Brachioradialis
60. Ulnar nerve
61. Lateral, medial, and posterior
62. C5-C8 and T1
63. 16 nerves
64. Nothing
65. Median nerve
66. Triceps brachii
67. Supinator
68. Extensor pollicis brevis
69. Hockey stick muscle
70. Abductor pollicis longus
71. Superficial anterior forearm
72. Radial nerve
73. Abduct and flex wrist
74. 10%–16%
75. Median nerve
76. Pronate forearm
77. 88%
78. Posterior arm and forearm and part of the skin on the posterior hand
79. Flex arm at shoulder
80. Deltoid and pectoralis major
81. Ulnar nerve
82. Flex at elbow
83. Biceps brachii

84. Inferior border of teres major
85. Axillary artery
86. Pass elbow
87. First rib
88. Right subclavian artery
89. Axillary artery
90. Deep arch
91. 3—pectoralis major, deltoid, coracobrachialis
92. 1.5—flexor carpi ulnaris and half of flexor digitorum profundus
93. 2—supraspinatus and deltoid
94. 4—rhomboid major and minor, levator scapulae, and serratus anterior
95. 5—pectoralis major, deltoid, latissimus dorsi, teres major, and subscapularis

1A-I Unit 1 Practice Test
1. c, d
2. b
3. e
4. e
5. e
6. d
7. a, c, d
8. b, c
9. a, c, e
10. ab
11. bc
12. ad and ae
13. b
14. b, c, d
15. a
16. a, c
17. c
18. ab, e
19. c
20. b
21. c
22. b, d
23. e
24. a
25. de
26. c
27. be, ce
28. d, e
29. b, c
30. ac
31. bc
32. b
33. b
34. c
35. ac
36. b
37. c
38. e
39. d
40. b, c
41. c, e
42. a, c, d, e
43. b, c
44. e
45. a
46. a, d
47. bd
48. b, ae
49. d
50. ad
51. c, e
52. d
53. a, b, c
54. b, e
55. a, e
56. c
57. c
58. a, e
59. d
60. a
61. d
62. a, b
63. b
64. d
65. b, c
66. b
67. ab, d, e
68. b

UNIT 2

Worksheets

2A Muscles of the Lower Extremity .... pp. 123–126
2B Nervous System in General .... pp. 127–130
2C Endocrine System................................... pp. 131–133
2D Brain... pp. 134–136
2E Spinal Cord and Meninges....................... pp. 137–140
2F Peripheral Nervous System (PNS)............ pp. 141–147
2G Special Senses and Receptors................. pp. 148–152
2H Autonomic Nervous System..................... pp. 153–156

Study Resources

2A Lower Limb Musculature .... pp. 158–160
2B Nervous System...................................... p. 161
2C Endocrine System................................... p. 162
2D Brain... pp. 163–164
2E Spinal Cord and Meninges....................... pp. 165–166
2F Peripheral Nervous System...................... p. 167
2G Special Senses and Receptors................. pp. 168–169

Practice Quizzes

2A Lower Limb Musculature
   Practice Quizzes....................................... pp. 171–177
2B Nervous System Practice Quiz .... pp. 178–184
2C Endocrine System Practice Quiz .... pp. 185–186
2D Brain Practice Quiz .... pp. 187–188
2E Spinal Cord and Meninges
   Practice Quiz.. pp. 189–190
2G Special Senses and Receptors
   Practice Quiz.. pp. 191–194
2H Autonomic Nervous System
   Practice Quiz.. pp. 195–196
2A–H Unit 2 Practice Test............................ pp. 197–210
Answer Key .... pp. 211–213

MUSCLES OF THE LOWER EXTREMITY

Gluteal Region (494,495)

Muscle	Origin	Insertion	Action	Innervation
Gluteus maximus m.	Ilium, sacrum, coccyx	Gluteal tuberosity	Extend and laterally rotate thigh at hip	Inferior gluteal n.
Gluteus medius m.	Ilium	Greater trochanter	Abduct and medially rotate thigh	Superior gluteal n.
Gluteus minimus m.	Ilium	Greater trochanter	Abduct and medially rotate thigh	Superior gluteal n.
Tensor fasciae latae m.	Iliac crest, ASIS	IT band	Flex and medially rotate thigh	Superior gluteal n.

Iliotibial Tract or Band (476) = IT Band

Lateral Rotators (495)

Muscle	Origin	Insertion	Action	Innervation
Piriformis m.	Anterior sacrum	Greater trochanter	Lateral rotation	Nerve to piriformis
Superior gemellus m.	Spine of ischium	OI tendon	Lateral rotation	Sacral Plexus n.
Obturator internus m. (OI)	Internal surface of obturator membrane	Greater trochanter	Lateral rotation	Sacral Plexus n.
Inferior gemellus m.	Ischial tuberosity	OI tendon	Lateral rotation	Sacral Plexus n.
Quadratus femoris m.	Ischial tuberosity	Intertrochanteric crest	Lateral rotation	Sacral Plexus n.
Obturator externus m.				

Anterior Thigh Muscles (492)

Muscle	Origin	Insertion	Action	Innervation
Iliopsoas m.	Iliac fossa, lumbar vertebrae	Lesser trochanter	Flexion of trunk	Femoral n.
Sartorius m.	ASIS	Upper medial tibia (pes anserinus)	Flex, abduct, laterally rotate thigh, Flex leg	Femoral n.
Quadriceps femoris				
Rectus femoris m.	AIIS, acetabulum	Tibial tuberosity	Flex thigh, extend leg	Femoral n.
Vastus lateralis m.	Greater trochanter, linea aspera	Tibial tuberosity	Extend leg	Femoral n.
Vastus medialis m.	Linea aspera	Tibial tuberosity	Extend leg	Femoral n.
Vastus intermedius m.	Upper femur	Tibial tuberosity	Extend leg	Femoral n.

Medial Thigh Muscles (492–493)

Muscle	Origin	Insertion	Action	Innervation
Gracilis m.	Pubis	Upper medial tibia (pes anserinus)	Adduct and flex thigh	Obturator n.
Pectineus m.	Pubis	Upper femur	Adduct and flex thigh	Femoral n.
Adductor longus m.	Pubis	Linea aspera	Adduct and flex thigh	Obturator n.
Adductor brevis m.	Pubis	Linea aspera	Adduct and flex thigh	Obturator n.
Adductor magnus m.	Adductor part: Ischiopubic ramus	Linea aspera	Adduct and flex thigh	Obturator n.
	Extensor part: Ischial tuberosity	Adductor tubercle	Extend thigh	Sciatic n.

Posterior Thigh Muscles (Hamstrings) (495, 502)

Muscle	Origin	Insertion	Action	Innervation
Semitendinosus m.	Ischial tuberosity	Upper medial tibia (pes anserinus)	Extend thigh, Flex leg	Sciatic n.
Semimembranosus m.	Ischial tuberosity	Medial condyle of tibia	Extend thigh, Flex leg	Sciatic n.
Biceps Femoris m.:				
Long head	Ischial tuberosity	Head of fibula	Extend thigh, Flex leg	Sciatic n.
Short head	Linea aspera		Laterally rotate leg at knee	Sciatic n.

Pes Anserinus

Common insertion into the upper medial surface of the tibia involving the tendons: (506)

Sartorius m.

Gracilis m.

Semitendinosus m.

Anterior Leg Compartment (519)

Muscle	Origin	Insertion	Action	Innervation
Tibialis anterior m.	Upper lateral tibia	Medial cuneiform, 1st metatarsal	Dorsiflex and invert foot	Deep fibular/ peroneal n.
Extensor hallucis longus m.	Middle fibula	Distal phalanx of toe 1	Extend big toe	Deep fibular/ peroneal n.
Extensor digitorum longus m.	Lateral condyle of tibia, upper fibula	Toes 2–5	Extend toes 2–5	Deep fibular/ peroneal n.
Fibularis (peroneus) tertius m.	Lower fibula	5th metatarsal	Dorsiflex and evert foot	Deep fibular/ peroneal n.

Lateral Leg Compartment (521)

Muscle	Origin	Insertion	Action	Innervation
Fibularis (peroneus) longus m.	Upper fibula	Medial cuneiform, 1st metatarsal	Evert foot	Superficial fibular/ peroneal n.
Fibularis (peroneus) brevis m.	Lower fibula	5th metatarsal	Evert foot	Superficial fibular/ peroneal n.

Superficial Posterior Leg Compartment (516–517)

Muscle	Origin	Insertion	Action	Innervation
Gastrocnemius m.	Lateral and medial condyles of femur	Calcaneus	Plantar flex foot	Tibial n.
Soleus m.	Upper tibia and Upper fibula	Calcaneus	Plantar flex foot	Tibial n.
Plantaris m. (nickname: freshman nerve)	Above lateral condyle of femur	Calcaneus	Plantar flex foot	Tibial n.

Deep Posterior Leg Compartment (518)

Muscle	Origin	Insertion	Action	Innervation
Tibialis posterior m.	Upper fibula and tibia	Tarsals, metatarsals 2–4	Invert foot	Tibial n.
Flexor digitorum longus m.	Middle tibia	Distal phalanx toes 2–5	Flex toes 2–5	Tibial n.
Flexor hallucis longus m.	Middle fibula	Distal phalanx toe 1	Flex toe 1	Tibial n.

Dorsum of Foot (530–531)

Muscle	Action	Innervation
Extensor digitorum brevis	Extend toes 1–4	Deep fibular/peroneal n.

Plantar Surface of Foot (Layers 1–4) (532–537)

Muscle	Action	Innervation
LAYER 1		
Abductor hallucis m.	Abduct big toe	Medial plantar n. (MPN)
Flexor digitorum brevis m.	Flex toe 2–5	MPN
Abductor digiti minimi m.	Abduct toe 5	Lateral plantar n. (LPN)
LAYER 2		
Quadratus plantae m.	Flex toes 2–5	LPN
Lumbricals	Flex toes 2–5	LPN and MPN
LAYER 3		
Flexor hallucis brevis m.	Flex big toe	MPN
Adductor hallucis m.	Adduct big toe	LPN
Flexor digiti minimi brevis m.	Flex little toe	LPN
LAYER 4		
Plantar interossei (1–3)	Adduct toes 3–5	LPN
Dorsal interossei (1–4)	Abduct toes 2–4	LPN

Note: Actions are listed as acting on a body part, for example flex thigh. Keep in mind that this refers to the same action as flex thigh at the hip joint. Actions involving movement of the thigh occur at the hip. Actions involving movement of the leg occur at the knee and actions of the foot occur at the ankle.

NERVOUS SYSTEM IN GENERAL

I. COORDINATING SYSTEMS OF THE BODY

A. NERVOUS SYSTEM: rapid activity.

　　1. Example: movement and thinking

B. ENDOCRINE SYSTEM: slow activity.

　　1. Example: _____

II. NERVOUS SYSTEM

A. DEFINITION: a coordinating system of the body composed of a group of highly _____ cells for conducting nerve impulses to a center so responses can be made.

　　1. The nervous system provides a control for the _____ activities of the body.

III. TWO MAJOR SUBDIVISIONS OF THE NERVOUS SYSTEM

A. CENTRAL NERVOUS SYSTEM (CNS)

　　1. _____

　　2. _____

B. PERIPHERAL NERVOUS SYSTEM (PNS)

　　1. Nerves

IV. PRIMARY FUNCTIONS OF NERVOUS TISSUE ARE:

1. To receive stimuli from the _____ (Receptor)

2. To transform these stimuli into nerve impulses (Receptor)

3. To transmit these impulses to the proper nerve center of the body (Neuron)

4. To process the information and determine the appropriate response (Brain, spinal cord)

5. This response is transmitted to the _____ organ (Neuron)

6. The effector organ carries out the response (_____)

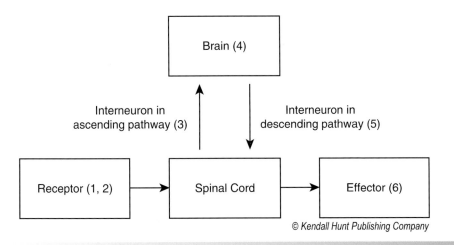

V. STRUCTURAL COMPONENTS OF THE NERVOUS SYSTEM

A. The nervous system consists of two principal types of cells:

    1. _____

    2. _____

B. The neuron is the functional unit of the nervous system.

© Kendall Hunt Publishing Company

(D) _____: cytoplasmic extensions that receive information and transmit it toward the cell body.

(CB) Cell body or soma: contains the nucleus and controls the metabolic activity of the neuron.

(AH) _____: connects the cell body to the axon (A).

(M) Myelin: insulating substance which allows axons to conduct impulses faster.

    1. Glial cells produce myelin.

       a. _____ produce myelin in the CNS

       b. _____ cells produce myelin in the PNS.

(NR) Nodes of _____: gaps between segments of myelin

(ST) Synaptic terminals: swellings at the end of the axon, involved in neurotransmitter release.

(S) _____: gap between the axon terminal of one neuron and the dendrite of another.

VI. NEUROGLIA: SUPPORTIVE CONNECTIVE TISSUE THAT NURTURES AND PROTECTS THE NEURONS.

A. There are six types:

    1. _____ cells (neurolemmocytes): form fatty myelin sheaths around the most axons in the PNS only.

       a. This insulatory material is not continuous along the axon but is interrupted at the nodes of Ranvier.

       b. The nerve impulses jump from node to node as they travel down the axon, a conduction called saltatory conduction.

    2. Oligodendrocytes: form similar myelin sheaths in the CNS only.

3. _____: phagocytic cells that migrate throughout the CNS removing debris; may migrate to areas where nervous tissue is injured.

4. _____: regulate the passage of molecules from blood to the brain; helps form the blood-brain barrier that regulates the passage of substances into the brain.

5. Ependymal cells: line the brain chambers called ventricles and help form the choroid plexus, which produces cerebrospinal fluid (CSF).

6. _____ cells: support neuron cell bodies in ganglia of the PNS.

VII. NEUROGLIA IN THE CNS CONSISTS OF:

A. Astrocytes

B. Microglia

C. Oligodendrocytes

D. _____ cells

VIII. NEUROGLIA IN THE PNS CONSISTS OF:

A. Schwann cells

B. _____ cells

IX. CLASSIFICATION OF NEURONS

A. Neurons can be classified structurally or functionally:

B. Structural classification:

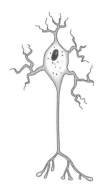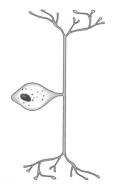

© Kendall Hunt Publishing Company

Multipolar	Bipolar	Unipolar
___ branches off the soma	___ branches off the soma	___ branch off the soma

   C. Functional classification:
      1. _____ NEURONS transmit sensory nerve impulses from receptors to the brain and spinal cord.
      2. EFFERENT NEURONS convey motor nerve impulses from the brain and spinal cord to effectors (muscles and glands).
      3. INTERNEURONS (aka internuncial neurons) carry impulses from one neuron to another.
         a. This group makes up the _____ of nerves in the body

X. NEURONAL ACTIVITY:

   A. Neurons are specialized to receive signals from sensory receptors or from other neurons in the body and transfer this information along the length of the axon.
   B. Impulses, known as _____ POTENTIALS, travel the length of the axon and invade the nerve terminal, thereby causing the release of neurotransmitter in to the synapse.

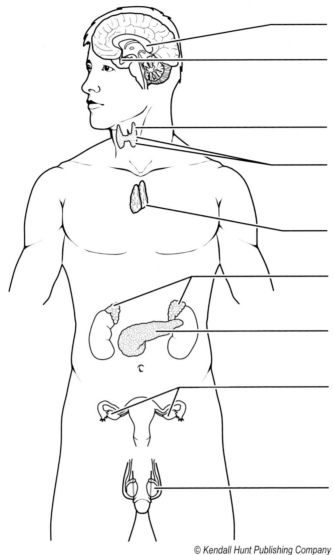

© Kendall Hunt Publishing Company

I. PITUITARY GLAND (OR HYPOPHYSIS) HANGS BY A STALK FROM THE HYPOTHALAMUS OF THE BRAIN.

A. Posterior pituitary: appears fibrous

    1. Neurons produce _____, an antidiuretic hormone, and oxytocin.

    2. ADH is stored in, and released from, the posterior pituitary gland in response to neural stimulation from the hypothalamus via the hypothalamohypophyseal system.

B. Anterior pituitary gland: appears glandular

    1. Develops from epithelial tissue that pinches off from the roof of the embryo's mouth.

2. Produces the hormones it secretes:
   a. _____ hormone (GH)
   b. Adrenocorticotropic hormone (ACTH)
   c. Thyroid-stimulating hormone (TSH)
   d. Luteinizing hormone (LH)
   e. Follicle-stimulating hormone (FSH)
   f. _____ (PRL)
   g. Melanocyte-stimulating hormone (MSH)

II. THYROID GLAND

A. Shaped like a bowtie or shield and lies just below the Adam's apple in the front of the _____.
B. _____helps set basal metabolic rate by stimulating the rate of cell respiration.
C. In children, thyroid hormones also promote growth and stimulate maturation of the CNS.

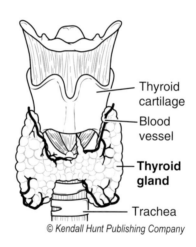

Thyroid cartilage
Blood vessel
Thyroid gland
Trachea

© Kendall Hunt Publishing Company

III. PARATHYROID GLANDS

A. Four small glands attached to the posterior surface of the thyroid gland.
B. Produces parathyroid hormone (PTH), which is involved in calcium homeostasis.

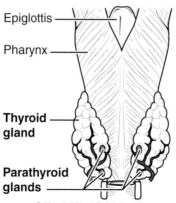

Epiglottis
Pharynx
Thyroid gland
Parathyroid glands

© Kendall Hunt Publishing Company

IV. ADRENAL GLANDS

A. It is located above each _____.

B. Each gland composed of inner portion (adrenal medulla) and outer layer (adrenal cortex).

C. Adrenal cortex

   1. Hormones from adrenal cortex are collectively referred to as _____.

D. Adrenal medulla

   1. Secretes epinephrine and norepinephrine in response to the ANS.

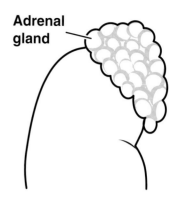

Adrenal gland

V. PANCREAS

A. It is located adjacent to the stomach and is connected to the _____ by the pancreatic duct.

B. Secretes insulin and a variety of digestive _____ into small intestine.

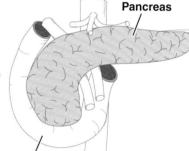

Pancreas

Duodenum

VI. OVARIES AND TESTES

A. Produce _____.

B. Associated with secondary sexual characteristics.

VII. PINEAL GLAND

A. Secretes _____.

B. Regulates biological clocks.

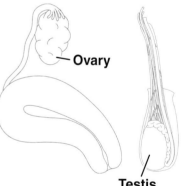

Ovary

Testis

VIII. ENDOCRINE DISRUPTING CHEMICALS

A. Chemicals that interfere with hormone function.

B. Any chemical that can bind to receptor proteins and mimic the effects of the hormone is called a hormone _____.

C. An example is chlorine, which the body interprets as estrogen. This causes an increase in female characteristics like gyneomastia and a reduction in sperm count.

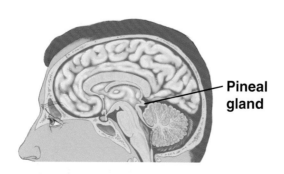

Pineal gland

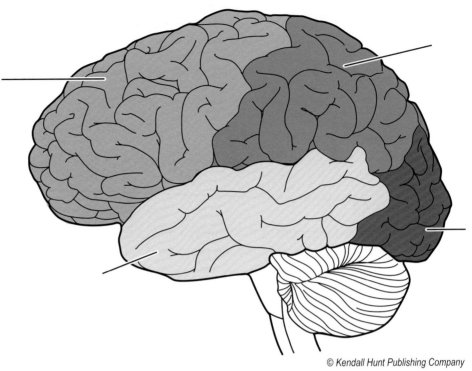

© Kendall Hunt Publishing Company

I. CEREBRUM

A. Largest part of the brain consisting of two _____.

B. Gyri: convolutions of the cerebrum separated by sulci.

C. Contains various fissures and large _____.

D. Four of these major fissures or sulci are named here:

1. Longitudinal fissure: separates the right and left hemispheres and is occupied by the falx _____.

2. Transverse fissure or sulcus: separates the cerebrum and cerebellum and is occupied by the _____ cerebelli.

3. Lateral sulcus or fissure: separates the temporal lobe from the rest of the cerebrum.

4. Central sulcus: separates the precentral (motor) and postcentral (_____) gyri.

   a. The primary motor cortex is precentral gyrus; it lies _____ to the central sulcus.

   b. The primary sensory cortex is postcentral gyrus; it lies posterior to the central sulcus.

E. 5 lobes

1. Frontal, parietal, occipital, _____, and insula.

2. The insula lies within the depths of the lateral sulcus.

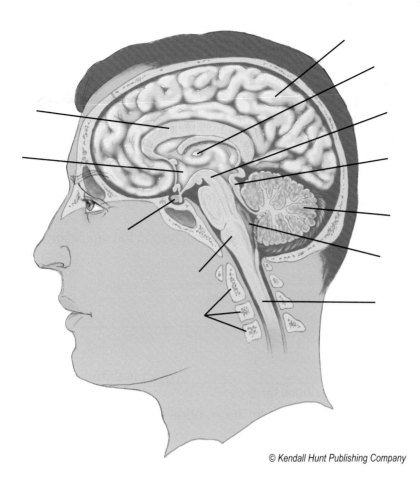

© Kendall Hunt Publishing Company

II. BASAL GANGLIA (NUCLEI)
A. Constitute the central _____ matter of the cerebrum.
B. Function in control of movement and posture.
   1. Diseases involve disturbances in voluntary _____ control.
      a. Example: Parkinson's disease, Huntington's chorea

III. THALAMUS
A. The most important _____ relay center of the brain.
   1. It sends incoming impulses from the receptors of the body to the cerebral cortex.

IV. HYPOTHALAMUS
A. It lies between and is associated with the:
   1. Optic chiasma: where optic tracts (CNII) cross.
   2. Mammillary bodies: sensory synaptic station.
   3. Pituitary gland: projects inferior from it and secretes many _____.

    B. Functions in the regulation of visceral activity:

       1. Body _____

       2. Carbohydrate and lipid metabolism

       3. Sleep, sexual activity, and _____

V. MEDULLA OBLONGATA

    A. Part of the brain directly continuous with the spinal cord and will contain most of the ascending and descending tracts of the spinal cord.

    B. Represents an area where pyramidal tract fibers lie, called the PYRAMIDS.

       1. Contains several nuclei involved in the regulation of vital body activities:

          a. _____

          b. Cardiac (heart rate)

          c. Vasomotor (blood _____)

VI. PONS

    A. Acts as a _____ connecting the right and left cerebellar hemispheres.

    B. Relay impulses from the cerebral cortex to the cerebellum.

VII. CEREBELLUM (LITTLE BRAIN)

    A. Connects with the midbrain, pons, and medulla oblongata.

    B. Consists of two hemispheres separated by a median _____.

    C. Outer cortex contains folia separated by fissures; folia means leaves.

    D. Internally presents white matter branching in the form of a tree, called the arbor _____.

    E. Functions to:

       1. Coordinate muscular activity

       2. Regulate muscle _____

       3. Maintain _____

VIII. CORPORA QUADRIGEMINA

    A. Consists of four elevations:

       1. Superior colliculi involved in the pathway of vision.

       2. Inferior colliculi involved in the pathway of _____.

IX. THE BRAINSTEM IS MADE UP OF THREE PARTS:

    A. Midbrain

    B. _____

    C. Medulla oblongata

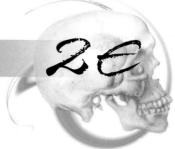
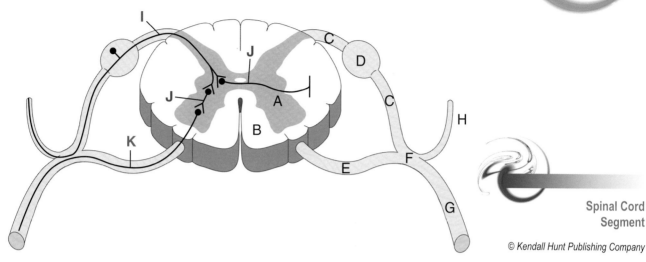

Spinal Cord
Segment

© Kendall Hunt Publishing Company

I. **SPINAL CORD IN GENERAL: ON THE RIGHT SIDE OF THE DIAGRAM.**

A. _____ of the spinal cord.

   1. Gray matter is an area of cell bodies within the CNS.

B. _____ of the spinal cord.

   1. White matter is an area of axons or fibers within the CNS.

C. _____ arising from the dorsal surface of the spinal cord.

   1. This contains sensory neurons only.

D. DORSAL ROOT _____:
an enlarged portion of the dorsal root.

   1. A ganglion is an area of cell bodies outside of the CNS.

   2. The dorsal root ganglion contains cell bodies of sensory neurons.

E. _____ROOT arising from the ventral surface of the spinal cord.

   1. This contains motor neurons only.

F. The ventral root joins with the dorsal root to form the SPINAL NERVE.

G. The spinal nerve divides into a larger VENTRAL _____, which supplies the entire anterior trunk as well as the appendages.

H. A smaller DORSAL _____.

   1. The dorsal ramus supplies all the structures of the back.

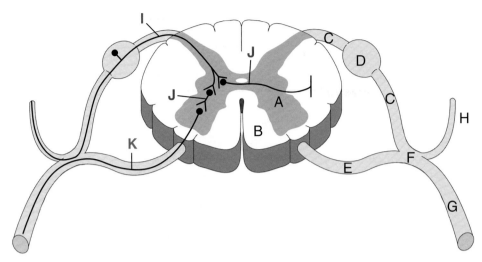

ON THE LEFT SIDE OF THE DIAGRAM:

I. _____ or afferent NEURON
with its cell body in the dorsal root ganglion.

J. _____or   INTERNUNCIAL
NEURON

1. One is shown synapsing with a motor neuron.

2. Another is shown crossing over to the other side of the cord, leaving the gray matter and entering the white matter, and beginning to ascend through the cord.

K. _____ or efferent NEURON
with its cell body in the gray matter of the cord, and its axon passing through the white matter into the ventral root.

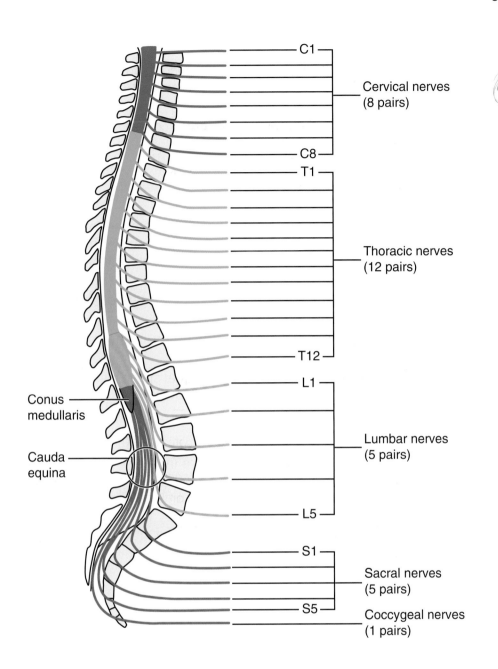

C1

Cervical nerves
(8 pairs)

C8

T1

Thoracic nerves
(12 pairs)

T12

L1

Conus
medullaris

Lumbar nerves
(5 pairs)

Cauda
equina

L5

S1

Sacral nerves
(5 pairs)

S5

Coccygeal nerves
(1 pairs)

**Spinal Cord and
Associated Structures**

© *Kendall Hunt Publishing Company*

II. ANATOMY OF THE SPINAL CORD AS A WHOLE

A. The spinal cord is a long cylindrical mass of nervous tissue that occupies the upper _____ of the vertebral canal.

B. It is connected to the brain superiorly where it is continuous with the medulla oblongata and extends to the level of _____.

C. It presents enlargements in the _____ and lumbar regions, where the cell bodies of the neurons for the _____ limb and lower limb are located.

D. The lower end of the cord has a conical shape and is termed the _____ MEDULLARIS.

E. Below the level of LV2, the vertebral canal is occupied by the CAUDA _____, which consists of the very long roots of the lower spinal nerves, which descend in a bundle from the conus medullaris.

III. MENINGES

A. The brain and spinal cord are surrounded and _____ by three layers of connective tissue, collectively termed meninges.

B. From external to internal, the meninges consist of the dura mater, arachnoid mater, and pia mater.

C. DURA MATER

   1. It is the outermost meninge, composed of _____ fibrous connective tissue.

   2. The dura of the spinal cord extends from the foramen magnum where it is continuous with the dura mater that surrounds the brain and then courses inferiorly to the coccyx in the vertebral canal.

   3. The space external to the dura mater is termed the _____ SPACE.

      a. This space contains adipose tissue in the form of globules of _____.

      b. In addition to this fat, the epidural space also contains the VERTEBRAL VENOUS PLEXUS.

D. ARACHNOID MATER

   1. It is the _____ meninge.

   2. It is a delicate, loose, netlike membrane that extends from the foramen magnum where it is continuous with the cerebral arachnoid inferiorly through the vertebral column to coccyx.

   3. It is separated from the pia mater by the SUBARACHNOID SPACE, which is the space containing CEREBROSPINAL FLUID (_____).

E. PIA MATER

   1. It is the innermost layer of meninges.

   2. It is very delicate connective tissue that _____ to the surface of the brain and spinal cord.

   3. It also extends from the foramen magnum to the coccyx.

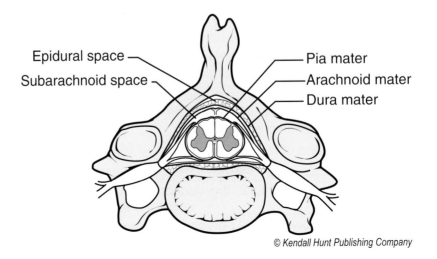

Epidural space ——
Subarachnoid space ——
—— Pia mater
—— Arachnoid mater
—— Dura mater

I. PNS IN GENERAL

A. Periphery means along the _____ .

B. PNS extends beyond the CNS; thus, it includes all the nervous tissue structures except the brain and spinal cord.

C. Most of the PNS is not protected by _____ , unlike the CNS.

II. PNS IS COMPOSED OF:

A. _____ pairs of cranial nerves

B. _____ pairs of spinal nerves

III. SPINAL NERVES ORIGINATE FROM THE SPINAL CORD

A. They are made up of:

1. _____ pairs of cervical spinal nerves
2. 12 pairs of thoracic spinal nerves
3. 5 pairs of lumbar spinal nerves
4. _____ pairs of sacral spinal nerves
5. 1 pair of coccygeal spinal nerves

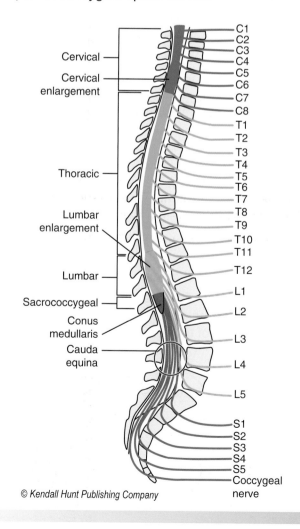

Cervical — C1, C2, C3, C4, C5
Cervical enlargement — C6, C7, C8
Thoracic — T1, T2, T3, T4, T5, T6, T7, T8, T9, T10, T11, T12
Lumbar enlargement
Lumbar — L1, L2, L3, L4, L5
Sacrococcygeal
Conus medullaris
Cauda equina — S1, S2, S3, S4, S5
Coccygeal nerve

IV. BRANCHES FROM SPINAL NERVE

A. Spinal nerves branch to form ventral and dorsal rami.

1. Dorsal rami will supply structures on the _____.

2. Ventral rami will supply structures on the front of the torso and the entire _____ (upper and lower limb).

    a. Thus, a nerve that passes through the ventral ramus supplies the back of the hand.

V. PLEXI OF THE BODY

A. Cervical plexus

1. Includes ventral rami _____.

2. Will supply muscles and skin of the neck.

3. Phrenic nerve comes off of C3, C4, and C5 and supplies the diaphragm.

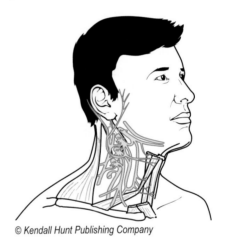

© Kendall Hunt Publishing Company

B. Brachial plexus

1. Includes ventral rami _____.

2. Supplies the entire upper limb except the trapezius muscle and the skin over the upper medial portion of the arm and part of the upper shoulder.

3. There is a total of 16 nerves that come off the plexus; we will focus on 4 of them:

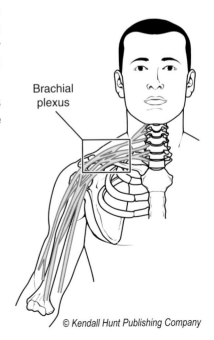

Brachial plexus

© Kendall Hunt Publishing Company

Nerve	Rami	Cord Derived from	Supplies	Special Notes
Musculocutaneous n.	C5–C7	Lateral	All anterior arm mm. and changes name to LATERAL ANTEBRACHIAL CUTANEOUS N (LAC), which supplies _____ _____ forearm.	50% of fibers supply muscle, 50% supply skin.
	C5–T1	Medial and lateral	Motor and sensory supply to some of the anterior forearm mm. and some anterior hand mm,	Only nerve to course through the carpal tunnel (canal).
Ulnar n.	C8, T1	Medial	Motor and sensory supply to some anterior forearm mm., and most of the hand mm.; in hand splits into a superficial and deep branch.	Lies _____ to the medial epicondyle.
	C5–T1	Posterior	Motor and sensory supply to posterior arm, forearm skin and mm; also supplies skin on posterior upper limb.	Supplies nearly all posterior structures of the upper limb.

C. LUMBOSACRAL PLEXUS

   1. Includes ventral rami L1–S4.

   2. Lumbar plexus begins and is located in the _____.

   3. Sacral plexus begins and is located in the pelvis.

   4. Lumbar plexus

      a. Ventral rami: L1–_____

      b. 2 major nerves:

         i. Femoral nerve (_____)

        ii. Obturator nerve (L2–L4)

           a) Obturator means "to stop up" or "fill up"

   5. Sacral plexus

      a. Ventral rami: L4–S4

      b. 5 major nerves:

         i. Posterior femoral cutaneous nerve: largest cutaneous nerve in body

        ii. _____ nerve (L4–S3): largest of all nerves in the body.

           a) Branches include tibial nerve and common fibular (peroneal) nerve.

              1) Tibial nerve supplies the posterior leg and majority of the _____.

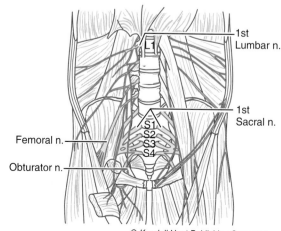

2) Common fibular (peroneal) nerve branches into the deep fibular nerve, which supplies the anterior leg and the superficial fibular (peroneal) nerve, which supplies the lateral leg.

iii. Superior gluteal nerve (L4, L5, S1) supplies gluteus medius, gluteus and tensor fasciae latae minimus.

iv. Inferior gluteal nerve (L5, S1, S2) supplies gluteus _____.

v. Pudendal nerve supplies genitalia.

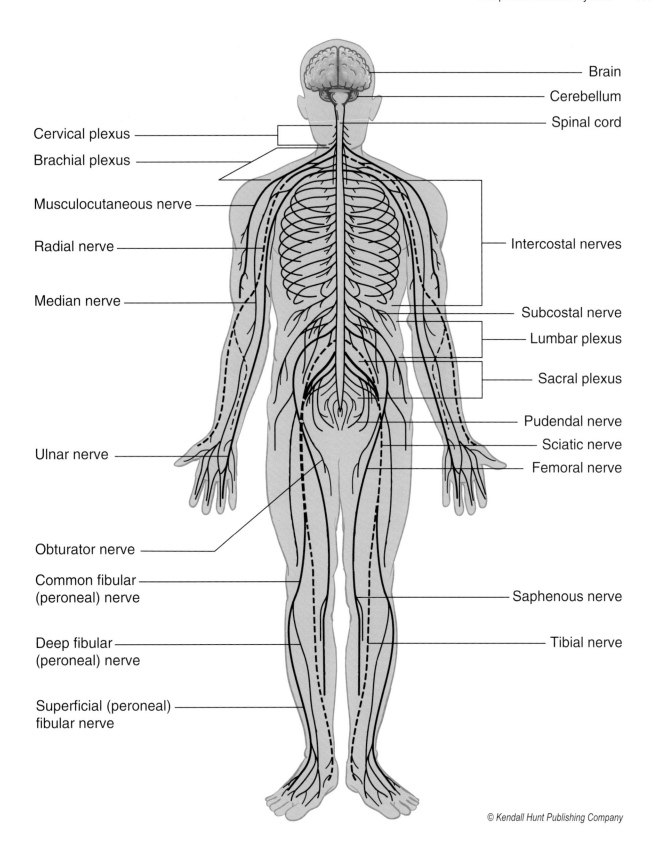

Brain

Cerebellum

Spinal cord

Cervical plexus

Brachial plexus

Musculocutaneous nerve

Radial nerve

Median nerve

Intercostal nerves

Subcostal nerve

Lumbar plexus

Sacral plexus

Ulnar nerve

Pudendal nerve

Sciatic nerve

Femoral nerve

Obturator nerve

Common fibular
(peroneal) nerve

Saphenous nerve

Deep fibular
(peroneal) nerve

Tibial nerve

Superficial (peroneal)
fibular nerve

CRANIAL NERVES

CN Name and Number	Type	Function	Cranial Exit	Pathway
Olfactory	Sensory	Smell	Cribriform plate	Olfactory nerve fibers pass through the cribriform plate to synapse in olfactory bulb and extend as olfactory tract to primary olfactory cortex.
Optic	Sensory	Vision	Optic canal	Fibers course from retina of eye in the optic nerve through the optic canal; some may cross over in the chiasma; nerves synapse on the thalamus and then run to the occipital cortex, where interpretation occurs.
Oculomotor	Motor	Intrinsic and extrinsic eye movement	Superior orbital fissure	Fibers extend from the ventral midbrain (near its junction with the pons) and pass through the superior orbital fissure to 4 of the extrinsic muscles of the eye.
Trochlear	Motor	Extrinsic eye movement	Superior orbital fissure	Fibers from the dorsal midbrain course through the superior orbital fissure with the oculomotor nerve. CN IV supplies the superior oblique muscle.
Trigeminal V_1–ophthalmic n. V_2–maxillary n. V_3–mandibular n.	Both	Sensation in head/ Muscles of mastication	V_1–Superior orbital fissure V_2–Foramen rotundum V_3–Foramen ovale	Fibers from the pons divide into ophthalmic, maxillary, and mandibular divisions which course through the superior orbital fissure, foramen rotundum, and foramen ovale, respectively. Supply to face and muscles of mastication.
Abducent or Abducens	Motor	Extrinsic eye movement (abducts eyeball)	Superior orbital fissure	Fibers from inferior pons enter orbit through superior orbital fissure to eye.
Facial	Both	Muscles of facial expression, taste	Internal acoustic meatus	Fibers from pons enter temporal bone through the internal acoustic meatus. CN VII gives off a branch for taste and courses to lateral side of face.

CN Name and Number	Type	Function	Cranial Exit	Pathway
Vestibulocochlear	Sensory	Hearing and equilibrium	Internal acoustic meatus	*Fibers arise from hearing and equilibrium is located within the inner ear of the temporal bone. They pass through the internal acoustic meatus and enter the brainstem at the pons-medulla border.* *Afferent nerves from hearing receptors (in cochlea) form the cochlear division and those from the equilibrium receptors (semicircular canals and vestibule) form the vestibular division. Both divisions merge to form the vestibulocochlear nerve*
Glossopharyngeal	Both	Muscles of pharynx, taste	Jugular foramen	*Fibers from the medulla leave the skull through the jugular foramen and course to structures in the throat area.*
Vagus	Both	Parasympathetic to major viscera, larynx and pharynx muscles	Jugular foramen	*Fibers emerge from the medulla and pass through the skull via the jugular foramen. Fibers descend through the neck region into the thorax and abdomen.*
Accessory	Motor	Innervates trapezius and sternocleidomastoid muscles	Jugular foramen	*Formed by the union of a cranial root and a spinal root, it emerges from the lateral side of the medulla and spinal cord. It exits through the jugular foramen and supplies the neck muscles.*
Hypoglossal	Motor	Tongue muscles	Hypoglossal canal	*Fibers arise from a series of roots from the medulla and exit from the skull through the hypoglossal canal to travel to the tongue.*

II. MNEMONICS TO MEMORIZE CRANIAL NERVES:

A. Oh, Oh, Oh, To Touch And Feel Very Good Velvet, AH!

B. Some Say Marry Money, But My Brother Says Bad Business Marrying Money. (S = sensory, M = motor, B = both sensory and motor)

SPECIAL SENSES AND RECEPTORS

I. RECEPTORS AND SENSATIONS

A. Receptors are structures that are specialized to receive environmental _____ and generate nerve impulses.

B. Receptors initiate nerve impulses; these impulses are conducted to the CNS.

C. Sensation and the _____ of stimuli are dependent on interpretation of the brain.

D. Receptors can be classified into _____ types.

II. TYPES OF RECEPTORS

A. Chemoreceptors are sensitive to chemical substances in the immediate area.

B. _____ are stimulated by mechanical forces, like pressure.

C. _____ sense the degree of muscle contraction, the movement of ligaments, and the stretch of tendons.

D. Thermoreceptors are stimulated by changes in temperature.

E. Pain receptors are technically called _____.

F. Photoreceptors detect light.

III. TWO TYPES OF SENSES

A. SOMATIC SENSES: senses that are associated with the skin, muscles, and joints are called _____ senses.

    1. Proprioception is a sense of knowing the position of the limbs.

B. SPECIAL SENSES

    1. The sense organs for taste, smell, vision, equilibrium, and _____.

IV. SKIN

A. The skin contains receptors for touch, pressure, _____, and temperature.

B. _____ occurs when a receptor becomes accustomed to stimulation and stops generating impulses, even though the stimulus is still present.

    1. For example, shortly after we put on an article of clothing, we are no longer aware of the sensation of clothes against our skin.

V. TASTE

A. Taste buds are groupings of cells found in the tongue epithelium and open at a taste _____.

B. Recent functional and molecular data have found that, contrary to popular belief, there is no tongue "map": where certain areas are responsive to the 5 basic modalities-bitter, sour, sweet, salty, and umami-all modalities are present in all areas of the tongue.

VI. OLFACTION

    A. Our sense of smell is dependent on olfactory cells found in the
        _____ of the nasal cavity.

VII. VISION

    A. The eyeball is an elongated sphere about _____ cm in diam-
        eter and has three layers, or coats: the sclera, the choroid, and
        the retina.

    B. The outer layer is called the sclera.

        1. It is white and fibrous except for the transparent _____,
           known as the window of the eye.

    C. The middle, dark, thin brown layer, the _____,
        is vascular and absorbs stray light rays.

        1. Toward the front, the choroid thickens and forms the ring-
           shaped ciliary body.

        2. The ciliary body contains the ciliary muscle, which controls
           the shape of the lens for near and far vision.

        3. Also, the choroid becomes a thin, circular, muscular,
           _____ diaphragm called the iris, which regu-
           lates the size of the pupil.

           a. The pupil is a hole in the center of the iris through which
              light passes into the eyeball.

Eye Anatomy

© Kendall Hunt Publishing Company

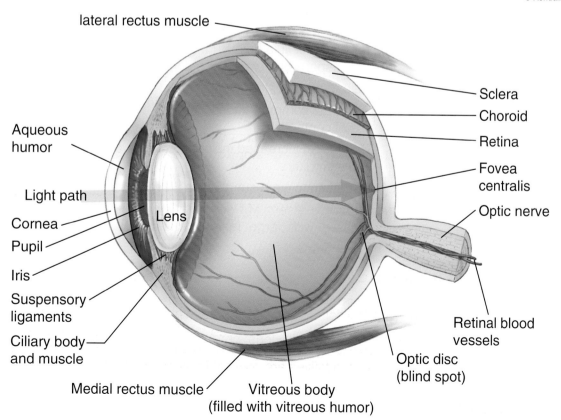

lateral rectus muscle

Sclera
Choroid
Retina
Fovea centralis
Optic nerve

Aqueous humor

Light path
Cornea
Pupil
Iris
Suspensory ligaments
Ciliary body and muscle

Lens

Retinal blood vessels

Optic disc (blind spot)

Medial rectus muscle   Vitreous body (filled with vitreous humor)

4. The lens, attached to the ciliary body via ligaments, divides the cavity of the eye into two smaller cavities:
  a. A clear, gelatinous material is called the _____ humor.
    i. It fills the posterior cavity, which lies behind the lens.
  b. The anterior cavity lying posterior to the cornea and anterior to the lens is filled with a clear, watery fluid.
    i. This fluid is secreted by the ciliary body and is called the _____ humor.
D. The inner layer of the eye, the retina, contains rods and the cones.
  1. The fibers of the ganglionic cells pass in front of the retina, forming the optic nerve, which pierces the layers of the eye as it exits posterior toward the brain.
  2. There are no cones or rods where the optic nerve passes through the retina.
    a. This is called the blind spot, where vision is _____.
  3. The retina contains a very special region that contains only cones.
    a. This oval, yellowish depression is called the fovea centralis.
    b. Vision is most acute in the fovea _____.
E. Diseases and preventing a loss of vision
  1. In diabetic _____, capillaries to the retina burst and blood spills into the vitreous humor. This blinds many people between 20 and 74 years old.
  2. _____ occurs when the eye drainage system fails, so that fluid builds up. This destroys the nerve fibers that are responsible for peripheral vision.
  3. Possible damage of the eye
    a. The most common cause of injury to the eye is careless use of contact _____.
    b. There is an increased incidence of cataracts in heavy cigarette smokers.
    c. Be certain to wear sunglasses that absorb _____ light.
    d. Glasses with large lenses offer better protection than smaller.

VIII. HEARING
A. The ear performs two sensory functions: equilibrium (balance) and _____.
B. The ear has three divisions: outer, middle, and inner.
  1. The outer ear consists of the pinna (external flap made of cartilage and skin) and the auditory canal.

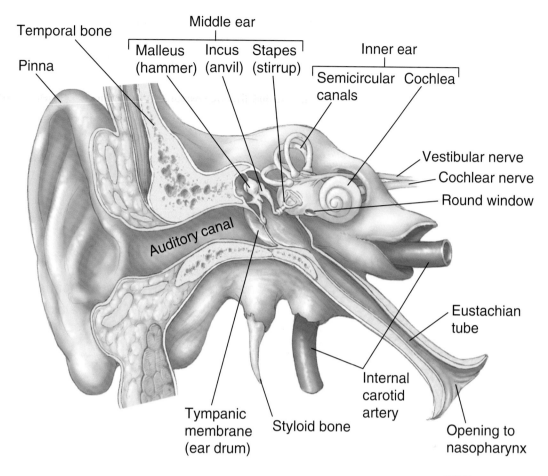

Temporal bone

Pinna

Middle ear

Malleus (hammer)   Incus (anvil)   Stapes (stirrup)

Inner ear

Semicircular canals   Cochlea

Vestibular nerve

Cochlear nerve

Round window

Auditory canal

Eustachian tube

Tympanic membrane (ear drum)

Styloid bone

Internal carotid artery

Opening to nasopharynx

Ear Anatomy

© Kendall Hunt Publishing Company

2. The middle ear
    a. The middle ear begins at the _____ membrane (eardrum) and ends at a wall containing the oval window (the round window is found near this area and it allows fluid in the cochlea to move).
    b. Three small bones are found between the tympanic membrane and the oval window.
    c. Collectively called the ossicles, they include the _____ or hammer, incus or anvil, and _____ or stirrup.
    d. The _____ attaches to the tympanic membrane, and the stapes contacts the oval window.
3. The inner ear has three regions:
    a. The semicircular canals and the vestibule are involved with equilibrium.
    b. The cochlea is involved with hearing.
    c. The inner ear contains semicircular canals that help maintain _____.
    d. It also contains the cochlea, which appears snail-shaped and is lined with small hairs called stereocilia.
    e. The movement of _____ transmits sensations to our brain to interpret as sound.

C. The Eustachian tube, also known as the auditory tube, extends from the middle ear to the nasopharynx.

   1. This permits equalization of air pressure when we swallow or yawn.

D. Preventing a loss of hearing

   1. Limiting exposure to loud noises aids in preventing stereocilia damage, which results in age-associated nerve deafness.

   2. Any noise above 80 decibels may damage hair cells of the organ of _____, and cause them to disappear completely.

   3. The first hint of danger could be temporary hearing loss, a "full" feeling in the ears, noises sounding muffled, or _____ (known as "ringing in the ears").

   4. One should modify listening habits immediately if one has any of these symptoms so as to prevent further damage.

   5. Exposure to intense sounds of short duration, such as a burst of gunfire, can result in an immediate hearing loss.

   6. Anticancer drugs and certain _____ may increase our sensitivity to loud noises and may result hearing loss. Hearing protection in this case is especially important.

AUTONOMIC NERVOUS SYSTEM

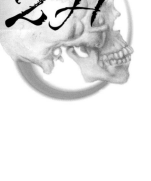

I. NERVOUS SYSTEM ORGANIZATION

1. The CNS is composed of the _____ and the spinal cord.

2. The PNS is composed of the _____ of the body.

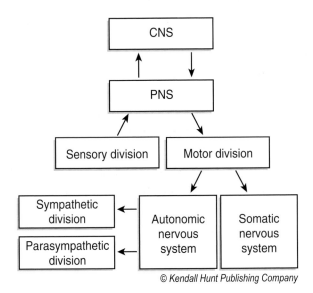

© Kendall Hunt Publishing Company

II. FUNCTIONAL DIVISIONS

1. Sensory neurons within peripheral nerves carry impulses from receptors to the CNS, whereas motor neurons carry impulses from the CNS to effectors.

2. The effectors of the body are muscles (_____, cardiac, skeletal) and glands (endocrine, _____).

3. In the body there are two systems: somatic and the ANS.

   This illustrates the pathway of neurons that we have already learned, which is found in the somatic system:

   RECEPTOR $\longrightarrow$ CNS $\longrightarrow$ EFFECTOR

           Sensory   Motor
           Neuron   Neuron

III. AUTONOMIC NERVOUS SYSTEM

A. The ANS is responsible for the control of:

   1. Smooth muscle
   2. Cardiac muscle
   3. Endocrine glands
   4. Exocrine glands

B. These effectors can function without any conscious knowledge and independent of the will.

C. The term autonomy means "self-government."

D. Anatomically, ANS differs from the somatic innervation of skeletal muscle in one extremely important way.

1. The pathway from CNS to the skeletal muscle effector involves only _____ neuron.

CNS   ——————→   EFFECTOR

Motor neuron

2. In the ANS, the pathway from CNS to effectors involves two neurons.

   a. A ganglion is defined as a collection of neuron cell bodies outside of the CNS.

   b. The name of the neuron that has its cell body in the CNS and courses to the autonomic ganglion is called the _____ NEURON.

   c. The neuron that has its _____ in the autonomic ganglion and carries the impulse from that ganglion to the effector is called the POSTGANGLIONIC NEURON.

CNS   ——————→   AUTONOMIC   ——————→   EFFECTOR

GANGLION

PREGANGLIONIC   POSTGANGLIONIC

NEURON   NEURON

IV. THE ANS IS DIVIDED INTO TWO SEPARATE SYSTEMS:

A. SYMPATHETIC SYSTEM

B. PARASYMPATHETIC SYSTEM

V. THERE ARE A NUMBER OF REASONS WHY THIS IS DONE:

A. Anatomical

1. The sympathetic system involves all the thoracic and the first two (sometimes three) lumbar spinal cord segments.

   a. Thus it is anatomically called the THORACOLUMBAR SYSTEM.

2. The parasympathetic system involves cranial nerves 3, 7, 9, and 10 and the sacral spinal cord segments S2, S3, and S4.

   a. Thus it is anatomically called the _____ SYSTEM.

B. Ganglia

1. Sympathetic ganglia are _____ the spinal cord.

2. Parasympathetic ganglia are near or within the wall of the organ innervated.

C. Length of fibers
1. Sympathetic system has _____ preganglionic and _____ postganglionic fibers.
2. Parasympathetic system has long preganglionic and short postganglionic fibers.
D. Actions:
1. In general the two systems have _____ actions in organs where both innervate.
E. Number of organs activated
1. The sympathetic system exhibits _____ action, where sympathetic stimulation activates many organs at one time.
2. The parasympathetic system stimulus involves only one organ at a time.

VI. AUTONOMIC EFFECTS ON VARIOUS ORGANS OF THE BODY

Target Organ/System	Sympathetic Effects	Parasympathetic Effects
Eye (iris)	Stimulates dilator muscles, dilates eye pupils	Stimulates constrictor muscles; constricts eye pupils
Glands (nasal, lacrimal, salivary, gastric, pancreas)	Inhibits secretory activity; causes vasoconstriction of blood vessels supplying the glands	Stimulates secretory activity
Sweat glands	Stimulates copious sweating	No effect
Arrector pilorum muscles	Stimulates to contract (erect hairs, goosebumps)	No effect
Heart muscle	Increases rate and force of heartbeat	Decreases rate; slows and steadies heart
Digestive tract organs	Decreases activity of glands and muscles of digestive system and constricts sphincters	Increased motility (peristalsis) and amount of secretion by digestive organs; relaxes sphincters to allow movement of food along tract
Blood vessels	Constricts most vessels and increases blood pressure; constricts vessels of abdominal viscera and skin	Little or no effect
Mental activity	Increases alertness	No effect

Brain and Spinal
Column

© Kendall Hunt Publishing Company

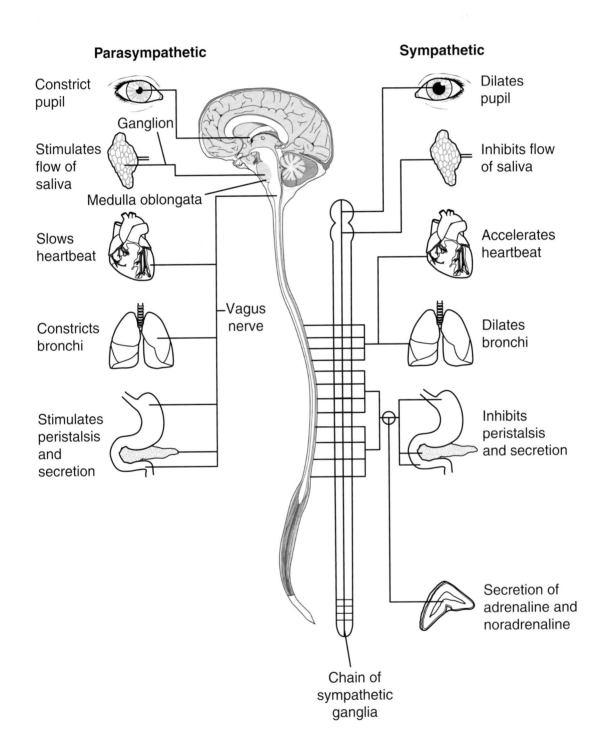

Parasympathetic

Constrict
pupil

Ganglion

Stimulates
flow of
saliva

Medulla oblongata

Slows
heartbeat

Constricts
bronchi

Stimulates
peristalsis
and
secretion

Vagus
nerve

Sympathetic

Dilates
pupil

Inhibits flow
of saliva

Accelerates
heartbeat

Dilates
bronchi

Inhibits
peristalsis
and secretion

Secretion of
adrenaline and
noradrenaline

Chain of
sympathetic
ganglia

STUDY RESOURCES

2A Lower Limb Musculature .... pp. 158–160
2B Nervous System................................... p. 161
2C Endocrine System................................. p. 162
2D Brain.. pp. 163–164
2E Spinal Cord and Meninges....................... pp. 165–166
2F Peripheral Nervous System...................... p. 167
2G Special Senses and Receptors................ pp. 168–169

2A LOWER LIMB MUSCULATURE

Muscle Associations of the Lower Limb—Origins and Insertions

Bone Structure	Muscle	Origin or Insertion	No. of Muscles That Attach
Ilium	Gluteus maximus	Origin	3 Origin
	Gluteus medius	Origin	
	Gluteus minimus	Origin	
ASIS	Tensor fasciae latae	Origin	2 Origin
	Sartorius	Origin	
Greater trochanter	Gluteus medius	Insertion	1 Origin 4 Insertion
	Gluteus minimus	Insertion	
	Piriformis	Insertion	
	Obturator internus	Insertion	
	Vastus lateralis	Origin	
Ischial tuberosity	Inferior gemellus	Origin	6 Origin
	Quadratus femoris	Origin	
	Adductor magnus, Extensor part	Origin	
	Semitendinosus	Origin	
	Semimembranosus	Origin	
	Biceps femoris, Long head	Origin	
Tibial tuberosity	Rectus femoris	Insertion	4 Insertion
	Vastus medialis	Insertion	
	Vastus lateralis	Insertion	
	Vastus intermedius	Insertion	
Linea aspera	Vastus lateralis	Origin	3 Origin 3 Insertion
	Vastus medialis	Origin	
	Biceps femoris, Short head	Origin	
	Adductor longus	Insertion	
	Adductor brevis	Insertion	
	Adductor magnus, Adductor part	Insertion	
Upper femur	Vastus intermedius	Origin	1 Origin
	Pectineus	Insertion	1 Insertion
Pubis	Gracilis	Origin	4 Origin
	Pectineus	Origin	
	Adductor longus	Origin	
	Adductor brevis	Origin	
Middle fibula	Extensor hallucis longus	Origin	2 Origin
	Flexor hallucis longus	Origin	
Lower fibula	Fibularis tertius	Origin	2 Origin
	Fibularis brevis	Origin	
5th metatarsal	Fibularis tertius	Insertion	2 Insertion
	Fibularis brevis	Insertion	
Upper fibula	Extensor digitorum longus	Origin	2 Origin
	Fibularis longus	Origin	
Upper fibula and upper tibia	Soleus	Origin	2 Origin
	Tibialis posterior	Origin	

Muscle Associations of the Lower Limb—Actions

Action	No. of Muscles	Muscle Name
Extend hip	5	Gluteus maximus Long head of biceps femoris Extensor part of adductor magnus Semitendinosus Semimembranosus
Laterally rotate hip	8	Gluteus maximus Piriformis Superior gemellus Inferior gemellus Obturator internus Quadratus femoris Obturator externus Sartorius
Abduct hip	3	Gluteus medius Gluteus minimus Sartorius
Medially rotate hip	3	Gluteus medius Gluteus minimus Tensor fasciae latae
Flex hip	8	Tensor fasciae latae Sartorius Rectus femoris Gracilis Pectineus Adductor longus Adductor brevis Adductor part of adductor magnus
Adduct hip	5	Gracilis Pectineus Adductor longus Adductor brevis Adductor part of adductor magnus
Flex trunk	1	Iliopsoas
Extend knee	4	Rectus femoris Vastus intermedius Vastus lateralis Vastus medialis
Flex knee	4	Sartorius Semitendinosus Semimembranosus Long head of biceps femoris
Laterally rotate knee	1	Short head of biceps femoris
Dorsiflex ankle	2	Tibialis anterior Fibularis (peroneus) tertius
Plantarflex ankle	3	Gastrocnemius Soleus Plantaris
Invert ankle	2	Tibialis anterior Tibialis posterior
Evert ankle	3	Fibularis (peroneus) tertius Fibularis (peroneus) longus Fibularis (peroneus) brevis
Extend big toe	1	Extensor hallucis longus
Extend toes 2–5	1	Extensor digitorum longus
Flex big toe	1	Flexor hallucis longus
Flex toes 2–5	1	Flexor digitorum longus

Muscle Associations of the Lower Limb—Innervations

Nerve	No. of Muscles	Muscle Name
Inferior gluteal n.	1	Gluteus maximus
Superior gluteal n.	3	Gluteus medius
		Gluteus minimus
		Tensor fasciae latae
Nerve to piriformis	1	Piriformis
Sacral plexus	4	Superior gemellus
		Obturator Internus
		Inferior gemellus
		Quadratus femoris
Femoral n.	7	Iliopsoas
		Sartorius
		Pectineus
		Rectus femoris
		Vastus lateralis
		Vastus medialis
		Vastus intermedius
Obturator n.	4	Gracilis
		Adductor longus
		Adductor brevis
		Adductor part of adductor magnus
Sciatic n.	4	Extensor part of adductor magnus
		Semitendinosus
		Semimembranosus
		Biceps femoris
Deep fibular (peroneal) n.	4	Tibialis anterior
		Extensor hallucis longus
		Extensor digitorum longus
		Fibularis tertius
Superficial fibular (peroneal) n.	2	Fibularis longus
		Fibularis brevis
Tibial n.	6	Gastrocnemius
		Soleus
		Plantaris
		Tibialis posterior
		Flexor digitorum longus
		Flexor hallucis longus

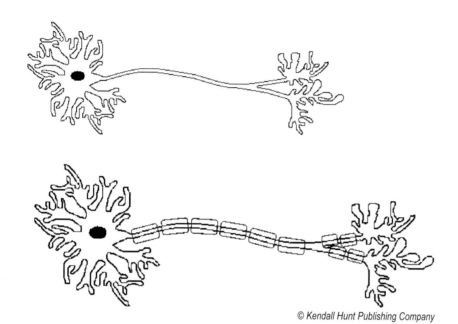

© Kendall Hunt Publishing Company

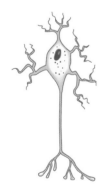

© Kendall Hunt Publishing Company

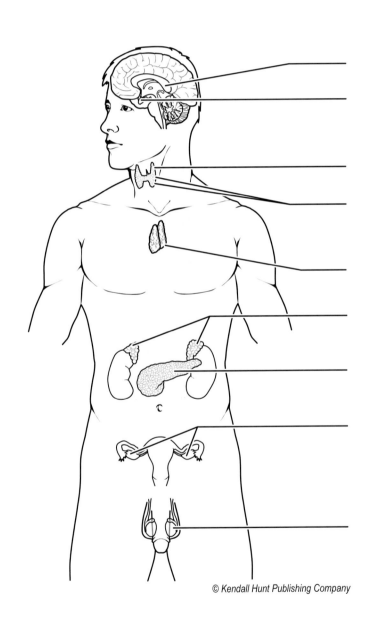

© Kendall Hunt Publishing Company

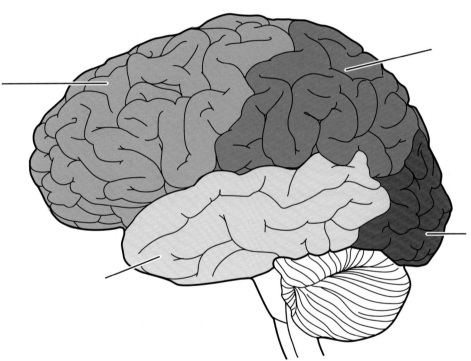

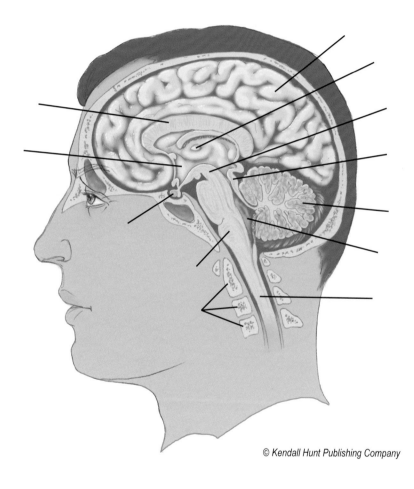

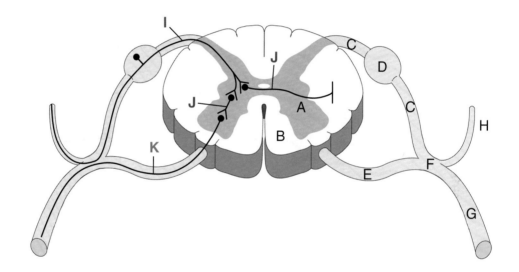

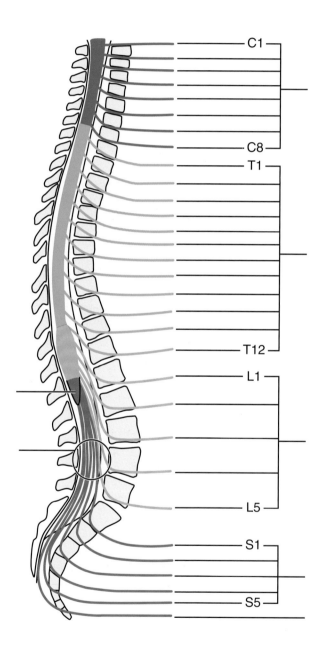

C1

C8

T1

T12

L1

L5

S1

S5

Nerves of the Body
Fill in the blanks.

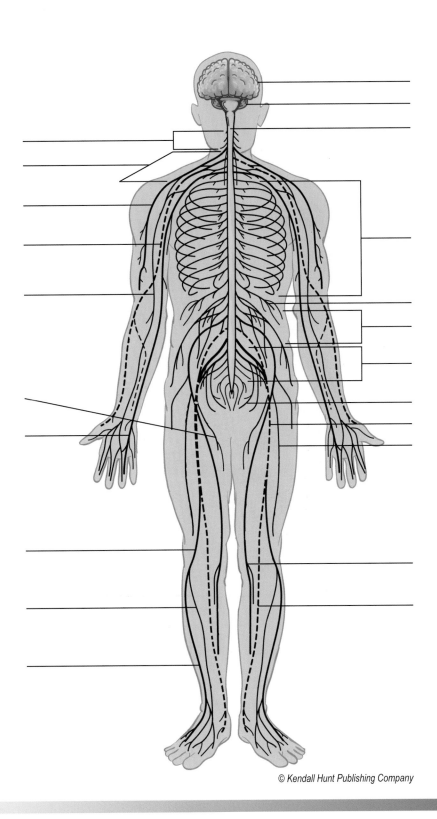

Fill in the blanks.

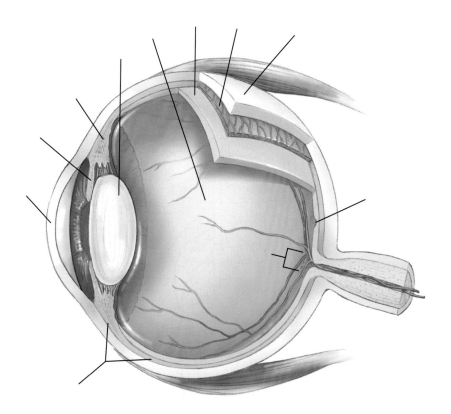

Fill in the blanks.

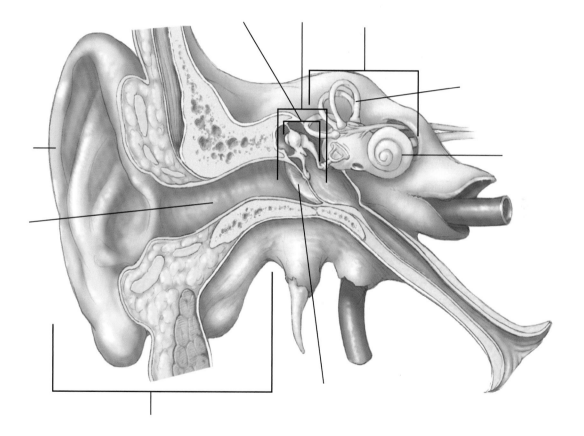

PRACTICE QUIZZES

2A Lower Limb Musculature
   Practice Quizzes .... pp. 171–177
2B Nervous System Practice Quiz .... pp. 178–184
2C Endocrine System Practice Quiz .... pp. 185–186
2D Brain Practice Quiz .... pp. 187–188
2E Spinal Cord and Meninges
   Practice Quiz.. pp. 189–190
2F Special Senses and Receptors
   Practice Quiz.. pp. 191–194
2H Autonomic Nervous System
   Practice Quiz.. pp. 195–196
2A–H Unit 2 Practice Test............................. pp. 197–210
Answer Key .... pp. 211–213

Lower Limb Musculature (Gluteal Region & Lateral Rotators) Practice Quizzes

1. The following muscles all originate from the ilium EXCEPT: (Choose all that apply.)
   a. Gluteus medius
   b. Gluteus minimis
   c. Inferior gemellus
   d. Gluteus maximus
   e. Piriformis

2. Choose the false statement:
   a. 2 of the 6 lateral rotators insert into the greater trochanter
   b. 2 of the 4 gluteal region muscles insert into the greater trochanter
   c. 3 of the 6 lateral rotators insert into the obturator internus tendon
   d. 1 of the 4 gluteal region muscles also laterally rotates
   e. 2 of the 6 lateral rotator muscles originate from the ischial tuberosity

Using the choices below, answer questions 3–8.

A. 1   B. 2   C. 3   D. 4   E. 5
AB. 6   AC. 7   AD. 8   AE. 9   BC. 10   BD. 11   BE. 12

3. How many muscles of the gluteal region and lateral rotators laterally rotate the hip?

4. How many muscles of the gluteal region and lateral rotators medially rotate the hip?

5. How many muscles of the gluteal region and lateral rotators are innervated by the superior gluteal nerve?

6. How many muscles of the gluteal region and lateral rotators insert into the greater trochanter?

7. How many muscles of the gluteal region and lateral rotators are innervated by the sacral plexus?

8. How many muscles of the gluteal region and lateral rotators abduct the hip?

9. Superior gemellus: (Choose all that apply.)
   a. Originates from the ischial tuberosity
   b. Inserts into the obturator internus tendon
   c. Inserts into the intertrochanteric crest
   d. Is innervated by the superior gluteal nerve
   e. Originates from the spine of the ischium

10. The tensor fasciae latae:
    a. Flexes and laterally rotates at hip
    b. Is the most popular drink at Starbucks
    c. Is innervated by the inferior gluteal nerve
    d. Originates from the iliac crest and AIIS
    e. Inserts into an area where thickening of fascia occurs on the lateral side of the thigh

11. The following statements are all true of the muscles that have the action lateral rotation at the hip EXCEPT:
    a. Originate from the anterior sacrum
    b. Insert into the intertrochanteric crest
    c. Originate from the ilium, sacrum, and coccyx
    d. Originate from the ischial tuberosity
    e. All of the above are true statements

Lower Limb Musculature (Anterior, Medial, and Posterior Thigh) Practice Quiz

1. Which muscle inserts into the upper femur?
   a. One that also originates from the tibial tuberosity
   b. One that originates from the ischial tuberosity
   c. One that extends the knee
   d. One that is innervated by the obturator nerve
   e. One that is innervated by the femoral nerve

2. Choose the false statement.
   a. 2 of the 5 medial thigh muscles are not innervated by the obturator nerve
   b. Only 1 muscle inserts into the lesser trochanter
   c. 2 muscles originated from the AIIS in the anterior thigh
   d. 3 muscles insert into the upper medial tibia
   e. 7 muscles are innervated by the femoral nerve

3. Which statement is correct? (Choose all that apply.)
   a. The vastus lateralis and vastus medialis share 4 things in common
   b. All the muscles of the quadriceps femoris insert into the ischial tuberosity
   c. All of the muscles of the quadriceps femoris extend the knee
   d. 1 of the 4 muscles of the quadriceps acts on 2 joints
   e. All of the above are correct

4. All of the following statements are true regarding the posterior thigh muscles that extend at the hip and flex the knee EXCEPT:
   a. One inserts into the upper medial tibia
   b. One originates from the linea aspera
   c. They are innervated by the sciatic nerve
   d. One inserts into the medial condyle of the tibia
   e. One inserts into the head of the fibula

5. All of the following muscles are flexors of the hip EXCEPT:
   a. Pectineus
   b. Adductor brevis
   c. Gracilis
   d. Sartorius
   e. Vastus lateralis

Using the choices below, answer questions 6–12.

A. 1   B. 2.5   E. 3   C. 3.5   D. 4
AB. 6   AC. 7   AD. 8   AE. 9   BC. 10   BD. 11   BE. 0

6. How many muscles of the anterior, medial, and posterior thigh muscles flex the knee?

7. How many muscles of the anterior, medial, and posterior thigh muscles are innervated by the obturator nerve?

8. How many muscles of the anterior, medial, and posterior thigh muscles are innervated by the femoral nerve?

9. How many muscles of the anterior, medial, and posterior thigh muscles extend the hip?

10. How many muscles of the anterior, medial, and posterior thigh muscles medially rotate the hip?

11. How many muscles of the anterior, medial, and posterior thigh muscles laterally rotate the hip?

12. How many muscles of the anterior, medial, and posterior thigh muscles attach to the ischial tuberosity?

Lower Limb Musculature (Anterior, Lateral, and Posterior Leg) Practice Quiz

1. Choose the false statement.
   a. The muscle that dorsiflexes and inverts the ankle also originates from the lower fibula
   b. All of the muscles of the superficial posterior leg compartment share the same insertion, action, and innervation
   c. A muscle from the anterior leg compartment and a muscle from deep posterior leg compartment have the same origin
   d. Only 2 muscles of the leg invert the ankle
   e. The muscle that flexes toes 2–5 also originates from the middle tibia

2. Choose the following muscles that share both origin and insertion (Choose 2):
   a. Fibularis longus
   b. Fibularis brevis
   c. Fibularis tertius
   d. Tibialis posterior
   e. Soleus

3. Choose the muscle(s) that dorsiflex the ankle. (Choose all that apply.)
   a. The muscle that also originates from the upper lateral tibia
   b. The muscle that is innervated by the superficial fibular (peroneal) nerve
   c. The muscle that is innervated by the deep fibular (peroneal) nerve
   d. The muscle that also originates from the lower fibula
   e. The muscle that also originates from the upper fibula and tibia

4. Choose the correct statement:
   a. 3 muscles originate from the lower fibula
   b. 4 muscles of the leg muscles originate from the upper fibula
   c. 3 muscles originate from the middle fibula
   d. Only 1 muscle originates from the upper tibia
   e. All of the above statements are correct

Using the choices below, answer questions 5–10.
         A. 1   B. 2   C. 3   D. 4   E. 5
    AB. 6   AC. 7   AD. 8   AE. 9   BC. 10   BD. 11   BE. 0

5. How many muscles of the anterior, lateral, and posterior leg muscles insert into the medial cuneiform?

6. How many muscles of the anterior, lateral, and posterior leg muscles originate from the middle and lower fibula?

7. How many muscles of the anterior, lateral, and posterior leg muscles evert the ankle?

8. How many muscles of the anterior, lateral, and posterior leg muscles plantar flex the ankle?

9. How many muscles of the anterior, lateral, and posterior leg muscles dorsiflex the ankle?

10. How many muscles of the anterior, lateral, and posterior leg muscles insert into the 5th metatarsal?

Lower Limb Musculature (Full Mix)
Practice Quiz

1. All of the following muscles originate from the ischium EXCEPT: (Choose all that apply.)
   a. Gluteus medius
   b. Gluteus minimus
   c. Quadratus femoris
   d. Inferior gemellus
   e. Gluteus maximus

2. All of the following originate from the linea aspera EXCEPT: (Choose all that apply.)
   a. Adductor longus
   b. Short head of biceps femoris
   c. Adductor part of adductor magnus
   d. Vastus lateralis
   e. Vastus medialis

3. Choose the false statement: (Choose all that apply.)
   a. 1 of the 4 gluteal muscles laterally rotates the hip along with 6 of the lateral rotators
   b. Only 1 anterior thigh muscle laterally rotates the hip
   c. Only 4 muscles of the lower limb abduct the hip
   d. 6 muscles adduct the hip
   e. Only 1 muscle laterally rotates the knee

4. The muscle that shares the same origin as extensor hallucis longus also:
   a. Inserts into distal phalanx toes 2–5
   b. Flexes toes 2–5
   c. Is innervated by the deep fibular (peroneal) nerve
   d. Extends the big toe
   e. Inserts into distal phalanx of toe 1

5. The ischial tuberosity:
   a. Serves as the origin for a muscle that inserts into the medial condyle of the tibia
   b. Serves as the origin for a muscle that inserts into the lateral condyle of the tibia
   c. Is the insertion of a muscle that causes laterally rotation of the thigh at the hip
   d. Is the insertion of a muscle that causes extension of the hip
   e. None of the above

6. All of the following muscles abduct the hip EXCEPT:
   a. Gluteus medius
   b. Gracilis
   c. Gluteus minimus
   d. Sartorius

7. Choose the false statement.
   a. 2 of the 6 anterior thigh muscles flex the hip
   b. 8 muscles of the lower limb flex the hip
   c. Only 2 muscles medially rotate the hip
   d. 5 medial thigh muscles flex the hip
   e. 5 muscles of the lower limb extend the hip

8. Choose the true statement:
   a. 6 muscles originate at the linea aspera
   b. 3 muscles attach to the middle fibula
   c. 2 muscles originate at both the upper fibula and tibia
   d. 2 muscles originate at the upper femur
   e. Pes anserinus can be found at the upper medial fibula

9. All of the following muscles can be found in layer 3 EXCEPT:
   a. Flexor hallucis brevis
   b. Flexor digiti minimi brevis
   c. Flexor digitorum brevis
   d. Adductor hallucis

Nervous System Practice Quiz

1. All of the following describe the nervous system EXCEPT:
   a. Provides control for rapid activity
   b. Highly specialized cells involved
   c. Movement and thinking are an example
   d. Growth is an example

2. The following is/are functions of a receptor: (Choose all that apply.)
   a. Transmit impulses to the proper nerve center of the body
   b. Processes information to determine appropriate response
   c. Receives stimuli from the environment
   d. Carries out the response
   e. Transforms stimuli into nerve impulses

3. The spinal cord uses a(n) _____ to transmit information to the effector.
   a. Sensory neuron
   b. Interneuron in ascending pathway
   c. Interneuron in descending pathway
   d. Motor neuron
   e. Brain

Match the letters from the picture below to questions 4–8.

4. This structure is produced by glial cells.

5. This structure controls metabolic activity of the neuron.

6. This structure is involved in neurotransmitter release.

7. This structure receives information and transmits it toward the structure indicated by the letter A.

8. This space is known as the synapse.

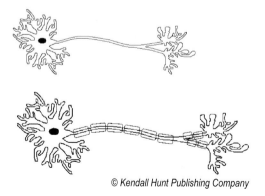

© Kendall Hunt Publishing Company

9. Choose the false statement: (Choose all that apply.)
   a. There are 6 types of neuroglia
   b. Oligodendrocytes form myelin sheaths in the peripheral nervous system (PNS) only
   c. Multipolar neurons can have 5 branches off the soma
   d. Interneurons are also called internuncial neurons
   e. Afferent neurons transmit motor nerve impulses from receptors to the brain and spinal cord

10. Neuronal activity:
    a. Involves impulses called action budding
    b. Receives signals from sensory receptors
    c. Involves recording information
    d. Travels through the bloodstream to get to its target
    e. Disposes of neurotransmitters

11. The peripheral nervous system includes all of the following EXCEPT: (Choose all that apply.)
    a. Brain
    b. 12 pairs of cranial nerves
    c. 31 pairs of spinal nerves
    d. Spinal cord
    e. Meninges

12. Spinal nerves branch laterally to form:
    a. Mixed spinal nerve
    b. Ventral and dorsal rami
    c. Ventral and dorsal roots
    d. Gray matter
    e. White matter

13. The gluteal region (both motor and sensory) is supplied by a nerve that passes through the:
    a. Ventral root
    b. Dorsal root
    c. Ventral ramus
    d. Dorsal ramus
    e. None of the above

14. The cervical plexus includes ventral rami:
    a. C5–T1
    b. L2–L4
    c. C2–C4
    d. C1–C4
    e. C1–C8

15. This nerve comes from C3–C5 alone:
    a. Median nerve
    b. Ulnar nerve
    c. Phrenic nerve
    d. Pudendal nerve
    e. Musculocutaneous nerve

16. This plexus supplies all the upper limb except the skin on part of the upper shoulder:
    a. The plexus that also supplies muscles and skin of the neck
    b. The plexus that includes ventral rami C5–T1
    c. The plexus that gives off the phrenic nerve
    d. The plexus that also supplies the skin over the upper medial portion of the arm
    e. The plexus that is located in the abdomen

17. All of the following nerves are motor and sensory EXCEPT:
    a. Median nerve
    b. Facial nerve
    c. Radial nerve
    d. Ulnar nerve
    e. None of the above

18. The lumbosacral plexus: (Choose all that apply.)
    a. Includes the ventral rami L1–L4 only
    b. Supplies the anterior thigh and medial thigh only
    c. Includes one of the largest nerves in the body
    d. Carries 2 plexi that can be found in the abdomen and pelvis
    e. Has a total of 16 nerves that come off the plexus

19. All of the following are features of the ulnar nerve EXCEPT:
    a. It is derived from the lateral cord
    b. Includes ventral rami C8, T1
    c. Splits into superficial and deep branch
    d. Supplies some anterior forearm muscles
    e. Can be found posterior to the medial epicondyle

20. Which pair is matched incorrectly?
    a. Lumbar plexus-femoral nerve
    b. Sacral plexus-common fibular nerve
    c. Lumbar plexus-medial thigh muscles
    d. Sacral plexus-lateral leg muscles
    e. All of the above are correctly matched

21. Which statement regarding the sciatic nerve is false? (Choose all that apply.)
    a. It branches into the tibial and common fibular nerve
    b. It branches distally to supply the majority of the foot
    c. The plexus it belongs to can be found in the pelvis
    d. After the sciatic nerve branches once, one of its nerves branches again to supply the anterior and posterior leg
    e. This is the largest cutaneous nerve in the body

22. All of the following are true regarding the trochlear nerve EXCEPT: (Choose all that apply.)
    a. It is cranial nerve IV
    b. It is motor in type
    c. Its function is intrinsic and extrinsic eye movement
    d. Its cranial exit is the superior orbital fissure
    e. Its cranial exit is the internal acoustic meatus

Match the letters in the diagram below with questions 23–33.

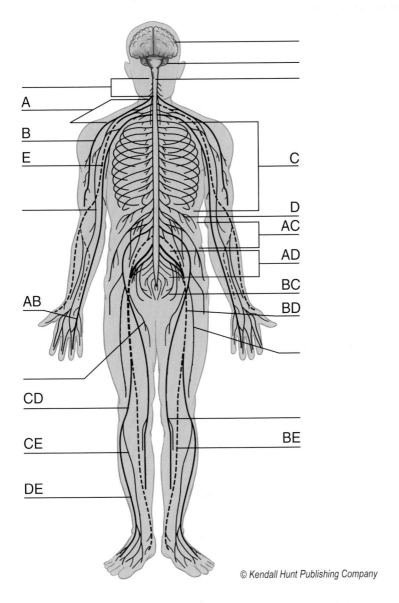

© Kendall Hunt Publishing Company

23. These nerves course through T1–T11.
24. This plexus includes the posterior femoral cutaneous nerve.
25. This nerve supplies the genitalia.
26. Supplies the entire upper limb muscles except the trapezius.
27. Choose the 2 nerves that split from the common fibular (peroneal) nerve.
28. Ventral rami L4–S3.
29. Derived from the lateral cord.

30. Ventral rami C5–T1 (Choose 2 structures).

31. Supplies 1.5 anterior forearm muscles

32. These 2 nerves are split inferiorly from BD

33. Identify the subcostal nerve

34. All of the following cranial nerves exit through the superior orbital fissure EXCEPT:
    a. CN VI
    b. CN III
    c. CN V$_2$
    d. CN IV
    e. All of the above exit through the superior orbital fissure

35. The following cranial nerves exit through the jugular foramen: (Choose all that apply.)
    a. One that functions in hearing and balance
    b. One that innervates the posterior third of the tongue
    c. One that innervates larynx and pharynx muscles
    d. One that is sensory only in type
    e. All of the above are characteristics of the cranial nerves that exit through the jugular foramen

36. Choose the structure(s) that contain(s) cell bodies: (Choose all that apply.)
    a. White matter
    b. Gray matter
    c. Dorsal root
    d. Ventral root
    e. Dorsal root ganglion

37. Choose the correct sequence if someone is stabbed with a knife in the right posterior arm and moves his/her other arm to remove it.
    a. Dorsal rami → spinal nerve → dorsal root → spinal cord → interneuron → ventral root → spinal nerve → ventral rami
    b. Ventral rami → spinal nerve → dorsal root → spinal cord → interneuron → ventral root → spinal nerve → ventral rami
    c. Ventral rami → spinal nerve → ventral root → spinal cord → interneuron → ventral root → spinal nerve → ventral rami
    d. Dorsal rami → spinal nerve → ventral root → spinal cord → interneuron → dorsal root → spinal nerve → dorsal rami
    e. Ventral rami → spinal nerve → ventral root → spinal cord → interneuron → ventral root → spinal nerve → dorsal rami

38. Choose the false statement.
    a. The ventral root arises from the ventral surface of the spinal cord
    b. The dorsal ramus is larger than the ventral ramus
    c. Interneurons are the most numerous neurons in the body
    d. Interneurons are also called internuncial neurons
    e. Interneurons can be found in both ascending and descending tracts

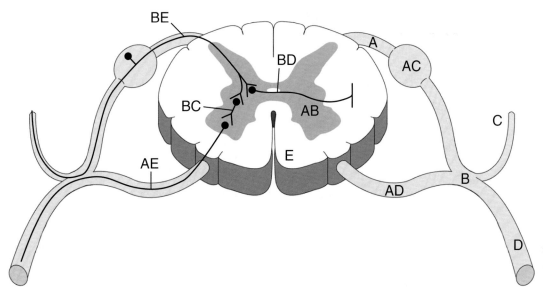

39. On the above picture, which statement is true?
    a. BE's cell body can be found in AC
    b. D contains cell bodies outside of the central nervous system (CNS)
    c. E contains cell bodies within the CNS
    d. A arises from the ventral surface of the spinal cord
    e. All of the above are true statements

40. On the above picture, which statement is false? (Choose all that apply.)
    a. A and AD come together to make a spinal nerve
    b. D is larger than C
    c. D supplies all structures of the back
    d. C supplies all the anterior trunk as well as the appendages
    e. AE has its axon passing through the white matter into the ventral root

41. Note the following statements:
    i. Cauda equina can be found below the level of LV2
    ii. The spinal cord is nervous tissue that occupies the upper three-fourths of the vertebral canal
    iii. The spinal cord is continuous with the medulla
    iv. The spinal cord has enlargements in the thoracic and sacral regions
    v. There are 61 total spinal nerves in the body

Which of the above are true?
    a. i, ii, iii, v   d. All of the statements
    b. iii only   e. None of the statements
    c. i and iii

42. All of the following are considered meninges EXCEPT:
    a. Dura mater
    b. Arachnoid mater
    c. One that has delicate connective tissue
    d. One that has netlike yet tough connective tissue
    e. One that has tough, fibrous connective tissue

43. Choose the false statement.
    a. Arachnoid mater can be found on the spinal cord
    b. Pia mater adheres to the brain and spinal cord
    c. The intermediate and outermost meninges extend from the foramen magnum
    d. The brain and spinal cord are protected and surrounded by 3 layers of meninges
    e. All of the above are true statements

Endocrine System Practice Quiz

1. Choose the false statement: (Choose all that apply.)
   a. The anterior pituitary develops from a pouch of epithelial tissue
   b. The posterior pituitary appears glandular
   c. The anterior pituitary pinches off the embryo's optic chiasm
   d. ADH is secreted by the posterior pituitary gland
   e. The anterior pituitary produces 7 hormones that it also secretes

2. The endocrine system includes all of the following EXCEPT:
   a. Pineal gland
   b. Pituitary gland
   c. Adrenal glands
   d. Thymus
   e. All of the above are part of the endocrine system

3. All of the following are hormones produced by the anterior pituitary EXCEPT: (Choose all that apply.)
   a. Growth hormone
   b. Adrenocorticotropic hormone
   c. Antidiuretic hormone
   d. Prolactin
   e. Oxytocin

4. Choose the false statement: (Choose all that apply.)
   a. Neurons release ADH and oxytocin in the posterior pituitary
   b. Each hormone is delivered in response to arterial stimulation from the hypothalamus in the posterior pituitary
   c. The pituitary gland hangs by the stalk from the hypothalamus of the brain
   d. Hormones in the posterior pituitary are released in response to neural stimulation from the thalamus

5. Choose the incorrect pair:
   a. Thyroid gland-thyroxine
   b. Ovaries and testes-androgens
   c. Pineal gland-melatonin
   d. Adrenal medulla-corticosteroids
   e. Pancreas-digestive enzymes

6. Choose the true statement.
   a. The melanin secreted from the pineal gland regulates biological clocks
   b. The thyroid gland can be found sitting on the heart
   c. The parathyroid hormone involves calcium homeostasis
   d. The adrenal glands are located in each kidney
   e. The pancreas is composed of an inner and an outer layer

7. The thyroid gland:
   a. Has a hormone that sets the biological clock
   b. Can be found on the kidney
   c. Has a hormone that sets the basal metabolic rate by stimulating the rate of cell respiration
   d. Releases Ca^{2+} into blood
   e. Secretes epinephrine and norepinephrine

8. Choose the false statement: (Choose all that apply.)
   a. The thyroid hormone stimulates maturation of the CNS
   b. The stomach is connected to the duodenum via the pancreatic duct
   c. Corticosteroids are hormones of the adrenal medulla
   d. The pancreas and the pineal gland secrete melatonin
   e. The pancreas is connected to the duodenum

Match the following that BEST matches for questions 9–15. (Letters may be used twice.)

   a. Adrenal medulla   e. Thyroid gland
   b. Adrenal cortex   ab. Anterior pituitary
   c. Pancreas   ac. Posterior pituitary
   d. PTH

 9. Corticosteroids   _____

10. Calcium homeostasis   _____

11. Digestive enzymes   _____

12. Promotes growth and maturation in the CNS   _____

13. Luteinizing hormone   _____

14. Insulin   _____

15. Appearance: fibrous   _____

16. A hormone agonist does all of the following EXCEPT:
    a. Binds to receptor proteins
    b. Interferes with hormone function
    c. Mimics the effect of the hormone
    d. All of the above are true of hormone agonist

Brain Practice Quiz

1. The fissure/sulcus that separates the cerebrum from the cerebellum is:
   a. Central sulcus
   b. Lateral fissure/sulcus
   c. Longitudinal fissure
   d. Transverse fissure/sulcus
   e. None of the above

For questions 2–4, match the function with the structure.
   a. postcentral gyrus
   b. central sulcus
   c. precentral gyrus

2. Separates primary motor cortex from the primary sensory cortex _____

3. This is anterior to the structure described in question 2 _____

4. This is posterior to the structure described in question 2 _____

5. A lobe of the cerebrum that lies within the depths of the lateral sulcus is the:
   a. Frontal lobe
   b. Parietal lobe
   c. Temporal lobe
   d. Occipital lobe
   e. None of the above

6. Choose the false statement regarding basal ganglia:
   a. It is a collection of cell bodies outside the CNS
   b. Disturbance can result in Parkinson's disease
   c. Basal nuclei would be a more correct term
   d. Contains gray matter
   e. Functions in controlling movement and posture

7. Choose the correct statement: (Choose all that apply.)
   a. The hypothalamus is an important sensory relay center of the brain
   b. The mammillary bodies serve as a sensory synaptic station
   c. One of the functions of the hypothalamus is coordination of muscular activity
   d. The mammillary bodies are associated with the limbic system
   e. The inferior colliculi involves a pathway of vision

For questions 8–13, match the function with the structure (letters may be used more than once).

a. Medulla oblongata
b. Cerebellum
c. Superior colliculi
d. Inferior colliculi
e. Hypothalamus
ab. Thalamus

8. Regulate muscle tone _____

9. Respiratory _____

10. Heart rate _____

11. Hearing _____

12. Regulation of visceral activity _____

13. Maintain equilibrium _____

14. The structure that relays impulses from the cerebral cortex to the cerebellum is:
a. Cerebellum
b. Medulla oblongata
c. Thalamus
d. Pons
e. Hypothalamus

Spinal Cord and Meninges Practice Quiz

For questions 1–10, match the questions with the letters indicating structures in the diagram on the left. Letters can be used more than once.

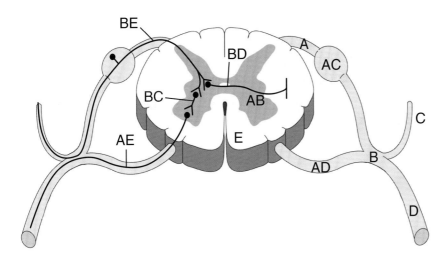

1. Identify the structure that contains cell bodies within the CNS.
2. Identify the structure that contains cell bodies within the PNS.
3. Identify the structure that contains sensory neurons only.
4. Identify the structure that contains sensory and motor neurons. (Choose all that apply.)
5. This structure is larger than C.
6. This structure supplies the back.
7. This structure has its axon passing through the white matter into AD.
8. Cell bodies of the sensory neuron can be found here.
9. This structure helps communicate one side of the spinal cord to the other. (Choose all that apply.)
10. This structure has its cell body in the gray matter of the cord
11. Choose the false statement.
    a. The spinal cord connects with the medulla
    b. Cell bodies of neurons create enlargements in the cervical and lumbar regions in the spinal cord
    c. Above the level of L2, the vertebral canal is occupied by the cauda equina
    d. The cauda equina consists of lower spinal nerves
    e. The cauda equina descends in a bundle from the conus medullaris

12. Choose the false statement.
    a. The brain and spinal cord are covered with 3 layers of connective tissue
    b. The meninges, from internal to external, are dura mater, arachnoid mater, and pia mater
    c. The space external to the dura mater is the epidural space
    d. External to the pia mater is the subarachnoid space
    e. The subarachnoid space contains CSF

13. Dura mater: (Choose all that apply.)
    a. Extends from the foramen magnum
    b. Is delicate, loose, netlike membrane
    c. Courses inferiorly to the coccyx in the vertebral canal
    d. Is the innermost meninges
    e. Is continuous with the cerebral arachnoid inferiorly

Special Senses and Receptors
Practice Quiz

1. Choose the false statement regarding receptors.
   a. Receptors are specialized to receive environmental stimuli
   b. Receptors generate nerve impulses
   c. Sensation is independent of the brain
   d. Receptors have 6 different types
   e. Receptors can become accustomed to stimulation

For questions 2–8, match the function with the structure. Letters can be used more than once; choose all that apply.)
   a. Proprioceptors   e. Nociceptors
   b. Mechanoreceptors   ab. Pain receptors
   c. Chemoreceptors   ac. Thermoreceptors
   d. Photoreceptors

2. Stimulated by pressure.   _____

3. Changes in temperature.   _____

4. Detects light.   _____

5. Sense the degree of muscle contraction.   _____

6. Respond to chemicals released by damaged tissues. _____

7. Sensitive to chemical substances in the immediate vicinity.

8. Sense movement of ligaments.

9. Touching your finger to your nose with your eyes closed is: (Choose all that apply.)
   a. A special sense
   b. Known as adaptation
   c. A somatic sense
   d. Known as proprioception
   e. A sense of knowing the position of the limbs

10. The skin contains receptors for all of the following EXCEPT:
   a. Touch   d. Equilibrium
   b. Pain   e. Pressure
   c. Temperature

11. In adaptation:
   a. A sensation becomes so accustomed to stimulation, it stops generating impulses
   b. The stimulus may still be present throughout the whole process
   c. An example would be if there was a bad smell in a room, one would smell it continuously
   d. Occurs only in the skin
   e. Receptors gain a sense of knowing the position of the limbs

12. Choose the false statement(s). (Choose all that apply.)
  a. Taste buds extend through the tongue muscle and then open
  b. The opening of a taste pore is called the taste bud
  c. There is no tongue map to the 5 basic modalities
  d. A sense of smell is dependent on olfactory cells
  e. Olfactory cells are modified neurons

Match the letters on the diagram below to the correct statement for questions 13–21. (Letters can be used more than once; choose all that apply.)

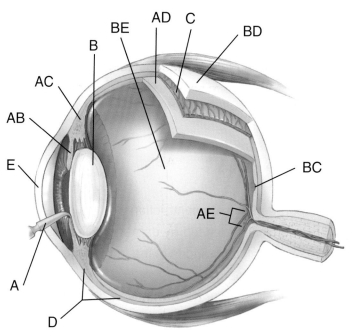

© Kendall Hunt Publishing Company

13. Choose the letters that make up the layers/coats of the eyeball.
14. This structure is transparent.
15. Dark brown layer.
16. Muscular, pigmented diaphragm.
17. Window of the eye.
18. Attached to the ciliary body by ligaments.
19. Clear, gelatinous material.
20. Fibers of the ganglionic cells pass in front of AD to make this structure.
21. Only cones can be found in the center of this area.

22. All of the following will help increase the chance of damaging vision EXCEPT:
    a. Careless use of contact lens
    b. Wearing plastic sunglasses
    c. Wearing large lenses
    d. Smoking cigarettes
    e. Getting poked in the eye

23. All of the following are true regarding diabetic retinopathy EXCEPT: (Choose all that apply.)
    a. Blinds people
    b. Effects people aged 20–74
    c. Capillaries burst
    d Destroys the nerve fibers responsible for peripheral vision
    e. Blood can be found in the aqueous fluid

Match the letters on the diagram below to the correct statement for questions 24–29. (Letters can be used more than once; choose all that apply.)

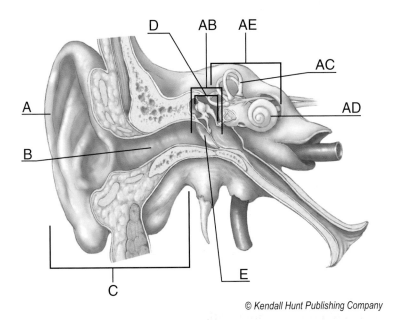

© Kendall Hunt Publishing Company

24. Identify the pinna.

25. Identify the auditory canal.

26. This region begins at tympanic membrane and ends at oval and round windows.

27. Choose the structure where 3 small bones can be found adjacent to laterally.

28. This structure is concerned with equilibrium.

29. This structure contains stereocilia.

30. Choose the false statement.
    a. Stereocilia transmits sounds to our brain to interpret
    b. The auditory tube can be found in the outer ear
    c. The eustachian tube permits equalization of air pressure
    d. The cochlea is snail shaped
    e. The cochlea is concerned with hearing

31. Choose the correct statement. (Choose all that apply.)
    a. Any noise below the level of 80 decibels could result in damage to hair cells
    b. Ringing in the ears is an effect from certain antibiotics
    c. Intense sounds of short duration can result in immediate hearing loss
    d. Tinnitus is a disease commonly associated with the cornea of the eye

Autonomic Nervous System
Practice Quiz

1. Choose the false statement. (Choose all that apply.)
   a. The PNS and autonomic nervous system (ANS) differ in 5 ways
   b. The CNS includes the brain and spinal cord
   c. The ANS is a subdivision of the PNS
   d. The word autonomy means "government"
   e. The parasympathetic division includes the thoracosacral system

2. Choose the correct statement.
   a. The sympathetic division will cause your pupil to constrict
   b. The parasympathetic division will cause copious sweating
   c. The preganglionic neuron of the sympathetic division is short, whereas the postganglionic neuron is long
   d. The parasympathetic division is known as the fight-or-flight response
   e. The autonomic nervous system has 5 effectors

3. Choose the correct statement. (Choose all that apply.)
   a. The parasympathetic includes cranial nerves 3, 5, 7, 9, 10, and S2–S5
   b. The sympathetic includes the thoracolumbar system
   c. The parasympathetic includes the craniosacral system
   d. The sympathetic includes T1–T11 and L2–L4 (sometimes L5)
   e. All of the above are true

4. All of the following are differences between the sympathetic and parasympathetic nervous systems EXCEPT:
   a. Ganglia   c. Length of fibers
   b. No. of neurons   d. Anatomy

5. This nervous system consists of a unit action:
   a. PNS   d. Parasympathetic
   b. ANS   e. Sympathetic
   c. CNS

6. Blood vessels are constricted in this nervous system:
   a. PNS   d. Parasympathetic
   b. ANS   e. Sympathetic
   c. CNS

7. Choose the false statement: (Choose all that apply.)
   a. Sympathetic and parasympathetic nervous systems have opposing actions where both innervate
   b. The parasympathetic nervous system activates organs simultaneously
   c. Sympathetic NS has its ganglia near or within the spinal cord
   d. Goosebumps are caused by the sympathetic nervous system
   e. Sympathetic system increases alertness

8. All of the following are effects of the sympathetic nervous system EXCEPT: (Choose all that apply.)
   a. Inhibits secretory activity
   b. Constricts eye pupils
   c. Steadies heart rate
   d. Increases blood pressure
   e. Increased motility (peristalsis)

UNIT 2 PRACTICE TEST

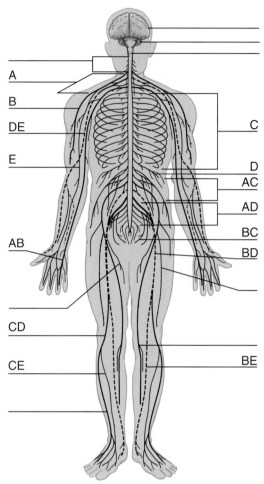

A

B

DE

E

C

D

AC

AD

BC

BD

AB

CD

CE

BE

© Kendall Hunt Publishing Company

1. Using the diagram above, which statement(s) is/are true? (Choose all that apply.)
   a. Letters AD includes the femoral and obturator nerve and has the ventral rami L1–L4
   b. CD is a branch of the nerve from the plexus indicated by the letters AC
   c. A does not innervate the skin over the upper medial portion of the arm
   d. The ventral rami of AB are L5–S2
   e. E has the same ventral rami of A and DE

2. Using the diagram on the previous page, choose the false statement. (Choose all that apply.)
   a. B comes from the lateral cord
   b. DE comes from the lateral and medial cord
   c. AB comes from the medial cord
   d. E comes from the posterior cord
   e. B, DE, AB, and E belong to the brachial plexus

3. The following statements are all true regarding the facial nerve EXCEPT:
   a. It is both motor and sensory in type
   b. Includes the function of taste
   c. Exits in the internal acoustic meatus
   d. It includes the function of facial expression
   e. All of the above are true statements

4. All of the following cranial nerves are sensory only in type EXCEPT: (Choose all that apply.)
   a. Olfactory   d. Vagus
   b. Abducent   e. Glossopharyngeal
   c. Vestibulocochlear

5. The efferent neuron:
   a. Conveys motor nerve impulses from the brain and spinal cord to effectors
   b. Carries impulses from one neuron to another
   c. Makes up the majority of nerves in the body
   d. Transmits sensory nerve impulses from receptors to the brain and spinal cord
   e. None of the above

6. Action potentials:
   a. Are impulses
   b. Travel the length of the axon
   c. Invade the nerve terminal
   d. Cause release of neurotransmitters
   e. All of the above are true

7. The neuroglia cell that produces myelin in the PNS is:
   a. Microglia   d. Ependymal cell
   b. Astrocyte   e. Schwann cell
   c. Oligodendrocyte

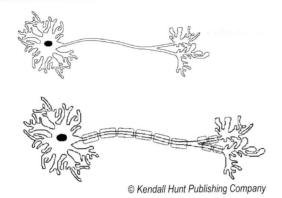

© Kendall Hunt Publishing Company

8. For the above picture, choose the false statement. (Choose all that apply.)
   a. E allows axons to conduct impulses faster
   b. AB is involved in neurotransmitter release
   c. D are gaps between segments of axons
   d. B controls metabolic activity of the neuron
   e. C receives information and transmits it toward A

9. For the above picture, choose the correct statement.
   a. AC is a function that occurs between a C of one neuron to a D of another neuron
   b. E is produced by glial cells
   c. C is also called the soma
   d. AC are cytoplasmic extensions
   e. All of the above are correct

10. All of the following are hormones from the anterior pituitary EXCEPT:
    a. LH
    b. TSH
    c. ADH
    d. PRL
    e. MSH

11. This endocrine organ promotes growth in children:
    a. Thymus
    b. Pancreas
    c. Pineal gland
    d. Adrenal glands
    e. Thyroid gland

12. Calcium homeostasis occurs in an endocrine organ that:
    a. Is shaped like a shield
    b. Produces the hormone thyroxine
    c. Secretes corticosteroids
    d. Can be found on the posterior thyroid
    e. Also regulates biological clocks

13. All of the following are hormones in the endocrine system EXCEPT:
    a. ACTH
    b. Insulin
    c. Parathyroid hormone
    d. Androgens
    e. All of the above are hormones in the endocrine system

14. The pancreas:
    a. Can be found next to the liver
    b. Secretes digestive enzymes into the large intestine
    c. Connects to the stomach via the pancreatic duct
    d. Digests insulin
    e. None of the above

15. The pituitary gland:
    a. Hangs by a stalk from the optic chiasm
    b. Is found below the hypothalamus
    c. Is made up of a medial and lateral part
    d. Is all controlled via neural stimulation
    e. All of the above are true

16. This fissure separates the primary motor cortex from the primary sensory cortex:
    a. Longitudinal fissure
    b. Transverse fissure
    c. Lateral sulcus
    d. Central sulcus
    e. Lobe fissure

17. This lobe is known for movement:
    a. Frontal
    b. Parietal
    c. Temporal
    d. Occipital
    e. Insula

18. All of the following are true statements regarding the basal ganglia EXCEPT:
    a. It is a collection of cell bodies inside the CNS
    b. Disturbs voluntary sensory control
    c. When disturbed can cause Huntington's disease
    d. Constituted of gray matter
    e. Functions in posture

19. The organ that functions in regulation of visceral (organ) activity also does all of the following EXCEPT: (Choose all that apply.)
    a. Body temperature
    b. Cardiac (heart rate)
    c. Carbohydrate and lipid metabolism
    d. Vasomotor (blood pressure)
    e. Sleep, sexual activity, and emotions

20. The organ that relays impulses from the cerebral cortex to the cerebellum is the:
    a. Medulla
    b. Hypothalamus
    c. Thalamus
    d. Cerebellum
    e. Pons

21. All of the following are associated with the cerebellum EXCEPT:
    a. Coordinate muscular activity
    b. Contains several nuclei
    c. Regulate muscle tone
    d. Maintain equilibrium
    e. Tree of life

22. Choose the false statement. (Choose all that apply.)
    a. Corpora quadrigemina are 4 glands found on the posterior thyroid gland
    b. The mammillary bodies are where the optic nerves cross
    c. The pons contains most of the ascending and descending tracts of spinal cord
    d. Superior colliculi involves pathway of vision
    e. Inferior colliculi involves pathway of hearing

23. Choose the correct statement.
    a. Folia separate the 2 hemispheres of the cerebellum
    b. The median vermis is found in the outer cortex of the cerebellum
    c. Arbor vitae are white matter found in the cerebrum
    d. The cerebellum connects to the brainstem including the pons, medulla, and midbrain
    e. All of the above are true

24. Choose the false statement. (Choose all that apply.)
    a. Optic chiasm is where optic tracts cross
    b. Pituitary gland secretes many hormones
    c. Mammillary bodies are known as the sensory synaptic station
    d. The pituitary gland is associated with limbic system
    e. The hypothamalus is found inferior to the optic chiasm, pituitary gland and the mammillary bodies

Answer questions 25–27 using the diagram below.

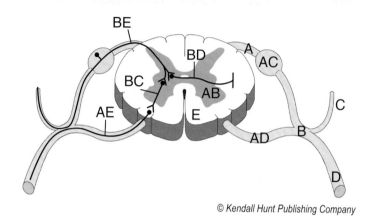

© Kendall Hunt Publishing Company

25. Choose the structure where cell bodies of motor neurons can be found.

26. Gray matter is surrounded by what letter(s)?

27. Choose the statement that is false.
    a. BD is called the internuncial neuron
    b. AE is only used for sensation
    c. AC contains cell bodies of sensory neurons
    d. BC are the most numerous neurons in the body
    e. B contains both sensory and motor neurons

28. If someone was to get a needle stuck right above their belly button and then uses his/her anterior abdominal muscles to flex the trunk, the pathway would be:
    a. Dorsal root → dorsal ramus → ventral ramus → ventral root
    b. Dorsal ramus → dorsal root → ventral ramus → ventral root
    c. Ventral ramus → dorsal ramus → ventral root → ventral ramus
    d. Ventral ramus → dorsal root → ventral root → ventral ramus
    e. Dorsal root → ventral ramus → dorsal root → ventral ramus

29. Choose the false statement regarding the spinal cord.
    a. It presents enlargements in the cervical and sacral regions
    b. It is connected to the brain superiorly
    c. The lower end of the cord is termed the conus medullaris
    d. The cauda equina consists of the very long roots of the lower spinal nerves
    e. The cauda equina descends in a bundle from the conus medullaris

30. If someone got her/his finger stuck in a beach chair and then used his/her forearm and arm to pull it away, the pathway would be:
    a. Ventral ramus → dorsal root → ventral root → ventral ramus
    b. Ventral ramus → dorsal root → ventral ramus → ventral root
    c. Dorsal root → dorsal ramus → ventral ramus → ventral root
    d. Dorsal root → ventral ramus → dorsal root → ventral ramus
    e. Ventral root → dorsal ramus → ventral root → ventral ramus

31. Choose the false statement regarding the meninges. (Choose all that apply.)
    a. There are 3 meninges surrounding the spinal cord
    b. Dura Mater is the outer most layer
    c. Arachnoid mater is surrounded by and is immediately deep to dura mater
    d. Pia mater lies right up against spinal cord and brain
    e. Pia mater is a very delicate connective tissue and can be separated from the brain

32. Choose the correct statement. (Choose all that apply.)
    a. The epidural space lies external to dura mater
    b. The subarachnoid space is filled with veins
    c. Veins found in the subarachnoid space are also known as the vertebral venous plexus
    d. The subarachnoid space is located below the arachnoid mater
    e. The epidural space contains CSF (cerebrospinal fluid)

33. Choose the false statement. (Choose all that apply.)
    a. Receptors are structures specialized to receive certain environmental stimuli and generate nerve impulses
    b. Nerve impulses received from receptors are sent to the CNS via neurons
    c. Chemoreceptors are sensitive to chemical substances in distinct and far apart areas
    d. Mechanoreceptors are stimulated by mechanical forces, which are most often pressure of some sort
    e. Proprioceptors sense the degree of muscle contraction, the tearing of tendons, and the movement of the larynx

34. Note the following statements:
    i. Somatic senses are associated with the head, limbs, spinal cord, and internal organs
    ii. Proprioception is a sense of knowing the position of your hand
    iii. Special senses consist of organs for taste, smell, vision, touch, and hearing
    iv. The skin contains receptors for touch, pressure, pain, and temperature

Which of the above are true?
    a. ii, iii, and iv   d. ii and iv
    b. ii and iii only   e. i and iii
    c. iii and iv

35. All the flavors sensed by the tongue are listed below EXCEPT:
    a. Bitter
    b. Salty
    c. Umami
    d. Sweet
    e. All of the above are flavors sensed by the tongue

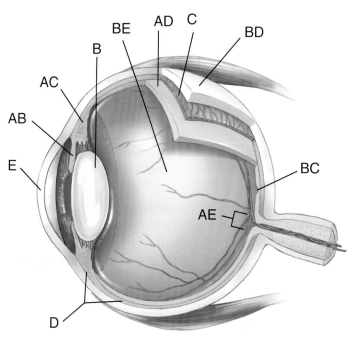

© Kendall Hunt Publishing Company

36. Using the diagram above, which of the following are false statements?
    a. BD is white and fibrous
    b. AC is attached to B via ligaments
    c. AC contains the ciliary muscle
    d. C absorbs stray lights
    e. AE contains cones only

37. Using the diagram above, which of the following is/are correct? (Choose all that apply.)
    a. Ganglionic cells pass behind AD
    b. Only rods can be found in the center of BC
    c. BE contains clear, gelatinous fluid behind the lens
    d. AB is the circular, muscular, and pigmented diaphragm
    e. AC controls the shape of AB

38. The following describes glaucoma: (Choose all that apply.)
    a. Blinds many people
    b. Occurs when the drainage system of the eyes fails
    c. Found in people between the ages of 20 and 50
    d. Destroys nerve fibers responsible for peripheral vision
    e. Capillaries to the retina burst and blood spills into the vitreous fluid

Use the diagram below for questions 39–42.

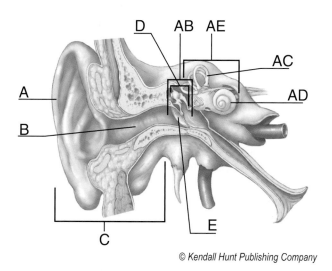

© Kendall Hunt Publishing Company

39. Using the diagram above, choose the letter(s) indicating the area that connects to the auditory tube.

40. Choose the letter(s) indicating the structure that involves equilibrium.

41. What do the structures indicated by the letter D sit between?
    a. Outer ear and middle ear
    b. E and the oval window
    c. E and the round window
    d. B and the beginning of AC
    e. A and AD

42. Stereocilia can be found in:
    a. The structure indicated by the A
    b. The structure indicated by the AC
    c. All structures found in AE
    d. The structure indicated by AB
    e. The structure indicated by AD

43. All of the following are false regarding the organ of Corti EXCEPT:
    a. Any noise above a level of 80 decibels could result in damage to the hair cells of the organ of Corti to disappear completely
    b. The movement of the small hair cells found in the organ of corti transmits sound to the brain to interpret
    c. The hair cells of organ of corti permit equalization of air pressure
    d. All of the above are true
    e. All of the above are false

44. Choose the false statement. (Choose all that apply.)
    a. Symptoms of temporary hearing loss include tinnitus
    b. To decrease chances of losing auditory abilities, one must modify listening habits immediately to prevent further damage
    c. Exposure to intense sounds of short duration can result in hearing loss forever
    d. Certain antibiotics may result in hearing loss if ears are not protected by loud noises
    e. Age-associated nerve deafness is due to hair cell damage of the organ of Corti

45. Choose the correct statement. (Choose all that apply.)
    a. The CNS and PNS interact to exchange signals attained from receptors
    b. The PNS includes both neurons that carry impulses from the receptors to the CNS and that carry impulses to the effectors from the CNS
    c. The ANS is part of the PNS and responsible for 3 effectors
    d. Effectors of the ANS cannot function without any conscious knowledge
    e. There are 5 differences between the PNS and ANS

46. The ANS: (Choose all that apply.)
    a. Can function with sensory neurons
    b. Was named so because it means "self-government"
    c. Involves only 1 neuron
    d. Has 2 important neurons: preganglionic and postganglionic
    e. All of the above are true

47. The preganglionic neuron:
    a. Is a neuron that has a long axon in the sympathetic nervous system
    b. Can carry an impulse from the ganglion to the receptor
    c. Is a neuron that has the cell body in the CNS
    d. Is short in the parasympathetic system
    e. All of the above are true

48. The sympathetic nervous system: (Choose all that apply.)
    a. Involves the first 2 lumbar spinal cord segments
    b. Have ganglia near or within the wall of the organ innervated
    c. Has an opposing action in organs where both sympathetic and parasympathetic innervate
    d. All of the above are true
    e. All of the above are false

49. The parasympathetic nervous system: (Choose all that apply.)
    a. Involves the S2–S4 spinal cord segments
    b. Have ganglia near or within the wall of the organ innervated
    c. Has an opposing action in organs where both sympathetic and parasympathetic innervate
    d. Has short preganglionic and long postganglionic fibers
    e. All of the above are true

Match the following answer choices with each statement for questions
50–52. Be specific as possible.
- a. Sympathetic
- b. Parasympathetic
- c. ANS
- d. PNS
- e. None of the above

50. Causes vasoconstriction of blood vessels supplying   _____
the glands.

51. Cause no effect in the sweat glands, arrector pilorum,   _____
and heart muscle.

52. Stimulates constrictor muscles of the eye (iris).   _____

53. All of the following are true EXCEPT:
- a. There are 8 pairs of cervical spinal nerves
- b. There are 12 pairs of thoracic spinal nerves
- c. There are 5 pairs of lumbar spinal nerves
- d. There are 5 pairs of sacral spinal nerves
- e. There are 5 pairs of coccygeal spinal nerves

54. The cervical plexus:
- a. Has the ventral rami: C5
- b. Supplies the upper limb
- c. Has the nerve that innervates the diaphragm
- d. Only supplies muscles in the neck
- e. Gives off a total of 16 nerves

Match the following answer choices with each statement for questions
55–60. Be specific as possible.
- a. Brachial plexus
- b. Cervical plexus
- c. Sciatic nerve
- d. Pudendal nerve
- e. Tibial nerve
- ab. Common fibular nerve
- ac. Lumbar plexus
- ad. Sacral plexus
- ae. Lumbosacral plexus
- bc. Inferior gluteal nerve
- bd. Superior gluteal nerve

55. Does not innervate the skin on the upper part of the   _____
shoulder but does supply the upper limb.

56. A plexus that includes a nerve that has the ventral   _____
rami C8, T1.

57. A plexus that has a nerve that supplies all of the posterior   _____
leg and foot.

58. A nerve that supplies the gluteus maximus.   _____

59. A nerve that supplies the genitalia.   _____

60. Has the ventral rami L1–S4.   _____

61. Choose the false statement: (Choose all that apply.)
    a. The lumbar plexus is located in the abdomen
    b. The sacral plexus includes the ventral rami L3–S3
    c. The common fibular nerve branches into a nerve that supplies the posterior leg and all of the foot
    d. The sciatic nerve is the largest of all nerves in the body
    e. All of the above are false

62. The obturator nerve: (Choose all that apply.)
    a. Has the same ventral rami as the femoral nerve
    b. Can be found in the lumbosacral plexus
    c. Innervates the anterior thigh
    d. Means to fill up
    e. All of the above are true

63. The musculocutaneous nerve:
    a. Comes from the medial cord
    b. Has the ventral rami C8, T1
    c. Branches to form a superficial and deep branch
    d. Innervates all anterior arm muscles
    e. Lies posterior to the medial epicondyle

64. The nerve that innervates anterior forearm muscles is/are: (Choose all that apply.)
    a. Musculocutaneous   d. Radial
    b. Median   e. Femoral
    c. Ulnar

65. Choose the false statement: (Choose all that apply.)
    a. The radial nerve is 50% of fibers that supply muscle and 50% fibers that supply skin
    b. The ulnar nerve is derived from the lateral cord
    c. The median nerve and the radial nerve share the same ventral rami
    d. The median, ulnar, and radial nerves are all motor and sensory
    e. The median nerve is the only nerve to course through the carpal tunnel

66. All of the following are true regarding the sacral plexus EXCEPT: (Choose all that apply.)
    a. It includes the posterior femoral cutaneous nerve
    b. It includes the sciatic nerve, which branches into the tibial nerve and superficial fibular (peroneal) nerve
    c. It has 5 major nerves
    d. It includes the superior gluteal nerve with the ventral rami: L4–S1
    e. It includes the superior fibular (peroneal) nerve that supplies the lateral leg

67. All of the following are innervated by the sciatic nerve EXCEPT:
    a. Biceps femoris
    b. Semitendinosus
    c. Extensor part of adductor magnus
    d. Semimembranosus
    e. Adductor longus

68. The femoral nerve supplies all of the following EXCEPT:
    a. Rectus femoris
    b. Pectineus
    c. Gracilis
    d. Iliopsoas
    e. Sartorius

69. Choose the false statement. (Choose all that apply.)
    a. Gluteus medius and minimus both laterally rotate
    b. Tensor fascia latae abducts the hip
    c. Sartorius flexes the hip and the knee
    d. Extensor part of adductor magnus inserts into the adductor tubercle
    e. All of the above are true

70. Choose the correct statement. (Choose all that apply.)
    a. Only 3 muscles abduct the hip
    b. 8 muscles flex the hip
    c. 6 muscles extend the hip
    d. 2 muscles evert the ankle
    e. Only 2 muscles medially rotate the hip

71. Choose the false statement.
    a. 5 muscles insert into the linea aspera
    b. Gluteus maximus originates from the sacrum
    c. 4 muscles originate from the pubis
    d. The short head of the biceps femoris originates from the linea aspera
    e. All muscles with the name that includes "adductor" insert into the linea aspera

72. Choose the true statement(s). (Choose all that apply.)
    a. 4 muscles originate from the iliac crest
    b. 2 muscles insert into ASIS
    c. 1 muscle originates from AIIS
    d. All of the above are true statements

73. All of the following are true regarding the anterior and medial thigh muscles EXCEPT:
    a. 2 muscles attach to the upper femur
    b. 2 muscles originate from the linea aspera in these compartments
    c. 2 muscles attach to the ischial tuberosity in these compartments
    d. 4 muscles extend the knee

Using the choices below, answer questions 74–80.

A. 1   B. 2   C. 3   D. 4   E. 5   AB. 6   AC. 7   AD. 8   AE. 9   BC. 10

74. How many muscles originate from the middle fibula?

75. How many muscles originate from the ischial tuberosity?

76. How many muscles insert into the 5th metatarsal?

77. How many muscles laterally rotate the hip?

78. How many muscles adduct the hip?

79. How many muscles flex the trunk?

80. How many muscles flex the knee?

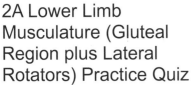

ANSWER KEY

For Unit 2 Practice Quizzes and Tests

2A Lower Limb Musculature (Gluteal Region plus Lateral Rotators) Practice Quiz
1. c, e
2. c
3. ac
4. c
5. c
6. d
7. d
8. b
9. b, e
10. e
11. e

Lower Limb Musculature (Anterior, Medial, and Posterior Thigh) Practice Quiz
1. e
2. c
3. a, c, d
4. b
5. e
6. d
7. d
8. ac
9. d
10. be
11. a
12. d

Lower Limb Musculature (Anterior, Lateral, and Posterior leg) Practice Quiz
1. a
2. b, c
3. a, c, d
4. b
5. b
6. d
7. c
8. c
9. b
10. b

Lower Limb Musculature (Full Mix) Practice Quiz
1. a, b, e
2. a, c
3. c, d
4. e
5. a
6. b
7. c
8. c
9. c

2B Nervous System Practice Quiz
1. d
2. c, e
3. d

4. e
5. a
6. ab
7. c
8. ac
9. b, e
10. b
11. a, d, e
12. b
13. c
14. d
15. c
16. b
17. e
18. c, d
19. a
20. e
21. d, e
22. c, e
23. c
24. ad
25. bc
26. a
27. ce, de
28. bd
29. b
30. a, e
31. ab
32. be, cd
33. d
34. c
35. b, c
36. b, e

37. b
38. b
39. a
40. c, d
41. c
42. d
43. e

2C Endocrine System Practice Quiz

1. b and c
2. e
3. c, e
4. b, d
5. d
6. c
7. c
8. b, c, d
9. b
10. d
11. c
12. e
13. ab
14. c
15. ac
16. d

2D Brain Practice Quiz

1. d
2. b
3. c
4. a
5. e
6. a
7. b, d
8. b
9. a
10. a
11. d
12. e
13. b
14. d

2E Spinal Cord and Meninges Practice Quiz

1. ab
2. ac
3. a
4. b, c and d
5. d
6. c
7. ae
8. ac
9. bd, bc
10. ae (can also be bc & bd)
11. c
12. b
13. a, c

2G Special Senses and Receptors Practice Quiz

1. c
2. b
3. ac
4. d
5. a
6. e, ab
7. c
8. a
9. c, d, e
10. d
11. b
12. a, b
13. bd, c, ad
14. e
15. c
16. ab (and a even though it is being retracted)
17. e
18. b
19. be
20. ae
21. bc
22. c
23. d, e

24. a
25. b
26. ab
27. e
28. ac
29. ad
30. b
31. c

2H ANS Practice Quiz

1. a, d, e
2. c
3. b, c
4. b
5. e
6. e
7. b, c
8. b, c, e

2A-H Unit 2 Practice Test

1. c, e
2. b, d
3. e
4. b, d, e
5. a
6. e
7. e
8. c, d
9. b
10. c
11. e
12. d
13. e
14. e
15. b
16. d
17. e
18. b
19. b, d
20. e
21. b
22. a, b, c

23. d
24. d, e
25. ab
26. e
27. b
28. d
29. a
30. a
31. e
32. a, d
33. c, e
34. d
35. e
36. e
37. c, d
38. b, d
39. ab
40. ac
41. b
42. e

43. a
44. c, e
45. a, b
46. b, d
47. c
48. a, c
49. a, b, c
50. a
51. e
52. b
53. e
54. c
55. a
56. a
57. ad
58. bc
59. d
60. ae
61. b, c
62. a, b, d

63. d
64. b, c
65. a, b
66. b, e
67. e
68. c
69. a, b
70. a, b
71. a
72. c
73. c
74. b
75. ab
76. b
77. ad
78. e
79. a
80. d

Worksheets

3A Heart...pp. 215–222
3B Heart Disease ....pp. 223–226
3C Blood Vessels and Lymphatic System ....pp. 227–230
3D Vasculature of the Body ....pp. 231–237
3E Respiratory System...pp. 238–242
3F Digestive System...pp. 243–249
3G Urinary System ....pp. 250–251
3H Male Reproductive System ....pp. 252–254
3I Female Reproductive System ....pp. 255–257

Study Resources

3A Heart...pp. 259–263
3C Blood Vessels and Lymphatic System ....p. 264
3D Vasculature of the Body ....pp. 265–272
3E Respiratory System...pp. 273–274
3F Digestive System...pp. 275–277
3G Urinary System ....p. 278
3H Male Reproductive System ....pp. 279–280
3I Female Reproductive System ....p. 281

Practice Quizzes

3A Heart Practice Quiz ....pp. 283–284
3B Heart Disease Practice Quiz..p. 285
3C Blood Vessels and Lymphatic System Practice Quiz..........pp. 286–287
3D Vasculature of the Body Practice Quiz...............................pp. 288–291
3E Respiratory System Practice Quiz ....pp. 292–293
3F Digestive System Practice Quiz ....pp. 294–295
3G Urinary System Practice Quiz..p. 296
3H&I Reproductive System Practice Quiz ....pp. 297–298
3A–H Unit 3 Practice Test...pp. 299–310
3A–H Student Written Practice Test for Unit 3.........................pp. 311–316
Answer Key ....pp. 317–318

HEART

I. **DEFINITION: IS A MUSCLE THAT FUNCTIONS IN PUMPING BLOOD THROUGH VESSELS OF THE CARDIOVASCULAR SYSTEM.**

    A. It is composed of striated muscle, cardiac in type.

    B. The heart has 4 internal cavities called CHAMBERS, 2 _____ and 2 VENTRICLES.

        1. The atria and ventricles are further differentiated by the side of the body; thus 1 can speak of the 4 chambers as the right atrium, left atrium, right _____, and left ventricle.

    C. The heart is positioned in such a way that the atria lie _____ (not superior) to the ventricles; thus, blood, when passing from atria to ventricles, moves horizontally rather than vertically.

    D. The heart is located in the thorax between the lungs, resting on the diaphragm.

II. **THERE ARE A NUMBER OF STRUCTURES THAT PROTECT THE HEART:**

    A. Anteriorly: sternum

    B. Laterally: ribs, intercostal muscles, lungs

    C. Posteriorly: thoracic vertebrae

    D. In addition to the previous, the heart is enclosed in a tough connective tissue sac called the _____.

III. **PERICARDIUM**

    A. It is a sac that encloses the heart.

    B. Its outer layer blends with the central tendon of the diaphragm inferiorly.

    C. Superiorly and posteriorly, the fibrous layer blends with the major blood vessels of the heart, the superior vena cava, _____ _____, and pulmonary trunk.

    D. The cardiac muscle itself is referred to as MYOCARDIUM.

    E. The inner epithelial lining of the chambers of the heart is referred to as ENDOCARDIUM.

IV. **EXTERNAL ANATOMY OF THE HEART**

    A. The heart is described as having an apex, a base, and 3 surfaces:

        1. Sternocostal surface: lying adjacent to the sternum and costal cartilages.

        2. _____ surface: adjacent to the diaphragm.

        3. Pulmonary surface: adjacent to the medial surface of the left & right lung.

    B. APEX: a rounded projection of the heart that points inferiorly and to the left.

C. BASE: generally the area where the great vessels attach to the heart. These vessels are the aorta, _____ trunk, and superior vena cava.

D. AURICLES: both the right and left atria have _____-like appendages attached to the lateral surface of the atria, and these are the auricles.

1. Clinically, the term *auricle* is also referred to as *the appendage*.

Heart—Anterior

© Kendall Hunt Publishing Company

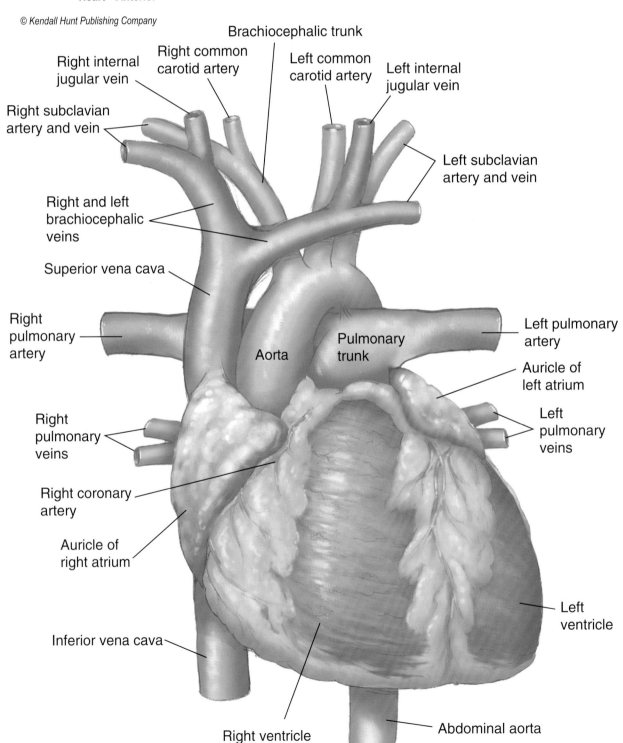

Brachiocephalic trunk

Right common carotid artery

Left common carotid artery

Right internal jugular vein

Left internal jugular vein

Right subclavian artery and vein

Left subclavian artery and vein

Right and left brachiocephalic veins

Superior vena cava

Right pulmonary artery

Aorta

Pulmonary trunk

Left pulmonary artery

Auricle of left atrium

Right pulmonary veins

Left pulmonary veins

Right coronary artery

Auricle of right atrium

Left ventricle

Inferior vena cava

Right ventricle

Abdominal aorta

Heart—Posterior

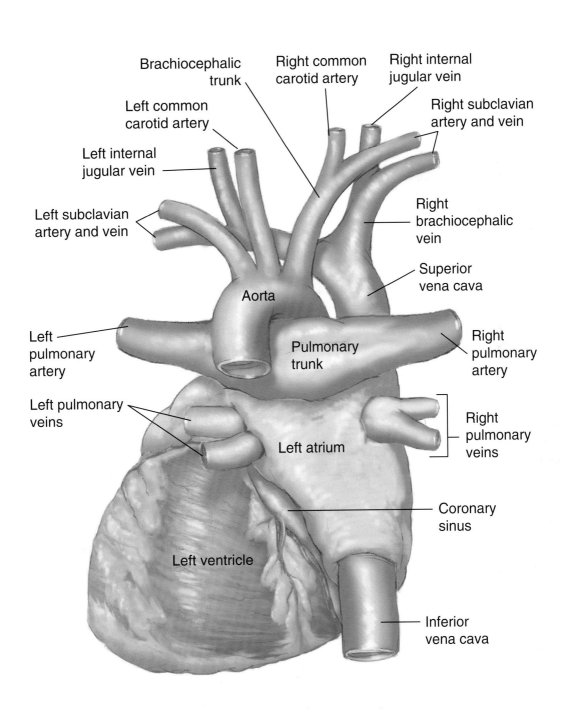

Brachiocephalic trunk

Right common carotid artery

Right internal jugular vein

Left common carotid artery

Right subclavian artery and vein

Left internal jugular vein

Left subclavian artery and vein

Right brachiocephalic vein

Aorta

Superior vena cava

Left pulmonary artery

Pulmonary trunk

Right pulmonary artery

Left pulmonary veins

Right pulmonary veins

Left atrium

Coronary sinus

Left ventricle

Inferior vena cava

V. INTERNAL ANATOMY OF THE HEART

A. RIGHT ATRIUM

1. A vertical muscular ridge is seen on the posterior wall of the right atrium. This is the CRISTA TERMINALIS.

2. From the crista terminalis are muscular ridge-like extensions called _____PECTINATI or PECTINATE MUSCLES.

   a. These musculi pectinati are found in the right atrium and in the right and left auricle.

3. There are 3 major venous openings into the right atrium:

   a. Superior vena caval opening:
      i. It is the opening of the superior vena cava, the main vein returning blood from the upper half of the body.

   b. _____ vena caval opening:
      i. It is the opening of the inferior vena cava, the main vein returning blood from the lower half of the body.

   c. Opening of the coronary sinus
      i. The coronary sinus is a venous chamber located on the posterior surface of the heart.
      ii. It receives the veins that drain the heart itself.
      iii. It opens into the right atrium just anterior and superior to the inferior vena cava.

4. Interatrial septum: the partition between the right atrium and the left atrium.

   a. On this septum in the right atrium lies an oval depression, the FOSSA OVALIS.
      i. This fossa ovalis is a remnant of a foramen that in the fetal stage of development existed between the right atrium and left atrium.

   b. This opening is called the FORAMEN OVALE.
      i. It closes at birth and remains in the adult as a fossa ovalis.

5. Anteriorly, the right atrium opens to the right ventricle via the right atrioventricular opening.

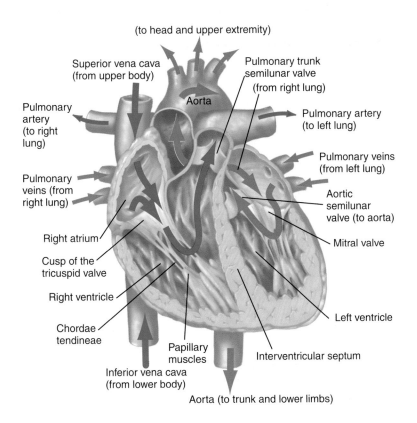

(to head and upper extremity)

Superior vena cava (from upper body)

Pulmonary trunk semilunar valve (from right lung)

Aorta

Pulmonary artery (to right lung)

Pulmonary artery (to left lung)

Pulmonary veins (from left lung)

Pulmonary veins (from right lung)

Aortic semilunar valve (to aorta)

Right atrium

Mitral valve

Cusp of the tricuspid valve

Right ventricle

Left ventricle

Chordae tendineae

Papillary muscles

Interventricular septum

Inferior vena cava (from lower body)

Aorta (to trunk and lower limbs)

Heart Interior

© Kendall Hunt Publishing Company

B. TRICUSPID (RIGHT ATRIOVENTRICULAR) VALVE

1. The right atrioventricular opening is guarded by the tricuspid or right atrioventricular valve.

2. VALVE: a _____ device that will allow for flow of blood in 1 direction only, thus preventing retrograde flow (flow in the wrong direction).

3. The heart is composed of 2 types of valves: ATRIOVENTRIC-ULAR VALVES and SEMILUNAR VALVES.

   a. An atrioventricular valve is characteristically composed of 3 parts:
      i. Cusps: flaps of connective tissue.
      ii. Chordae tendineae: connective tissue _____ that attach to the lower surface of the cusps.
      iii. _____ muscle: internal folds of ventricular muscle that give attachment to the chordae tendineae.

4. The tricuspid valve functions in closing during contraction of the right ventricle.

   a. When closed, it will prevent backflow of blood from the right ventricle to the right atrium.

      b. The valve is held in a closed position via the chordae tendineae that are attached to the lower surface of the cusps, and are thus not _____ into the atrium.

C. RIGHT VENTRICLE

    1. The internal surface of the ventricle consists of irregular ridge-like projections of muscle called TRABECULAE CARNEAE.

        a. Papillary muscles are a type of trabeculae carneae.

    2. A band of muscle in the chamber is called the MODERATOR BAND or SEPTOMARGINAL TRABECULA.

        a. It contains important fibers of the _____ system of the heart.

    3. The only openings of the right ventricle are the:

        a. Right atrioventricular opening, guarded by the tricuspid valve.

        b. _____ trunk opening.

    4. Blood will leave the right ventricle and enter the pulmonary trunk by passing through the pulmonary trunk opening.

    5. This opening is guarded by a valve, the PULMONARY SEMI-LUNAR VALVE.

D. PULMONARY SEMILUNAR VALVE

    1. A semilunar valve, unlike the atrioventricular valves, does not possess papillary muscles and chordae tendineae.

        a. Rather, it exists merely as pocket-like flaps surrounding an opening.

    2. For each semilunar valve there are 3 flaps or cusps.

        a. The free edge of each cusp has a small central thickening of fibrous tissue, the _____.

        b. This fills the small gap left at closure of the 3 flaps.

    3. In the pulmonary semilunar valve, there are 3 such flaps.

    4. Between these cusps and the wall of the pulmonary trunk, there are 3 sinuses.

    5. When flow of blood is from right ventricle into pulmonary trunk, the valve opens. If the flow is _____, it closes.

E. PULMONARY CIRCULATION

1. Blood will flow through the pulmonary trunk into the right and left pulmonary arteries, to the right and left lungs.

2. In the lungs, blood will give off CO_2 and _____ O_2.

3. Oxygenated blood will return to the heart via 4 PULMONARY VEINS, 2 from the right lung and 2 from the left lung.

4. All _____ pulmonary veins will enter the left atrium.

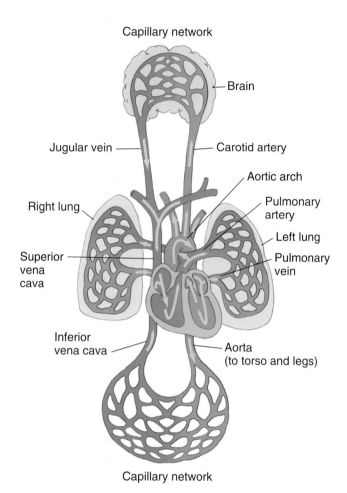

Capillary network

Brain

Jugular vein

Carotid artery

Aortic arch

Pulmonary artery

Right lung

Left lung

Superior vena cava

Pulmonary vein

Inferior vena cava

Aorta (to torso and legs)

Capillary network

Diagrammatic Circulation

© Kendall Hunt Publishing Company

F. LEFT ATRIUM

1. The left atrium has its musculi pectinati located within the left _____ only.

2. The main part of the left atrium is taken up by the 4 separate openings of the pulmonary veins.

3. The only other opening of the left atrium is the LEFT ATRIO-VENTRICULAR OPENING.

G. BICUSPID VALVE (MITRAL; LEFT ATRIOVENTRICULAR)

1. The left atrioventricular opening is guarded by the bicuspid valve.

2. Being an atrioventricular valve, it has papillary muscles and chordae tendineae.

3. It contains _____ cusps.

    4. Supporting papillary muscles connect to the cusps.

    5. Blood will flow from the left atrium into the left ventricle through the bicuspid valve.

H. LEFT VENTRICLE

    1. Contains internal muscular ridgelike folds, TRABECULAE CARNEAE.

    2. Papillary muscles of the bicuspid valve are a type of trabeculae carneae.

    3. One major difference between the right ventricle and the left ventricle is the _____ of the wall itself.

        a. The wall of the left ventricle is usually more than twice as thick as that of the right.

        b. The reason for this is the right ventricle must pump blood only to 1 organ, the _____.

        c. The left ventricle must pump blood to every other organ in the body, and thus performs more work, and is larger.

    4. The only openings of the left ventricle are:

        a. Left atrioventricular opening

        b. Opening of the _____.

    5. When the left ventricle contracts, blood will leave and enter the aorta.

    6. The opening of the aorta is guarded by a valve, the AORTIC SEMILUNAR VALVE.

I. AORTIC SEMILUNAR VALVE

    1. This valve possesses _____ cusps located at the opening of the aorta.

    2. These cusps possess nodules and lunulae as did pulmonary semilunar valves.

    3. Similarly, the spaces between the cusps and the wall of the aorta are termed AORTIC SINUSES and differ from the pulmonary sinuses in that the right aortic sinus and left aortic sinus are the sites of origins of the right and left coronary arteries, respectively.

    4. Blood will then leave the left ventricle and enter the aorta and then pass to all parts of the _____.

HEART DISEASE

I. GENERAL INFORMATION

A. Heart disease refers to the heart's ability to function _____.

B. Heart disease is a major cause of disability and is the leading cause of death in the United States.

C. Nearly _____ people die of heart disease each year in the United States.

    1. This is approximately _____% of all U.S. deaths.

D. Heart disease encompasses many specific heart conditions.

E. Coronary heart disease is the most common heart disease in the United States; it can lead to _____.

II. CORONARY HEART DISEASE (CHD)

A. CHD is the most _____ type of heart disease.

B. CHD occurs when the _____ arteries that supply blood to the heart become hardened and narrowed due to the buildup of plaque.

C. The buildup of plaque and the hardening and subsequent narrowing of the arteries is called atherosclerosis. Plaques are a mixture of fatty substances including _____ and other lipids.

D. With the restriction of blood flow, oxygen supply to the heart can be reduced or even fully blocked.

E. Plaques may also break off and cause blood clots that block arteries so that tissues do not receive adequate blood supply.

F. CHD can lead to a heart attack. Angina can also occur.

G. Eventually, CHD can weaken the heart muscle and lead to heart failure.

    1. This is a serious problem resulting in the inability of the heart to pump blood the way that it should.

H. Also, an irregular heartbeat, called _____, can develop.

III. HEART ATTACK

A. A heart attack is also called a _____.

B. If the blood supply to the heart is severely reduced or completely blocked, heart muscle cells may not receive enough oxygen and begin to _____.

C. The more time that passes without treatment to restore blood flow, the greater is the damage to the heart.

D. This damage can cause _____ heart rhythms or even sudden cardiac arrest or stopping of the heart beat.

E. Death can result.

F. Coronary artery disease is the _____ underlying cause of a heart attack.

IV. ANGINA

A. Chest pain or discomfort that occurs when the heart muscle is not getting enough blood.

B. Angina may feel like _____ or a squeezing pain in the chest.

C. The pain may also occur in the shoulders, arms, neck, jaw, or back, and it may feel like _____.

D. Angina is a symptom of coronary heart disease.

E. Angina may be stable or unstable.

1. Stable angina is chest pain that occurs on physical exertion or under mental or emotional stress.

2. Unstable angina is chest pain that occurs even while at rest, without apparent reason.

V. ACUTE CORONARY SYNDROME

A. A term that is sometimes used to describe people who have either an acute myocardial infarction or unstable angina.

VI. AORTIC ANEURYSM AND DISSECTION

A. A condition where the aorta stretches or _____ (aneurysm) and _____ (dissection).

VII. ARRHYTHMIAS

A. Irregular, or abnormally fast or slow, _____ of the heart.

B. The heartbeat is controlled by electrical impulses.

C. When the timing or frequency of these electrical impulses is disrupted, arrhythmias develop.

D. Some arrhythmias are quite serious.

1. An example is ventricular _____, a severely abnormal heart rhythm that causes death unless treated right away by providing an electrical shock to the heart (called *defibrillation*).

E. Others are less severe but can develop into more serious conditions over time.

1. A particular concern is atrial fibrillation.

2. Atrial fibrillation is rapid, irregular beating of the upper chambers of the heart.

a. The chambers can quiver instead of beating in a regular pattern.

b. Blood is not fully pumped out of them and may pool and _____.

VIII. CARDIOMYOPATHY

A. A _____ of the heart muscle or a change in heart muscle structure.

B. It often results in inadequate heart pumping or other heart function abnormalities.

C. These can result from various causes, including prior heart attacks, _____ or bacterial infections, and others.

IX. CONGENITAL HEART DISEASE

A. Malformations of heart structures, present during pregnancy or at _____.

B. These may be caused by genetic factors or by adverse exposures during pregnancy.

C. Examples include holes in the walls that divide the heart chambers, abnormal heart valves, and others.

D. Congenital heart defects can disrupt the normal flow of blood through the heart.

E. Congenital heart defects are the most common type of _____ birth defect.

X. HEART FAILURE

A. This may also be called _____ heart failure or chronic heart failure.

B. Heart failure is a condition where the heart cannot pump enough blood and oxygen to meet the needs of other body organs.

C. Heart failure does not mean that the heart has stopped, but that it cannot pump blood the way that it should. Heart failure is a serious condition.

D. There is no cure for heart failure at this time, except a heart _____.

E. Once diagnosed, medicines are needed for the rest of the person's life.

XI. PERIPHERAL ARTERIAL DISEASE (PAD)

A. _____ of the arteries that supply blood to the arms and legs.

B. PAD is usually the result of atherosclerosis, the buildup of plaque and narrowing of the arteries.

C. Blood flow and oxygen to the _____ in the arms and legs can be reduced or even fully _____.

D. Painful leg muscles, numbness, swelling in the ankles and feet, and _____ pulse in the feet are some of the signs and symptoms of PAD.

XII. MITRAL VALVE PROLAPSE

A. The heart's mitral valve helps blood on the _____ side of the heart flow in 1 direction.

B. It closes to keep blood from moving backwards when the heart beats (contracts).

C. If the valve does not open and close properly, it is called mitral valve prolapse.

D. Many different things can cause it.

   1. In most cases, it is _____ and patients usually do not know they have the problem.

   2. In a small number of cases, it can cause blood to leak backwards (_____ mitral regurgitation).

      a. This requires treatment with surgery.

XIII. ARTERIOSCLEROSIS

A. Arteries are blood vessels that carry oxygen and nutrients from the heart to the rest of the body.

B. Healthy arteries are flexible, strong, and elastic.

C. Over time, however, too much pressure in your arteries can make the walls thick and stiff—sometimes restricting blood flow to your organs and tissues.

D. This process is called arteriosclerosis, or _____ of the arteries.

   1. Atherosclerosis is a specific type of arteriosclerosis, but the terms are often used interchangeably (although we will not be doing that in this class or on the exam).

BLOOD VESSELS AND LYMPHATIC SYSTEM

I. DEFINITION

1. The structures that carry blood from the heart to the organs of the body and back to the heart again are called BLOOD VESSELS.

II. STRUCTURE

1. The space within the blood vessel is called its _____.

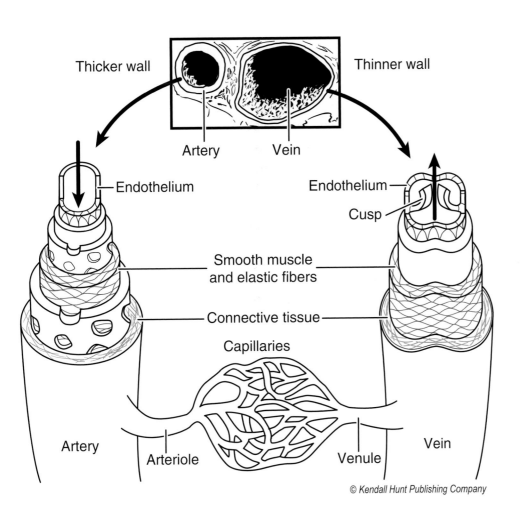

Thicker wall   Thinner wall

Artery   Vein

Endothelium   Endothelium

Cusp

Smooth muscle and elastic fibers

Connective tissue

Capillaries

Artery   Arteriole   Venule   Vein

III. THERE ARE 5 TYPES OF BLOOD VESSELS:

A. _____: a vessel that carries blood away from the heart (regardless of whether it carries oxygenated or deoxygenated blood).

   1. Artery walls are composed of smooth muscle and elastic fibers that allow for extension of the vessels and the carrying of a pulse.

B. _____: small arteries that arise via branching of large arteries.

   1. Smooth muscle and elastic fibers are also located in the walls of arterioles.

   2. Arterioles branch to form capillaries.

C. _____: connections between arterioles and venules.

   1. It is at the capillary level where oxygen and nutrients pass from the blood into the tissues and where carbon dioxide and waste materials pass from the tissues into the blood.

D. _____: small veins formed by the junction of a number of capillaries.

E. VEIN: a vessel formed by the junction of a number of venules.

   1. Veins are said to be formed by tributaries and carry blood back to the heart.

   2. They have a thinner wall than the corresponding artery.

   3. In certain veins, especially those that carry blood against gravity, veins contain _____ that allow for the flow of blood only in 1 direction, toward the heart.

   4. Blood moves past the valves via contraction of surrounding muscles.

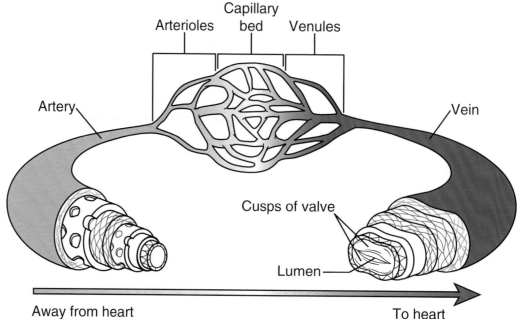

LYMPHATIC SYSTEM

I. FLUID FILTERED OUT OF BLOOD CAPILLARIES EACH DAY EXCEEDS THAT REABSORBED.

   A. This excess is returned to the blood via lymphatics.

II. THE CAPILLARIES THAT PICK UP THIS _____ FLUID ARE CALLED LYMPHATIC CAPILLARIES, AND THEY DIFFER FROM BLOOD CAPILLARIES IN THAT THEY ARE ENDOTHELIAL TUBES THAT BEGIN BLINDLY.

   A. They are not open at both ends.

   B. They will conduct the excess fluid called LYMPH toward veins.

      1. As they do this, a number of them will join to form an AFFERENT LYMPHATIC VESSEL.

         a. Lymphatic vessels consist of similar layers that comprise blood vessels.

         b. They contain folds termed valves, which allow for flow of lymph in 1 direction, toward veins.

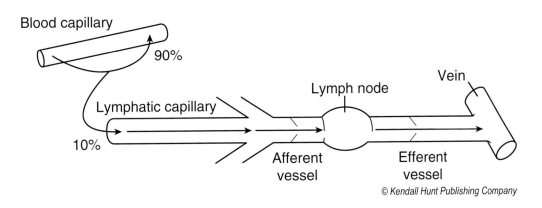

© Kendall Hunt Publishing Company

   C. Afferent lymphatic vessels convey lymph to LYMPH NODES, which function in filtering the lymph.

      1. Each node has a CORTEX and a MEDULLA, through which lymph will filter.

   D. Leaving the lymph node will be several EFFERENT LYMPHATIC VESSELS that also contain valves.

      1. They will pass the lymph to the venous system.

III. IMPORTANT LYMPHATIC DUCTS

1. RIGHT _____ DUCT: drains the right half of the head, neck, chest, and right upper limb.
2. _____ DUCT: drains the rest of the body.

A. Both ducts end in their respective brachiocephalic veins.

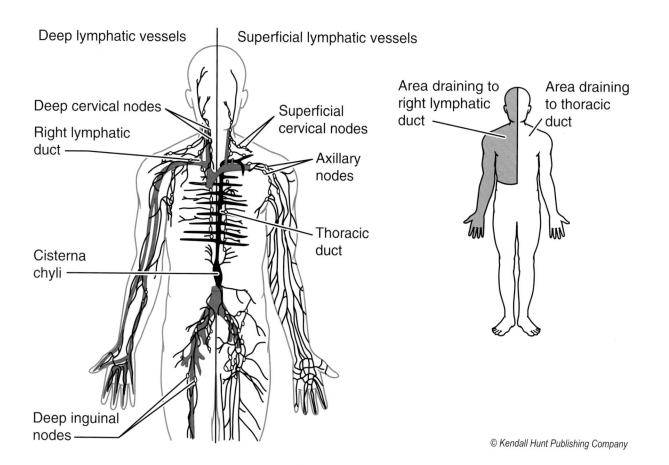

Deep lymphatic vessels   Superficial lymphatic vessels

Deep cervical nodes

Right lymphatic duct

Superficial cervical nodes

Axillary nodes

Thoracic duct

Cisterna chyli

Deep inguinal nodes

Area draining to right lymphatic duct

Area draining to thoracic duct

© Kendall Hunt Publishing Company

IV. LYMPH NODES ARE PREVALENT IN THE FOLLOWING REGIONS:

A. Neck

B. Axilla

C. Inguinal region (Groin)

VASCULATURE OF THE BODY

Arteries of the Body

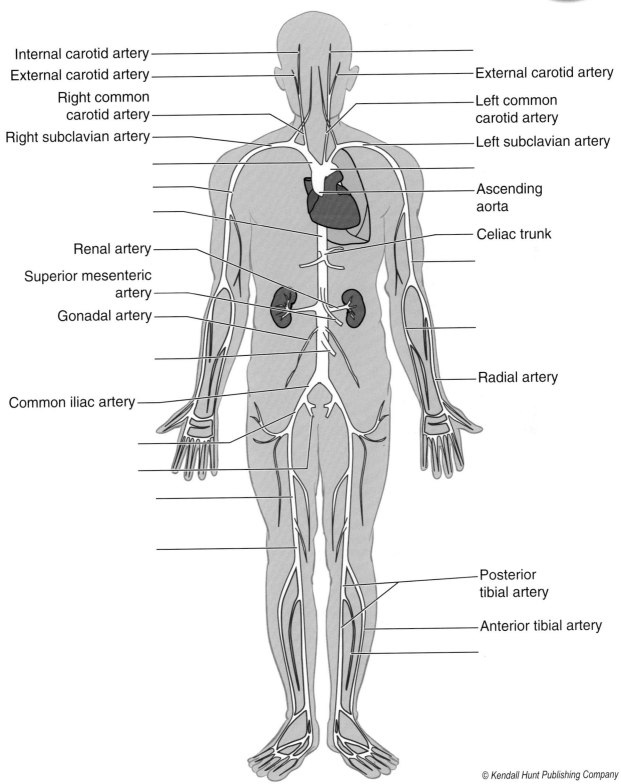

Internal carotid artery

External carotid artery

Right common carotid artery

Right subclavian artery

Renal artery

Superior mesenteric artery

Gonadal artery

Common iliac artery

External carotid artery

Left common carotid artery

Left subclavian artery

Ascending aorta

Celiac trunk

Radial artery

Posterior tibial artery

Anterior tibial artery

© Kendall Hunt Publishing Company

231

Head/Neck Arteries

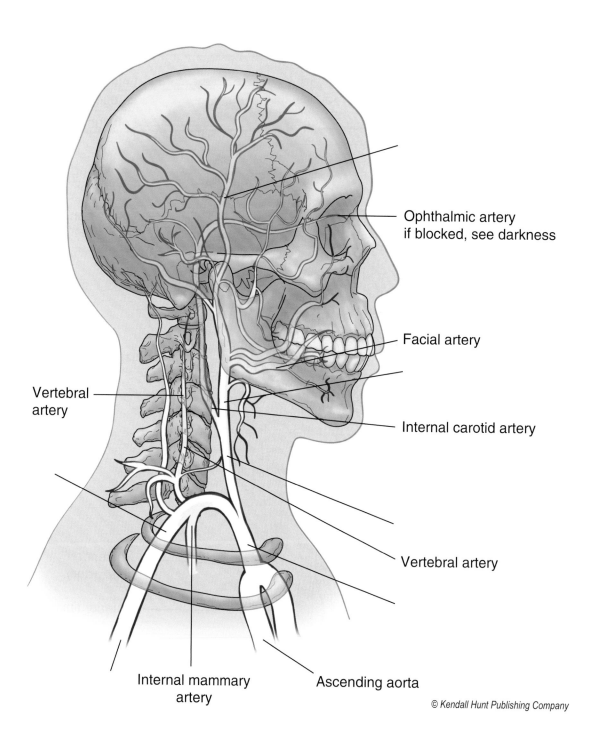

Ophthalmic artery
if blocked, see darkness

Facial artery

Vertebral
artery

Internal carotid artery

Vertebral artery

Internal mammary
artery

Ascending aorta

Upper Limb Arteries

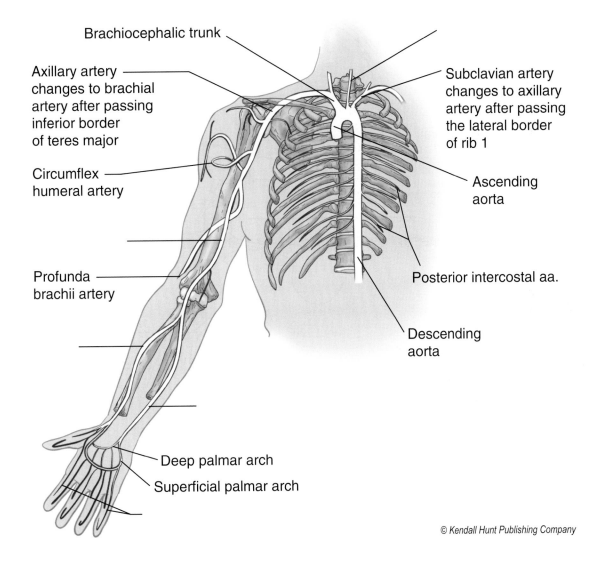

Brachiocephalic trunk

Axillary artery
changes to brachial
artery after passing
inferior border
of teres major

Circumflex
humeral artery

Profunda
brachii artery

Subclavian artery
changes to axillary
artery after passing
the lateral border
of rib 1

Ascending
aorta

Posterior intercostal aa.

Descending
aorta

Deep palmar arch

Superficial palmar arch

Abdominal Arteries

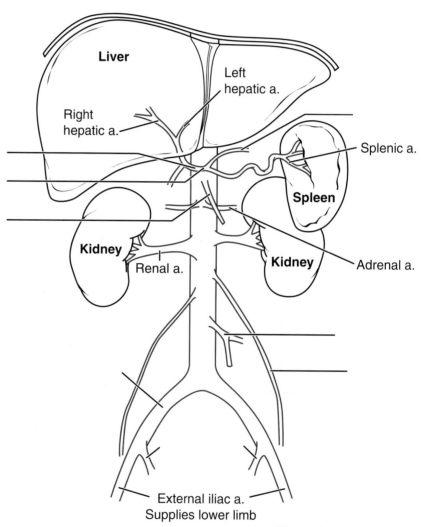

Liver

Left
hepatic a.

Right
hepatic a.

Splenic a.

Spleen

Kidney

Kidney

Adrenal a.

Renal a.

External iliac a.
Supplies lower limb

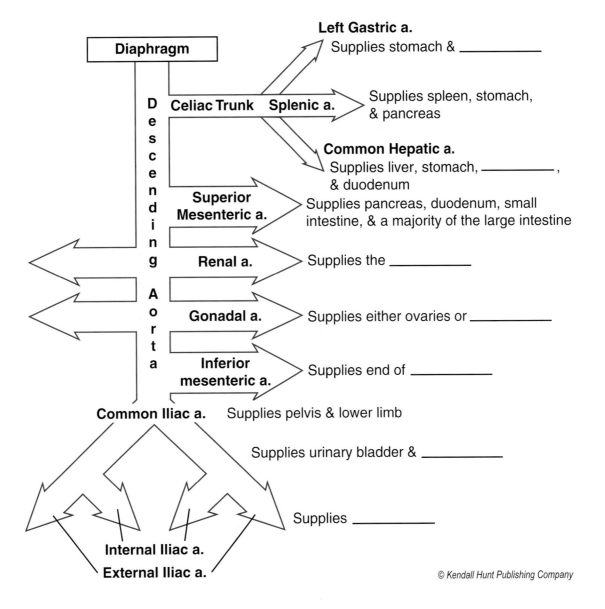

Left Gastric a.
Supplies stomach & _____

Diaphragm

Descending Aorta

Celiac Trunk   Splenic a.   Supplies spleen, stomach, & pancreas

Common Hepatic a.
Supplies liver, stomach, _____, & duodenum

Superior Mesenteric a.   Supplies pancreas, duodenum, small intestine, & a majority of the large intestine

Renal a.   Supplies the _____

Gonadal a.   Supplies either ovaries or _____

Inferior mesenteric a.   Supplies end of _____

Common Iliac a.   Supplies pelvis & lower limb

Supplies urinary bladder & _____

Supplies _____

Internal Iliac a.
External Iliac a.

Lower Limb Arteries

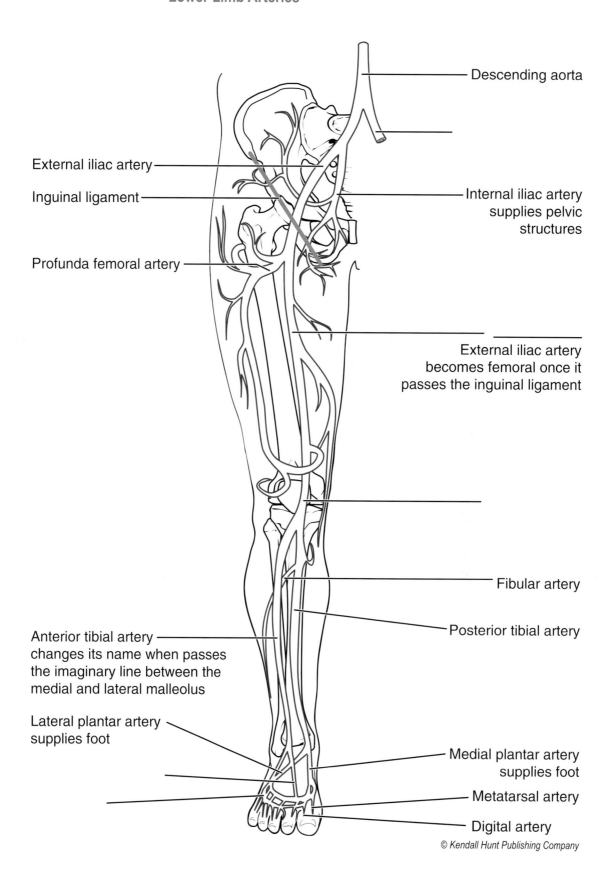

Descending aorta

External iliac artery

Inguinal ligament

Internal iliac artery supplies pelvic structures

Profunda femoral artery

External iliac artery becomes femoral once it passes the inguinal ligament

Fibular artery

Posterior tibial artery

Anterior tibial artery changes its name when passes the imaginary line between the medial and lateral malleolus

Lateral plantar artery supplies foot

Medial plantar artery supplies foot

Metatarsal artery

Digital artery

Full Body Veins

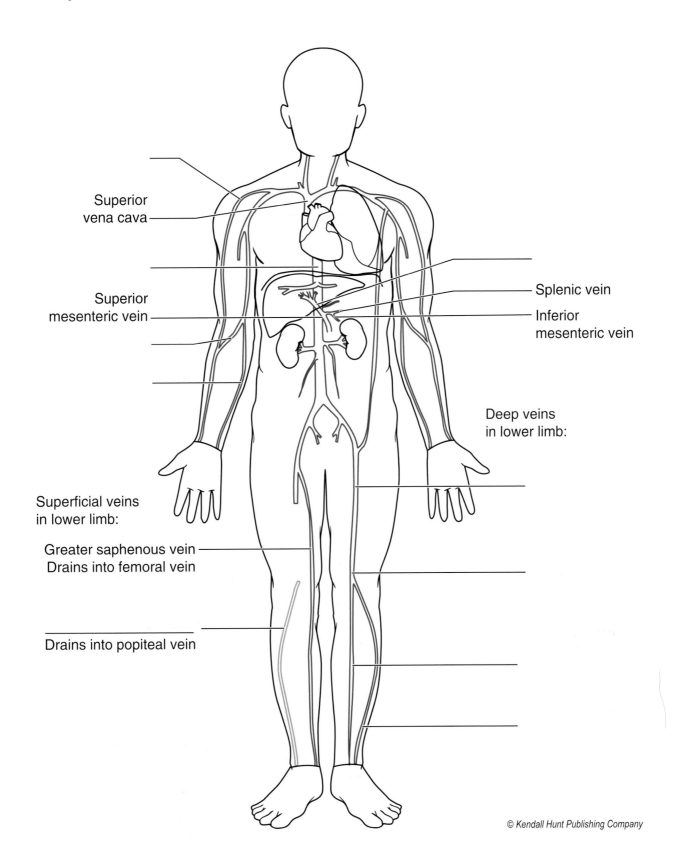

Superior
vena cava

Superior
mesenteric vein

Splenic vein

Inferior
mesenteric vein

Deep veins
in lower limb:

Superficial veins
in lower limb:

Greater saphenous vein
Drains into femoral vein

Drains into popiteal vein

I. **DEFINITION:** The system of the body concerned with gas transport and exchange.

II. **IT EXISTS IN 2 PHASES:**

    A. _____ PHASE: concerned with the movement of gases from the outer environment through the respiratory tubes to the lungs.

    B. _____ EXCHANGE PHASE: concerned with the exchange of O_2 and CO_2 between the blood and the air sacs of the lungs.

III. **ORGANS OF THE RESPIRATORY SYSTEM**

    A. Organs are discussed in the order that air passes from the outer environment to the lungs:

        1. Nasal cavity (or oral cavity): referred to as the nose and mouth regions.

        2. Pharynx: muscular tube for passageway of air and food.

        3. _____: cartilage tube for the passageway of air, contains the vocal folds.

        4. Trachea

        5. _____

        6. Lungs

IV. TRACHEA

A. The trachea is a cartilaginous and membranous tube extending from the larynx above, to the point at which it bifurcates into 2 primary bronchi below.

B. It is called the _____ by lay people.

C. It is about 15 cm in length in vivo.

D. It is composed of a series of 16 to 20 C-shaped rings of hyaline cartilage, so that each almost encircles the lumen.

E. The open ends of these incomplete cartilaginous rings are directed posteriorly, and the gap between the 2 ends of each ring is bridged by connective tissue and smooth muscle.

    1. This connective tissue bridge is adjacent to the posteriorly related _____.

F. The tracheal bifurcation marks the end of trachea and the beginning of 2 primary bronchi.

    1. It is the primary bronchi that will enter the substance of the lungs.

Trachea: anterior ⟶

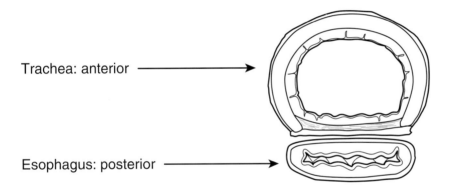

Esophagus: posterior ⟶

V. BRONCHI

A. The trachea terminates by bifurcating onto 2 _____. BRONCHI, called, respectively, the RIGHT PRIMARY BRONCHUS and the LEFT PRIMARY BRONCHUS.

VI. RIGHT PRIMARY BRONCHUS

A. It is _____, shorter and straighter (forms a less-acute angle with the trachea) than the left.

B. It is approximately 2.5 cm in length.

C. Enters the right lung at the hilus of the right lung and divides into 3 SECONDARY BRONCHI, 1 for each of the lobes of the right lung.

    1. Each of these 3 secondary bronchi will divide into a number of TERTIARY BRONCHI that will supply a BRONCHOPULMONARY SEGMENT.

        a. The term bronchopulmonary segment is applied to the largest segment within a lobe of the lung.

        b. Bronchopulmonary segments are separated from each other by connective tissue septa that prevent diffusion of air from 1 segment to another.

VII. LEFT PRIMARY BRONCHUS

A. It is smaller in caliber but about twice as long as the right (5 cm).

B. Makes more of an acute angle with the trachea than the right.

   1. Thus, objects falling through the trachea would most likely lodge in the right primary bronchus since it is more in line with the trachea than the left primary bronchus.

C. It enters the left lung through the hilus and it divides into 2 secondary bronchi, 1 for the upper lobe and 1 for the lower lobe.

D. Tertiary bronchi subdivide numerous times and eventually into many _____.

VIII. THE MAIN DIFFERENCES BETWEEN BRONCHI AND BRONCHIOLES ARE:

A. Bronchioles, as their name indicates, are much smaller and more numerous than bronchi.

B. Bronchioles do not require cartilage in their walls to keep them from collapsing on inspiratory movements because they are inside the substance of the lung which itself is expanded during inspiratory movements.

IX. THE TERMINAL BRONCHIOLES IN TURN DIVIDE INTO _____ BRONCHIOLES.

A. These are very short tubes composed of connective tissue and smooth muscle.

B. A few alveoli bud off of the respiratory bronchioles and are the reason why these bronchioles are termed respiratory bronchioles.

   1. The respiratory bronchioles branch and radiate conelike into 2 to 11 alveolar ducts.

X. THE _____ DUCTS ARE LONG THIN-WALLED TUBES OF CONNECTIVE TISSUE AND SMOOTH MUSCLE.

A. From the alveolar ducts arise single alveoli and alveolar sacs containing 2 or more alveoli.

XI. AT THE LEVEL OF THE _____, THERE IS NO LONGER ANY CARTILAGE OR SMOOTH MUSCLE.

A. All that remains as the alveolar wall is a thin layer of epithelium and connective tissue.

B. The most conspicuous feature of the alveoli is the presence of numerous _____ adjacent to them.

   1. The capillaries are so situated that a great portion of their surface is directed toward the alveolus.

   2. This is understandable since it is the alveolar wall plus the capillary wall that constitute the respiratory membrane, the membrane through which gas exchange will occur.

XIII. LUNGS

A. There are 2 lungs in the body, properly called the RIGHT LUNG and the LEFT LUNG.

B. Each lung presents an APEX (the rounded superior end of the lung), a BASE, and 3 SURFACES:

1. _____ SURFACE: the surface adjacent to the thoracic wall (sternum, ribs, costal cartilages, intercostal muscles).

2. DIAPHRAGMATIC SURFACE (BASE): that part of the lung adjacent to the upper surface of the diaphragm.

   a. Since the diaphragm projects upward forming 2 domes, the diaphragmatic surface is concave.

3. MEDIAL SURFACE: that part of the lung adjacent to the heart and other thoracic organs.

   a. The medial surface presents a locus, the HILUS or hilum, where all structures that will enter or leave the lung will pass.

Respiratory
System

© Kendall Hunt Publishing Company

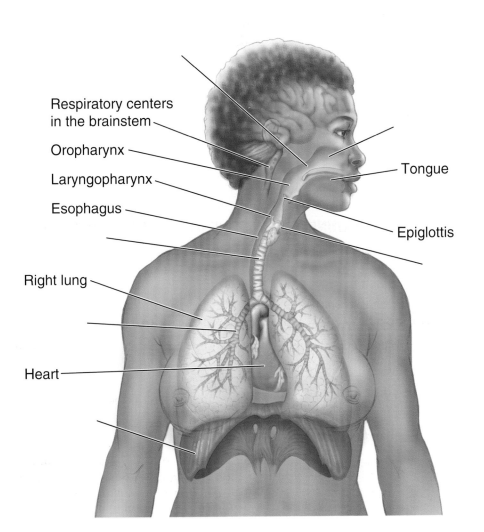

Respiratory centers
in the brainstem

Oropharynx

Laryngopharynx

Esophagus

Right lung

Heart

Tongue

Epiglottis

C. The name that is given collectively to all of the structures that enter or leave the lung at the hilus is _____ of the lung.

1. The structures forming the root are:

   a. PULMONARY ARTERY: a branch of the pulmonary trunk that will bring deoxygenated blood from the heart to the lung.

   b. PULMONARY _____ (2): will carry oxygenated blood from the lung back to the heart.

   c. PRIMARY BRONCHUS: branch of the trachea.
      i. It will serve as a passageway for air.

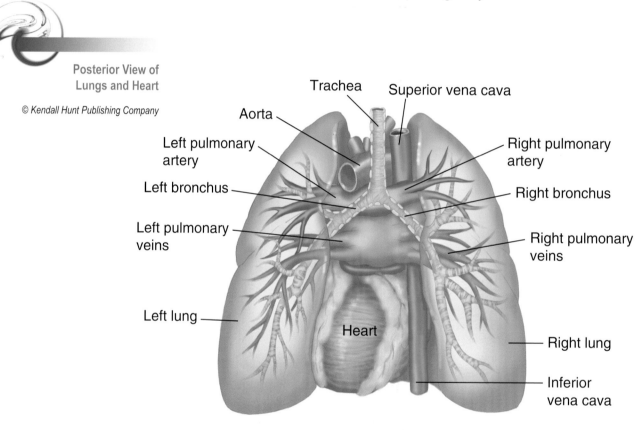

Posterior View of Lungs and Heart

© Kendall Hunt Publishing Company

Trachea · Superior vena cava · Aorta · Left pulmonary artery · Right pulmonary artery · Left bronchus · Right bronchus · Left pulmonary veins · Right pulmonary veins · Left lung · Heart · Right lung · Inferior vena cava

D. Lobes and fissures of the lungs:

1. The right lung has 2 fissures:

   a. _____ FISSURE

   b. _____ FISSURE
      i. These fissures subdivide the right lung into 3 lobes: UPPER (or superior), MIDDLE, and LOWER (or inferior) LOBES.

2. The left lung has 1 fissure:

   a. OBLIQUE FISSURE
      i. This fissure subdivides the left lung into 2 lobes: UPPER and _____ LOBES.

DIGESTIVE SYSTEM

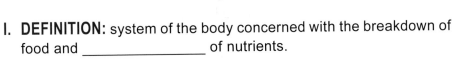

I. **DEFINITION:** system of the body concerned with the breakdown of food and _____ of nutrients.

II. **IT IS ALSO REFERRED TO AS THE:**
   A. Digestive tract
   B. Gastrointestinal tract
   C. _____ canal

III. **THE ORGANS OF THE DIGESTIVE SYSTEM EXIST AS A CONTINUOUS TUBE EXTENDING FROM THE ORAL CAVITY TO THE ANUS.**

IV. **PERITONEUM**
   A. **DEFINITION:** a large, highly folded, _____ membrane located in the abdomen.

V. **PERITONEAL FOLDS AND MEMBRANES:**
   A. **FALCIFORM LIGAMENT:** extends from the liver to the anterior abdominal wall.
      1. It contains in its free edge the ROUND LIGAMENT OF THE LIVER (obliterated umbilical vein).
   B. _____ **OMENTUM:** extends from the greater curvature of the stomach to the transverse colon, forming a fatty apron over the small intestines.
   C. **MESENTERY:** supports and suspends the jejunum and ileum.

VI. **DIGESTIVE SYSTEM STRUCTURES**
   A. **ORAL CAVITY**
      1. It is also referred to as the mouth.
      2. It contains the tongue, teeth, and openings of the salivary glands.
         a. **TONGUE:** a skeletal muscular organ, which functions in the sense of taste, mastication, and the movement of food.

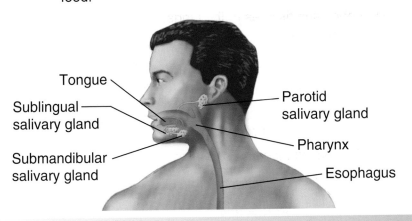

Tongue
Sublingual salivary gland
Submandibular salivary gland
Parotid salivary gland
Pharynx
Esophagus

Digestive System

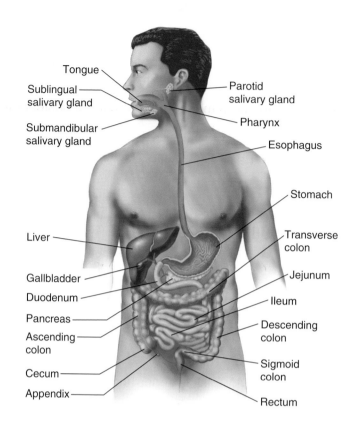

b. TEETH: _____ in the adult: 4 types (incisors, canines, _____, and molars).

c. SALIVARY GLAND OPENINGS: there are 3 pairs of salivary glands called the parotid, submandibular, and sublingual glands.

   i.   They are all exocrine glands since they are drained by a duct, all of which empty the gland secretions (SALIVA) into the oral cavity.

B. PHARYNX

1. Composed of _____ muscle.

2. Functions in swallowing.

3. It is divided into 3 parts:

   a. NASOPHARYNX posterior to the NASAL CAVITY.

   b. OROPHARYNX posterior to the _____ CAVITY.

   c. LARYNGOPHARYNX posterior to the LARYNX.

      i.   The laryngopharynx is continuous with the esophagus.

      ii. This is also called the _____ clinically.

C. ESOPHAGUS

1. A muscular tube extending _____ cm from the lower end of the pharynx above to the cardiac opening of the stomach below.

2. Exhibits 3 regions known as the cervical, thoracic, and abdominal parts.

   a. CERVICAL: in the neck where it lies posterior to the trachea.

   b. THORACIC: in the thorax where it lies posterior to the trachea in the upper half and posterior to the _____ in the lower half of the thorax.

   c. ABDOMINAL: after piercing the diaphragm at the esophageal opening of the diaphragm, it enters the abdomen.

      i. It runs a very short course in the abdomen and terminates by joining the _____ (gastroesophageal junction).

D. STOMACH

1. It is the digestive organ responsible for the _____ of food.

2. It presents 3 parts:

   a. _____: the part of the stomach above the level of entrance of the esophagus.

   b. BODY: located between the fundus and the pyloric part of the stomach, it comprises the main mass of the stomach.

   c. _____ PART: extends toward the right from the lower part of the body of the stomach.

      i. It ends at the PYLORIC OPENING, which is the opening between the stomach and the first part of the duodenum.

      ii. The pyloric opening is surrounded by a circular smooth muscle termed the PYLORIC SPHINCTER.

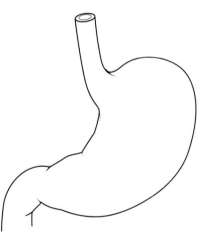

3. The stomach presents 2 curvatures:

   a. GREATER CURVATURE: name given to the margin of the stomach that courses over the fundus and inferiorly on the left side of the stomach to the inferior side of the pyloris.

      i. The greater curvature is a convex curve in its entirety.

   b. _____ CURVATURE: the name given to the margin that is located on the right side of the stomach, its curvature being concave.

4. The stomach presents 2 openings:

   a. CARDIAC OPENING: opening between the cavity of the esophagus and the cavity of the stomach.

      i. It is located at the upper junction of the greater and lesser curvatures.

      ii. It is called "cardiac" because of its close relationship with the part of the diaphragm upon which the heart rests.

b. PYLORIC OPENING: opening between the stomach and the first part of the duodenum.

    i. It is surrounded by a _____ smooth muscle termed the PYLORIC SPHINCTER.

5. The internal surface of the stomach present folds called _____.

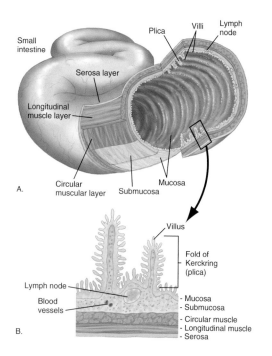

Small intestine

Plica   Villi   Lymph node

Serosa layer

Longitudinal muscle layer

A.   Circular muscular layer   Submucosa   Mucosa

Villus

Fold of Kerckring (plica)

Lymph node

Blood vessels

B.

- Mucosa
- Submucosa
- Circular muscle
- Longitudinal muscle
- Serosa

E. SMALL INTESTINE

1. That part of the intestine between the _____ sphincter (where it is connected to the stomach) and the iliocecal junction (where it joins the _____ intestine).

2. Its length is approximately 7 meters.

3. Its diameter gradually diminishes through its length.

4. It is subdivided into 3 parts:

    a. DUODENUM: the first part of the small intestine and extends from the pyloric sphincter to where it joins the jejunum.

       i. It is a C-shaped organ with its concave medial border receiving the openings of ducts draining the liver, gallbladder, and pancreas.

5. _____: the proximal two-fifths of the remainder of the small intestine.

6. ILEUM: the distal three-fifths of the remainder of the small intestine.

F. ILEOCECAL JUNCTION

1. It is the junction of the ileum portion of the small intestine and the cecum of the large intestine.

G. LARGE INTESTINE OR COLON

1. The part of the intestine extending from the ileocecal junction to the anus.

2. It is subdivided into the following parts:

    a. _____: the part of the large intestine that lies at and below the level of entrance of the ileum.

    b. APPENDIX: a lymphatic organ attached to the posteromedial surface of the cecum.

    c. _____ COLON: the portion of the large intestine that extends superiorly from the right side of the posterior abdominal wall to the liver.

       i. Since it cannot course above the liver, it bends forming the RIGHT COLIC or _____ FLEXURE, and courses to the left.

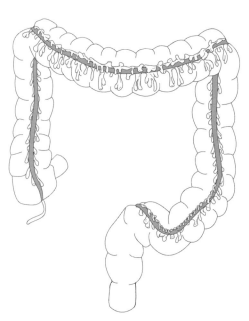

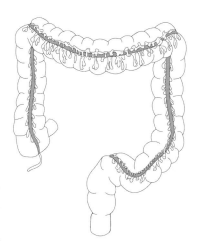

d. TRANSVERSE COLON: portion of the large intestine that extends from the right colic flexure on the right side of the abdomen to the spleen on the left side.

    i. When it reaches the spleen, it will bend and course inferiorly forming the LEFT COLIC or SPLENIC FLEXURE.

e. _____ COLON: portion of the large intestine, which extends from the left colic flexure inferiorly along the left side of the posterior abdominal wall.

f. SIGMOID COLON: part of the large intestine, which extends from the descending colon to the pelvis, where it is continuous with the rectum.

    i. It forms a loop, the shape and position of which depend upon the degree of filling.

H. RECTUM

1. Portion of the digestive system between the sigmoid colon and the anus.

    a. It narrows inferiorly, forming the _____ CANAL.

I. ANUS

1. Sphincteric muscle is located at the termination of the anal canal, which functions in the retention of _____.

VII. ASSOCIATED GLANDS OF THE DIGESTIVE SYSTEM

A. LIVER

1. It is an exocrine gland that produces a substance called BILE, which is conveyed via hepatic ducts to the duodenum.

2. It presents 4 lobes of the liver: RIGHT, LEFT, QUADRATE, and _____.

3. The structures that enter and exit the liver (right and left hepatic arteries, portal vein, right and left hepatic ducts) do so

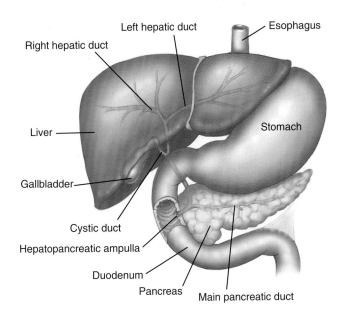

**Associated glands
of the digestive system**

© Kendall Hunt Publishing Company

at the _____ HEPATIS, at the junction of the 4 lobes.

   a. The hepatic veins do not exit here.

B. GALL BLADDER

1. It is located on the visceral surface of the liver between the right lobe and the quadrate lobe.

2. Bile is _____ and concentrated here.

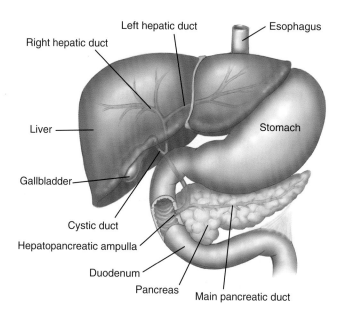

C. PANCREAS

1. It is both an endocrine and an exocrine gland.

   a. As an exocrine gland, it produces digestive enzymes that pass via a duct to the duodenum.

   b. As an endocrine gland, it produces the hormone _____ _____.

2. Anatomically, it presents the following parts:

   a. HEAD: located in the concavity of the duodenum.

   b. BODY: courses from the head toward the left across the vertebrae.

   c. _____: the left end of the gland, which approximates the spleen.

D. DUCT SYSTEM

1. The RIGHT HEPATIC DUCT drains the right half of the liver, and the LEFT HEPATIC DUCT drains the left half of the liver.

2. These 2 ducts join to form the _____ HEPATIC DUCT.

3. The gallbladder is drained by the _____ DUCT.

4. The cystic duct joins the common hepatic duct to form the BILE DUCT; this may also be called the common bile duct.

   a. This drains into the _____.

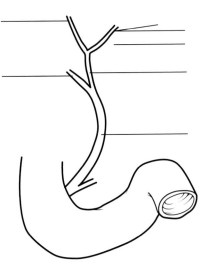

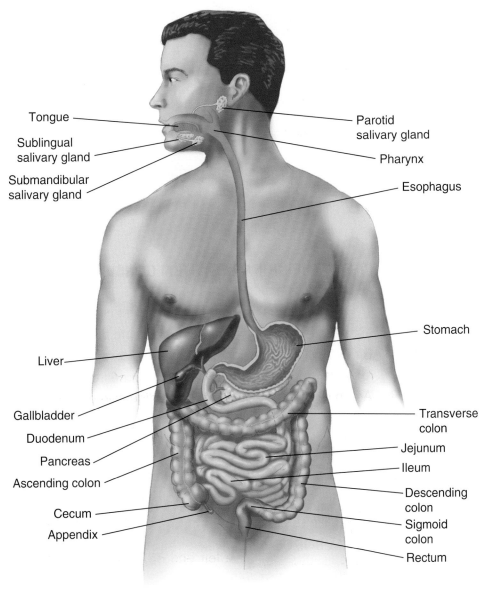

Tongue
Sublingual salivary gland
Submandibular salivary gland
Liver
Gallbladder
Duodenum
Pancreas
Ascending colon
Cecum
Appendix

Parotid salivary gland
Pharynx
Esophagus
Stomach
Transverse colon
Jejunum
Ileum
Descending colon
Sigmoid colon
Rectum

Digestive System

URINARY SYSTEM

I. DEFINITION: SYSTEM OF THE BODY THAT IS RESPONSIBLE FOR THE PRODUCTION AND ELIMINATION OF _____.

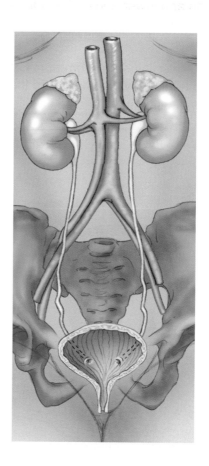

Urinary System

II. **ANATOMICALLY, THE URINARY SYSTEM CONSISTS OF 4 DIFFERENT ORGANS:**

    A. _____: urine production occurs here.

    B. URETER: a tube conveying urine from kidney to the bladder.

    C. URINARY BLADDER: functions in storage of urine.

    D. _____: a tube that conveys urine from the urinary bladder to the outside of the body.

III. **KIDNEY**

    A. The kidney is a bean-shaped organ that is situated in the posterior portion of the abdominal cavity on either side of the vertebral column.

    B. There are 2 kidneys, called the RIGHT KIDNEY and the LEFT KIDNEY.

    C. The LATERAL BORDER is convex.

D. The MEDIAL BORDER is concave and presents a point at which all the structures that will enter or leave the kidney will pass.

   1. This location is the _____, which marks the entrance into a cavity that is called the RENAL SINUS.

E. The upper end and lower end of the kidney are referred to respectively as the SUPERIOR POLE and the INFERIOR _____.

   1. The suprarenal gland lies upon the superior pole.

F. Internally, the cortex lies at the periphery and the medulla lies internal to this.

   1. The medulla contains the medullary pyramids.

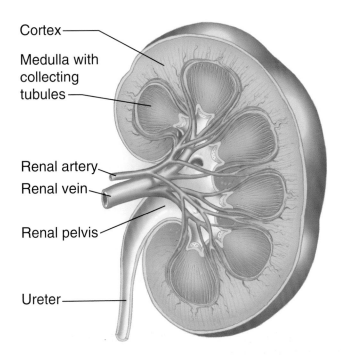

Cortex

Medulla with collecting tubules

Renal artery

Renal vein

Renal pelvis

Ureter

Kidney

© Kendall Hunt Publishing Company

IV. URETER

A. DEFINITION: a muscular tube that conveys urine from the renal pelvis to the urinary bladder.

B. There are 2 ureters, 1 draining each kidney.

C. They are approximately _____ cm in length.

D. They descend along the posterior abdominal wall toward the bladder.

E. The ureter will open into the cavity of the urinary bladder.

V. URINARY BLADDER

A. DEFINITION: a musculomembranous sac which acts as a _____ for the urine.

B. It is located in the pelvis, resting upon the pubis.

C. The urinary bladder is drained by the _____, a fibromuscular tube that extends from the internal urethral orifice to the outside of the body.

I. SPERM COURSES THROUGH THE ORGANS OF THE MALE REPRODUCTIVE SYSTEM IN THE FOLLOWING ORDER:

A. Testes (scrotum)

B. Epididymis

C. Ductus deferens

D. _____ vesicle

E. Ejaculatory duct

F. Prostate gland

G. Urethra

H. Penis

Male Reproductive
System

© Kendall Hunt Publishing Company

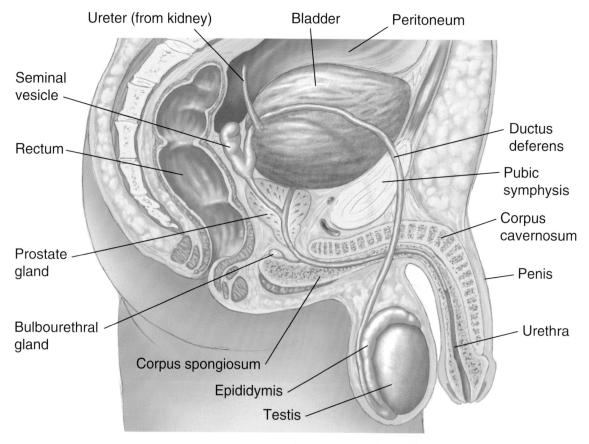

II. TESTES (SINGULAR = TESTIS)

A. A testis is the male gonad that contains many SEMINIFEROUS _____ that function in the production of the male sex cell (SPERM or SPERMATAZOA) and the male hormone (TESTOSTERONE).

B. There are 2 testes in the male reproductive system.

C. They are located external to the abdominal cavity within a skin pouch called the SCROTUM.

D. The reason why the testes are located in the scrotum is that the production of sperm (SPERMATOGENISIS) cannot occur at body temperature but will occur at a temperature slightly less than body temperature; hence, the location external to abdominal cavity in the scrotum.

E. Sperm will leave the seminiferous tubules via efferent ducts and pass to the epididymis.

III. EPIDIDYMIS

A. A C-shaped structure located on the _____ surface of each testis.

B. It receives sperm from the testis and stores the sperm until the sperm are released in the process of ejaculation.

IV. DUCTUS DEFERENS

A. Is also referred to as the _____ DEFERENS.

B. A ductus deferens will begin at each epididymis and will have a lengthy course within the SPERMATIC CORD, through the _____ CANAL, along the superior surface of the bladder and inferiorly along the posterior surface of the urinary bladder where it terminates.

C. The ductus deferens on each side terminates by joining the duct of the seminal vesicle and thereby forming the ejaculatory duct.

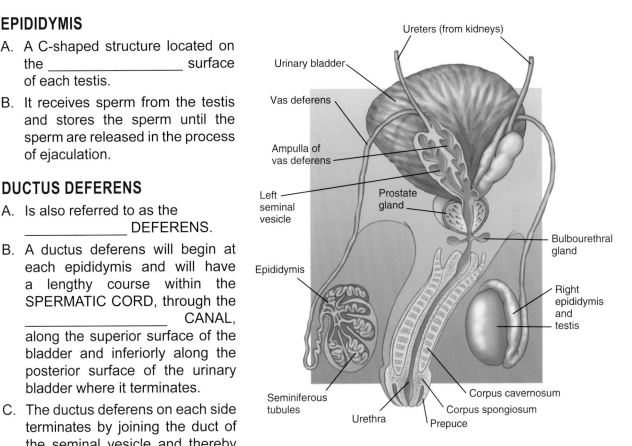

Male Reproductive
System—Posterior

© Kendall Hunt Publishing Company

V. SEMINAL VESICLE

A. Exocrine glands functions in producing seminal fluid which is added to the sperm.

B. Seminal vesicles are 1 of the 3 types of glands that function in the production of seminal fluid.

1. Collectively, these glands are referred to as _____ GLANDS of the male reproductive system.

VI. EJACULATORY DUCT

A. The ejaculatory duct is formed by the _____ of the ductus deferens and the duct of the seminal vesicle on each side.

B. This union occurs posterior to the urinary bladder and just above the prostate.

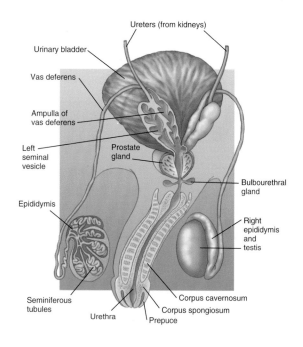

Ureters (from kidneys)
Urinary bladder
Vas deferens
Ampulla of vas deferens
Left seminal vesicle
Prostate gland
Epididymis
Bulbourethral gland
Right epididymis and testis
Seminiferous tubules
Corpus cavernosum
Corpus spongiosum
Urethra
Prepuce

VII. PROSTATE GLAND

A. The prostate gland is the second accessory gland of the male reproductive system and _____ seminal fluid that is added to the seminal fluid produced by the seminal vesicles.

B. It is located in the pelvis posterior to the pubis and below the urinary bladder.

C. Within the substance of the prostate gland, the 2 ejaculatory ducts join with the duct draining the urinary bladder to form the urethra.

VIII. URETHRA

A. It is a fibromuscular tube that carries urine during urination and sperm during ejaculation.

B. The urethra is subdivided into _____ parts:

1. PROSTATIC URETHRA: part that traverses the prostate gland.
2. MEMBRANOUS URETHRA
3. SPONGY URETHRA: part that traverses the penis.

IX. BULBOURETHRAL GLANDS

A. This is the 3rd and final accessory gland of the male reproductive system.

B. The ducts draining this gland will empty the secretion (additional seminal fluid) directly through the spongy urethra.

X. PENIS

A. It is an external genital organ through which the urethra passes.

B. It is the male organ involved in sexual intercourse.

C. It is composed of 3 longitudinal connective tissue structures that are filled with _____ spaces called VENOUS SINUSES that fill with blood resulting in an erection.

1. Two of these connective tissue structures are called COR-PORA CAVERNOSA and are made up of venous sinuses only.

2. The 3rd is called the CORPUS SPONGIOSUM, which in addition to venous sinuses also contains the spongy _____.

   a. Corpus cavernosa
   b. Corpus spongiosum
   c. Spongy urethra

Penis, Cross-Section

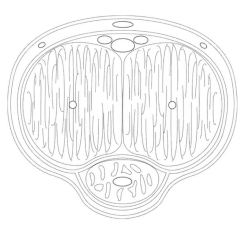

I. OVA COURSE THROUGH THE ORGANS OF THE FEMALE REPRODUCTIVE SYSTEM IN THE FOLLOWING ORDER:

A. Ovary

B. Uterine tube

C. Uterus

II. ADDITIONAL ORGANS OF THE FEMALE REPRODUCTIVE SYSTEM NOT INVOLVED IN OVA PRODUCTION AND TRANSPORTATION ARE:

A. Vagina

B. Greater vestibular glands

C. _____ minora

D. Labia majora

E. Clitoris

F. Mons _____

III. OVARY

A. It is the female gonad that contains many _____ that function in the production of the female sex cell (OVUM) and in the production of the female sex hormones (ESTROGEN and _____).

B. There are 2 ovaries in the female reproductive system.

C. They are located on the lateral wall of the pelvis.

Female
Reproductive
System

© Kendall Hunt Publishing Company

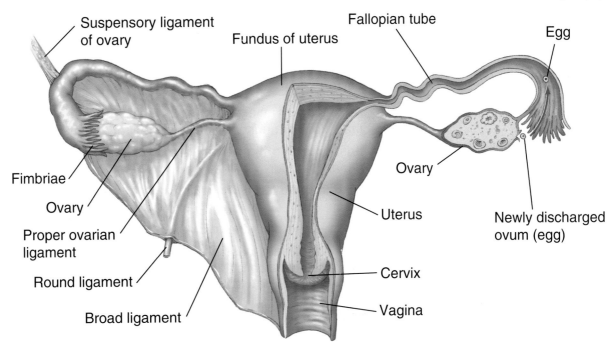

Suspensory ligament of ovary

Fundus of uterus

Fallopian tube

Egg

Fimbriae

Ovary

Proper ovarian ligament

Round ligament

Broad ligament

Ovary

Uterus

Cervix

Vagina

Newly discharged ovum (egg)

D. Ova will leave an ovary by being expelled from the follicle at the surface of the ovary.

   1. The ovum then enters the abdominal cavity, where it is immediately picked up by the uterine tube.

IV. UTERINE TUBE

A. It is also referred to as the FALLOPIAN TUBE or the

   _____.

B. There are 2 uterine tubes in the female reproductive system.

C. The uterine tube extends from the ovary where the ovarian end of the tube presents numerous finger-like processes called _____, to the uterus where the tube attaches to the lateral wall of the uterus.

D. The uterine tube conveys the released ovum from the ovary toward the uterus.

   1. If fertilization is to occur, it will occur within the uterine tube.

   2. If fertilization does not occur, the ovum _____ within the tube.

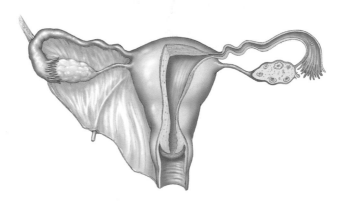

V. UTERUS

A. An organ with an extremely thick muscular _____ that expands during the development of a fetus.

B. It is located in the pelvis lying upon the superior surface of the urinary bladder.

C. It exhibits the following parts:

   1. _____: the part of the uterus that lies above the opening of the uterine tubes.

   2. BODY: main mass of the uterus that extends posteriorly to a constriction called the isthmus.

   3. ISTHMUS: the constricted part of the uterus located between the body and the cervix.

   4. _____: the lower part of the uterus that opens into the vagina.

VI. VAGINA

A. A canal that extends from the cervix of the uterus inferiorly to the vestibule of the vagina, the inferior opening of the vagina.

B. It is located _____ to the rectum and posterior to the urinary bladder.

C. It is a separate and distinct canal from the urethra. The urethra in the female does not join the reproductive organs as it does in the male reproductive system.

D. It is the female organ involved in sexual intercourse.

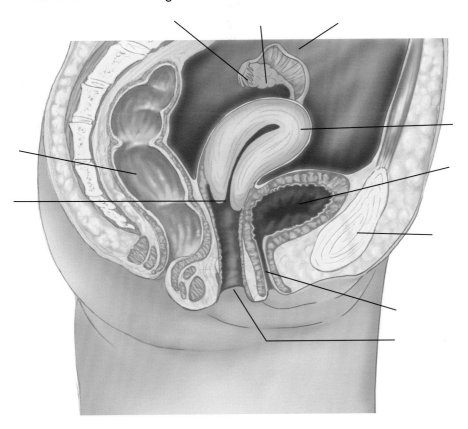

VII. LABIA MINORA

A. Two small folds of skin located at either side of the vestibule of the vagina.

   1. They are usually hidden by the labia _____.

VIII. LABIA MAJORA

A. Two elongated folds of skin that extend posteriorly from the pubis.

B. The outer surface is covered with course hairs, whereas the inner surface is smooth.

IX. CLITORIS

A. It is homologous to the penis and contains _____ tissue that, when it becomes filled with blood, results in an erection.

B. It is located where the 2 labia minora join anteriorly.

STUDY RESOURCES

3A Heart.. pp. 259–263

3C Blood Vessels and Lymphatic System .... p. 264

3D Vasculature of the Body .... pp. 265–272

3E Respiratory System.................................. pp. 273–274

3F Digestive System..................................... pp. 275–277

3G Urinary System .... p. 278

3H Male Reproductive System .... pp. 279–280

3I Female Reproductive System .... p. 281

Heart Game (answers follow)

Right Atrium	Left Atrium	Right Ventricle	Left Ventricle	General Heart
100 Name what kind of muscle can be found here.	100 How many cusps can be found in the atrioventricular valve that can be found in this chamber?	100 What kind of muscle can be found here?	100 What is the name of the muscular ridge like folds you find in this chamber?	150 The aorta sends _____ blood to the _____ body.
200 What structure can be found on the interatrial septum in a person who is 12 years old?	200 Name where musculi pectinati can be found in this chamber.	200 What kind of blood can be found in this chamber?	200 The wall of this chamber is ___ as that of the right.	250 Name the 3 layers of the heart that you have learned from this class.
300 Name only the venous structures that drain into the right atrium.	300 Give all names of the atrioventricular valve in this chamber.	300 Name the 2 valves that open to the right ventricle.	300 Name the valve(s) that open to the left ventricle.	350 Name the 4 vessels that bring oxygenated blood into the left atrium.
400 What is the vessel that drains into the coronary sinus and what is their function?	400 How many openings can be found in this chamber including valve(s)?	400 A semilunar valve ___ when the blood is passed into the pulmonary trunk and _____ when flow is retrograde.	400 The aortic valve contains the sites of origins of _____.	450 Describe pulmonary circulation of the heart starting from the 3 vessels that bring _____ blood into the heart.
500 What is the valve we find in the right atrium and what is its function when the ventricles contract?	500 Name what kind of muscle can be found in this chamber (this was only said in SI and you do not have to know this for the exam).	500 Name the vessel(s) in which blood is passed from the right ventricle to the lungs.	500 This chamber pumps blood through a valve, which travels to the aorta. What are the 3 branches coming off the aortic arch?	550 Name all structures that protect the heart anteriorly, laterally, posteriorly and all over.

Heart Game Answers

Right Atrium	Left Atrium	Right Ventricle	Left Ventricle	General Heart
100 Musculi pectinati	**100** 2	**100** Trabeculae carneae	**100** Trabeculae carneae	**150** Oxygenated; whole
200 Fossa ovalis	200 In the left auricle	200 Deoxygenated	200 >2 times	250 Pericardium, myocardium, and endocardium
300 Coronary sinus, superior and inferior vena cava	300 Mitral, bicuspid, and left atrioventricular valve	300 Tricuspid and pulmonary semilunar valve	300 Mitral and aortic semilunar valve	350 2 right pulmonary veins and 2 left pulmonary veins
400 Cardiac veins, drain the heart itself	400 5	400 Opens; closes	400 Right and left coronary arteries	450 *See below
500 Tricuspid; valve closes	500 Smooth cardiac muscle (this was only said in SI and you do not have to know this for the exam)	500 Pulmonary arteries (2 total)	500 Brachiocephalic trunk, left common carotid artery, and left subclavian artery	550 Sternum, ribs, intercostal mm, lungs, thoracic vertebrae, and pericardium

*Coronary sinus and inferior and superior venae cavae bring deoxygenated blood into the right atrium. This blood flows through the tricuspid valve into the right ventricle. The blood is then sent through the pulmonary semilunar valve into the pulmonary trunk to exit through the 1 right and 1 left pulmonary arteries. The arteries send blood to the lungs to become oxygenated. Once oxygenated, the blood is returned via 2 right and 2 left pulmonary veins into the left atrium. The bicuspid valve opens to allow the oxygenated blood from the left atrium to flow into the left ventricle. From the left ventricle, the blood exits through the aortic semilunar valve to go up through the ascending aorta, aortic arch, and descending aorta.

Note: The aortic arch contains (from right to left) the brachiocephalic trunk (branches into the right subclavian artery and right common carotid artery), left common carotid artery, and left subclavian artery.

DIAGRAM OF THE HEART
Fill in the blanks.

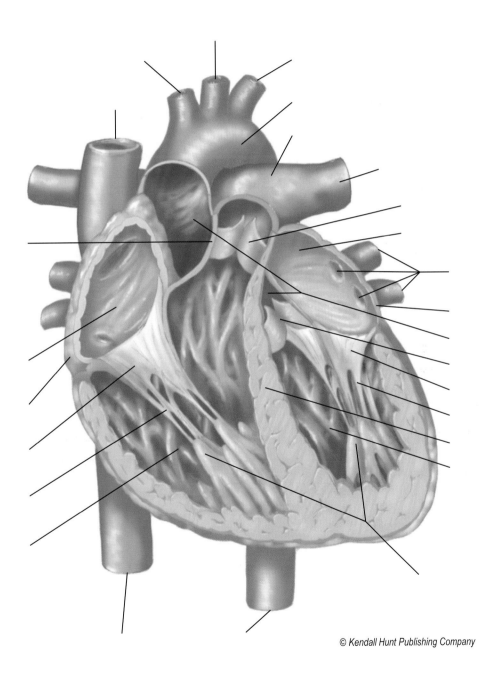

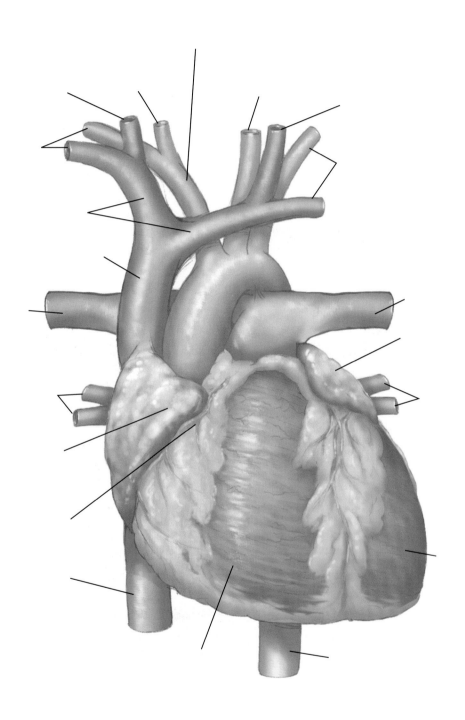

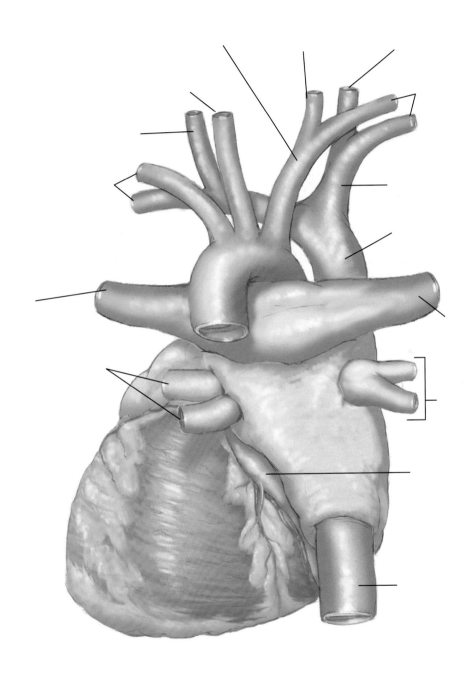

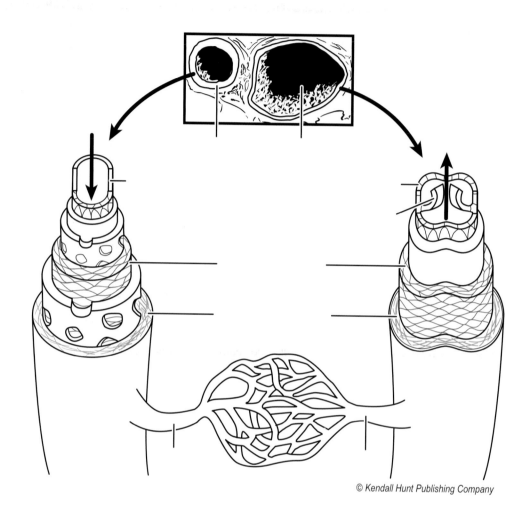

© Kendall Hunt Publishing Company

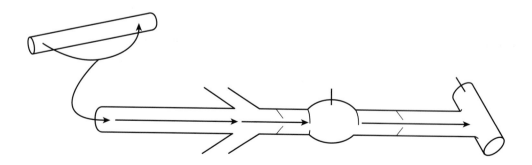

© Kendall Hunt Publishing Company

Major Abdominal Arteries and What They Supply

Organ Supplied	Abdominal Arteries
Stomach	Left gastric a.
	Splenic a.
	Common hepatic a.
Esophagus	Left gastric a.
Spleen	Splenic a.
Pancreas	Splenic a.
	Superior mesenteric a.
Liver	Common hepatic a.
Gallbladder	Common hepatic a.
Duodenum	Common hepatic a.
	Superior mesenteric a.
Small intestine (referring just to the jejunum and ileum)	Superior mesenteric a.
Large intestine	Superior mesenteric a. (majority of L. I.)
	Inferior mesenteric a. (end of L. I.)
Kidneys	Renal a.
Ovaries/testes	Gonadal a.
Rectum	Inferior mesenteric a.
Lower limb	Common iliac a. (splits to become E. I.)
	External iliac a.
Pelvis	Common iliac a. (splits to become I.I.)
	Internal Iliac a.
Urinary bladder	Internal Iliac a.

Note: Keep in mind that if you are asked what supplies the small intestines this includes the duodenum, jejunum, and ileum unless stated otherwise. You will be learning about this in the digestive system.

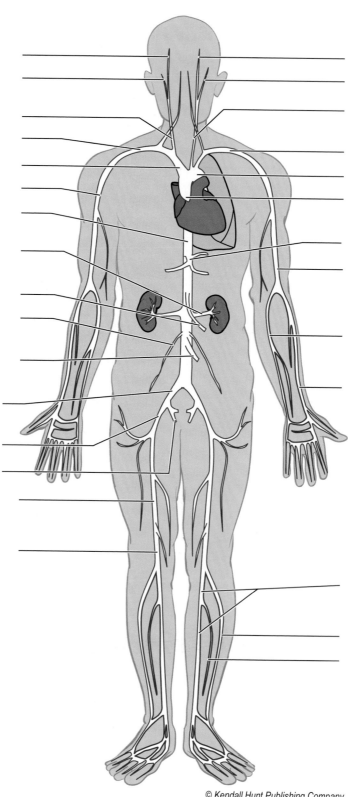

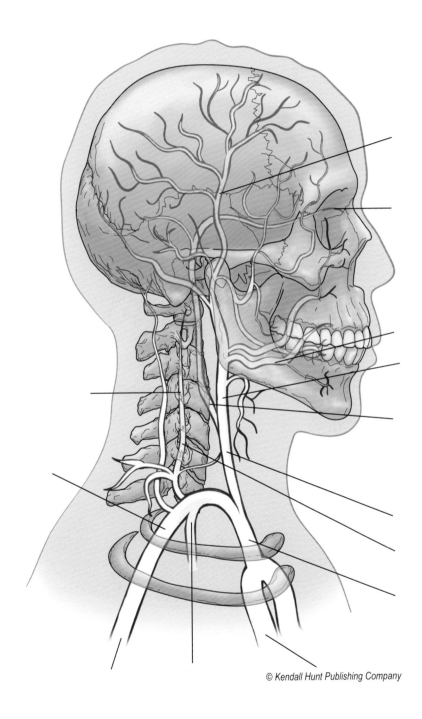

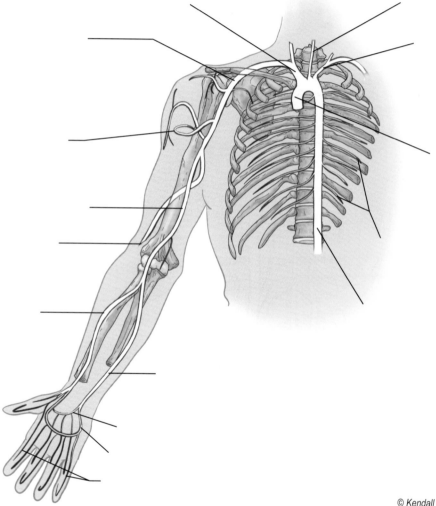

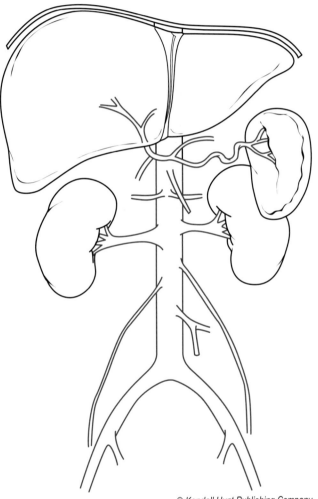

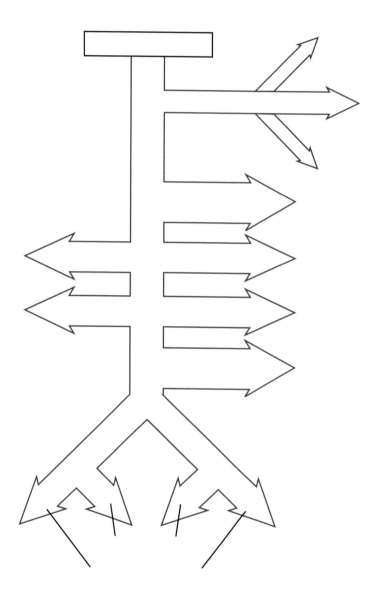

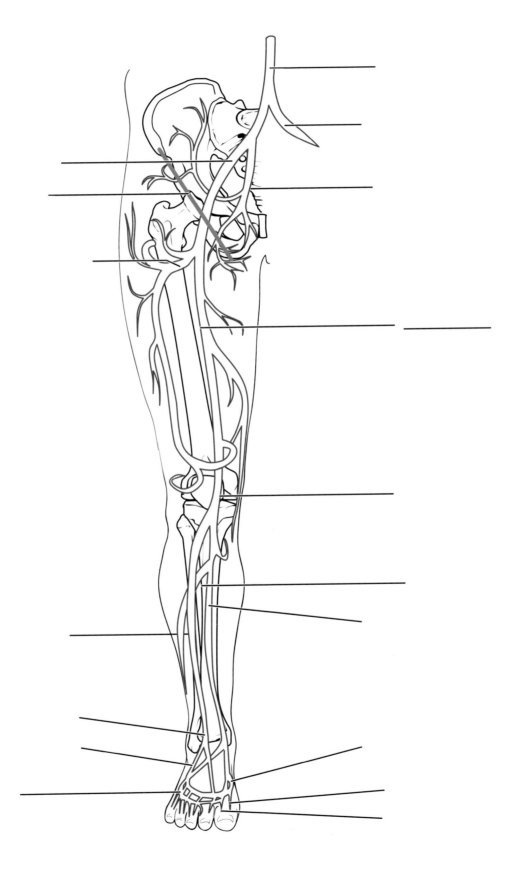

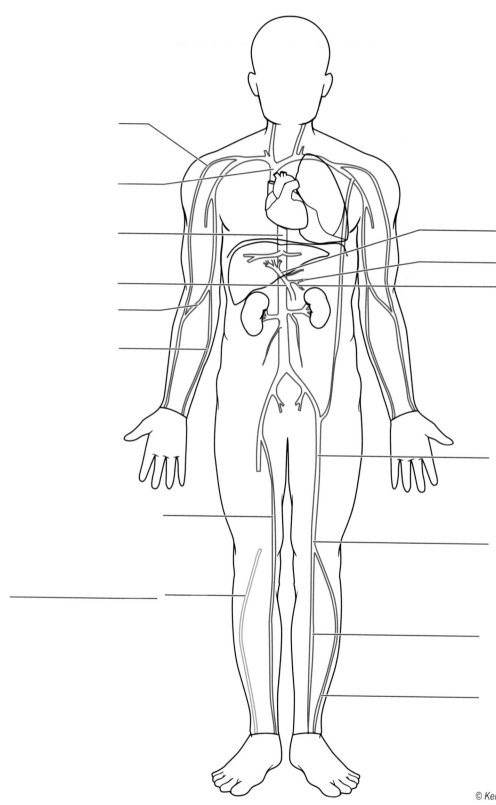

Breakdown of Respiratory System

Trachea → left and right primary bronchi (which supply the left and right lung, respectively)

Left and right primary bronchi → secondary bronchi (left lung has 2, right lung has 3—1 to supply each lobe)

Secondary bronchi → tertiary bronchi

Tertiary bronchi → bronchioles → terminal bronchioles → respiratory bronchioles

Respiratory bronchioles → alveolar ducts → alveoli and alveolar sacs

Breakdown of Tissues and Cartilage of Respiratory System
(only including what you need to know)

Trachea: hyaline cartilage and membranous (gap posterior contains connective tissue and smooth muscle)

Primary bronchi: hyaline cartilage

Bronchioles: no cartilage

Alveolar ducts: connective tissue and smooth muscle

Alveoli: epithelium and connective tissue (no cartilage or smooth muscle)

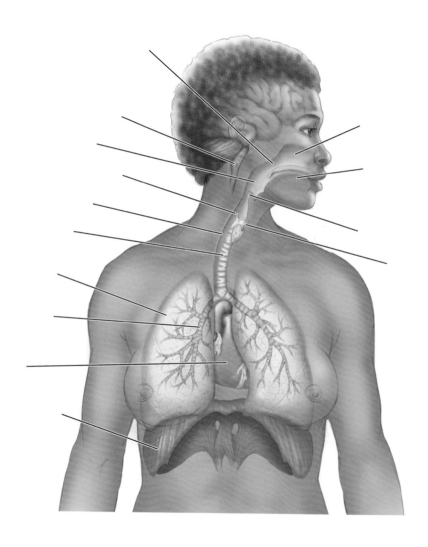

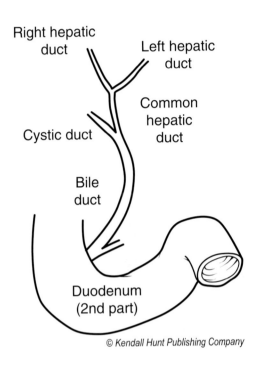

Right hepatic duct

Left hepatic duct

Common hepatic duct

Cystic duct

Bile duct

Duodenum (2nd part)

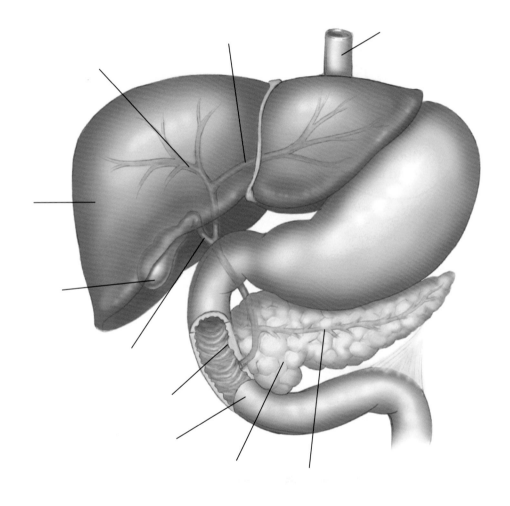

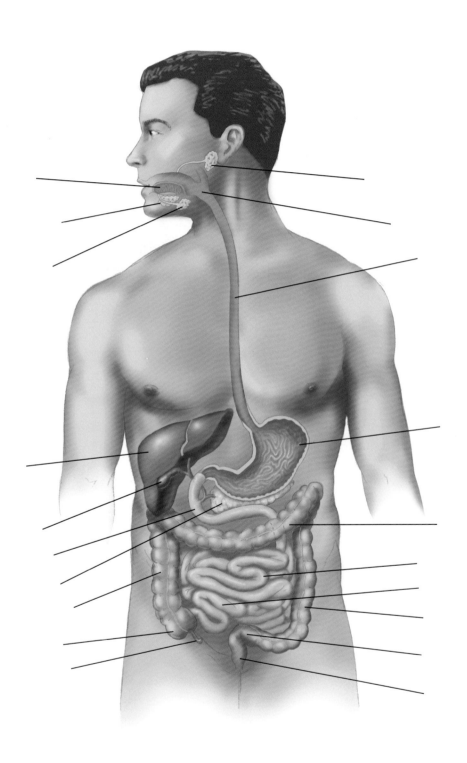

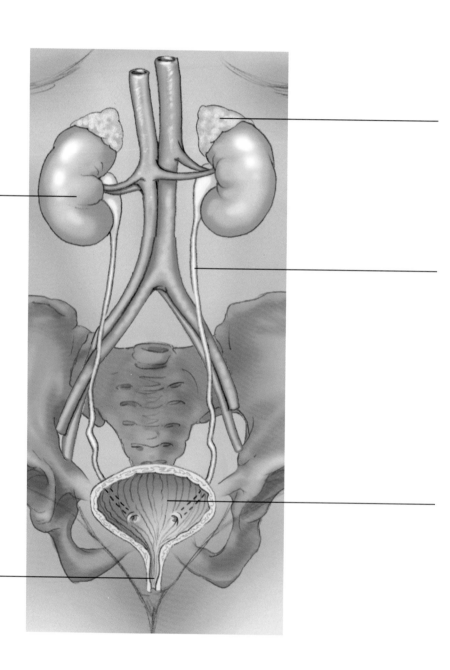

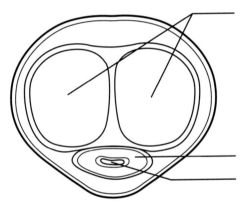

© Kendall Hunt Publishing Company

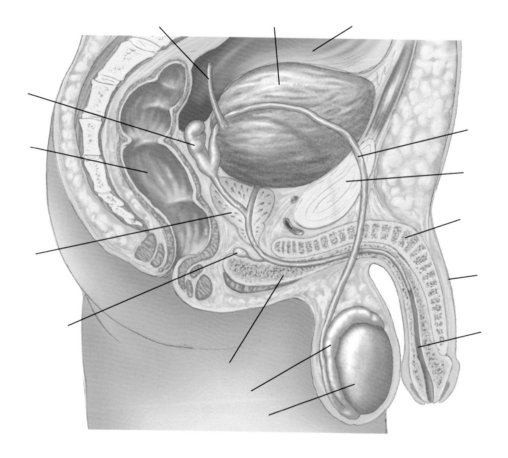

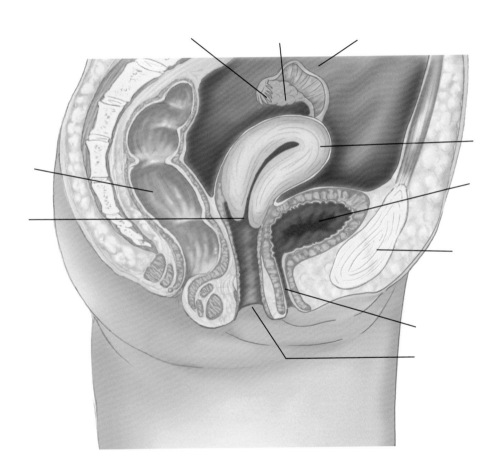

PRACTICE QUIZZES

3A Heart Practice Quiz ....pp. 283–284

3B Heart Disease Practice Quiz ....p. 285

3C Blood Vessels and Lymphatic System
Practice Quiz..pp. 286–287

3D Vasculature of the Body Practice Quiz......pp. 288–291

3E Respiratory System Practice Quiz ....pp. 292–293

3F Digestive System Practice Quiz ....pp. 294–295

3G Urinary System Practice Quiz...........................p. 296

3H&I Reproductive System Practice Quiz......pp. 297–298

3A–H Unit 3 Practice Test..............................pp. 299–310

3A–H Student Written Practice Test for Unit 3 pp. 311–316

Answer Key ....pp. 317–318

Heart Practice Quiz

1. All of the following protect the heart laterally EXCEPT:
   a. Ribs
   b. Sternum
   c. Intercostal muscles
   d. Lungs
   e. Pericardium

2. The pericardium blends: (Choose all that apply.)
   a. Into the diaphragm inferiorly
   b. Into the myocardium
   c. Into the endocardium
   d. Into the great vessels coming off the heart superiorly
   e. All of the above

3. The apex of the heart points:
   a. Superiorly and to the right
   b. Superiorly and to the left
   c. Laterally and to the left
   d. Laterally and to the right
   e. Inferiorly and to the left

4. All of the following structures contain musculi pectinati EXCEPT:
   a. Right atrium
   b. Left atrium
   c. Right auricle
   d. Left auricle

5. Choose the following that have 3 cusps: (Choose all that apply.)
   a. Right atrioventricular valve
   b. Left atrioventricular valve
   c. Pulmonary semilunar valve
   d. Aortic semilunar valve
   e. Pulmonary trunk

6. The pulmonary semilunar valve opens when:
   a. Flow is retrograde
   b. Blood moves from the left ventricle into the pulmonary trunk
   c. Blood moves from the right ventricle to the aorta
   d. When the aortic semilunar valve closes
   e. None of the above

7. All of the following are openings of the right atrium EXCEPT: (Choose all that apply.)
   a. Coronary sinus
   b. Superior vena cava
   c. Inferior vena cava
   d. Left atrioventricular valve
   e. 4 pulmonary veins

Use the diagram above to answer questions 8–17.

8. Choose the letter(s) of the chamber(s) where trabeculae carneae can be found.

9. Choose the semilunar valve, which transports oxygenated blood.

10. Choose the exact location where the fossa ovalis in an adult can be found.

11. How many of the structures indicated by the BC are found in the heart?
    a. 1   d. 4
    b. 2   e. 5
    c. 3

12. The structure indicated by the BD is the:
    a. Left subclavian
    b. Right common carotid
    c. Brachiocephalic trunk
    d. Right subclavian
    e. Left common carotid

13. Choose all the letters indicating the structure(s) where musculi pectinati can be found.

14. How many openings can be found in the chamber indicated by the AE (including valves)?
    a. 1   c. 3   e. 5
    b. 2   d. 4

15. Choose the letter(s) that indicate(s) the right auricle.

16. Choose the letter(s) that indicate(s) the structure that has the thickest ventricular wall.

17. Choose the letter(s) that indicate(s) the pulmonary semilunar valve.

Heart Disease Practice Quiz

1. Heart disease: (Choose all that apply.)
   a. Is a minor problem in the United States
   b. Accounts for about 29% of all deaths in the United States
   c. Can lead to heart attack, which can lead to cardiac arrest
   d. Is a condition is which hardening of the arteries occurs in the arteries that supply the arms and legs
   e. In most cases is harmless

2. All of the following are false EXCEPT (Choose all that apply):
   a. Cardiac arrest cannot result in death
   b. Heart failure is when the heart cannot pump blood the way it should
   c. The heart muscles may not receive enough oxygen and begin to die during a heart attack
   d. CHD involves venuosclerosis
   e. All of the above are true

3. All of the following are true regarding mitral valve prolapse EXCEPT:
   a. In most cases it is harmless
   b. May need to be treated with surgery if severe
   c. Patients may not know they have the problem
   d. A symptom may be numbness
   e. May become severe mitral regurgitation

4. Atherosclerosis is seen in all of the following EXCEPT:
   a. Heart disease
   b. CHD
   c. PAD
   d. All of the above including atherosclerosis

5. Cardiomyopathy can be caused by all of the following EXCEPT:
   a. Prior heart attacks
   b. Multiple heart defects
   c. Viral infection
   d. Bacterial infections

6. Symptoms and sign of PAD include: (Choose all that apply.)
   a. Numbness
   b. Chest pain
   c. Swelling of chest
   d. Weak pulse in feet
   e. Softening of artery walls

7. Arteriosclerosis:
   a. Is a type of atherosclerosis
   b. Can cause blood to leak backward
   c. Is when the aorta stretches and dilates
   d. Includes irregular heartbeats
   e. None of the above

Blood Vessels and Lymphatic System Practice Quiz

1. Vessels that contain oxygenated blood are: (Choose all that apply.)
   a. Arteries
   b. Arterioles
   c. Veins
   d. Capillaries
   e. All of the above

2. Veins and arteries have all of the following in common EXCEPT: (Choose all that apply.)
   a. Smooth muscle
   b. Elastic fibers
   c. Contain cusps
   d. Can carry deoxygenated blood
   e. Can carry blood toward the heart

3. Which of the following allows extension of the vessels and carrying of a pulse?
   a. Capillaries
   b. Tributaries
   c. Cusps or valves
   d. Elastic fibers and smooth muscle

4. Choose the false statement. (Choose all that apply.)
   a. In the capillaries, carbon dioxide and waste materials are passed from tissues into the bloodstream.
   b. The wall of a vein is thicker than the wall of a artery.
   c. Arterioles branch to form capillaries.
   d. Arteries carry blood to the heart.
   e. Blood vessels carry blood from the heart to organs and then back to the heart.

5. Choose the true statement. (Choose all that apply.)
   a. Cusps help separate the flow of blood into 2 directions: 1 toward the heart and 1 away from the heart.
   b. Smooth muscle and elastic fibers can be found in arteries.
   c. The smooth muscle contractions in veins help bring blood back up to the heart.
   d. Venules are formed by the junction of a number of capillaries.
   e. All veins contain at least 3 cusps.

6. Choose the correct pathway.
   a. Blood capillary → lymphatic capillary → efferent vessel → lymph node → afferent vessel → vein
   b. Blood capillary → lymphatic capillary → lymph node → afferent vessel → efferent vessel → vein

c. Blood capillary → lymphatic capillary → afferent vessel → lymph node → efferent vessel → artery

d. Blood capillary → lymphatic capillary → afferent vessel → lymph node → efferent vessel → vein

e. Blood capillary → lymphatic capillary → lymph node → efferent vessel → afferent vessel → artery

7. The afferent lymphatic vessel does all of the following EXCEPT:
   a. Allows lymph to flow through
   b. Has valves
   c. Has a structure that allows lymph to flow in 2 directions
   d. Sends lymph to an artery

8. Using the diagram on the bottom right of this page, choose the correct statement.
   a. E can be found in the neck, axilla, and groin
   b. AE drains into the left subclavian vein.
   c. C drains into the left subclavian and left internal jugular vein
   d. E drains the entire head and neck
   e. The right upper limb is drained by C

Use the letter/letters from the diagrams below to answer questions 9 and 10.

9. The duct that drains AD

10. The duct that drains AE

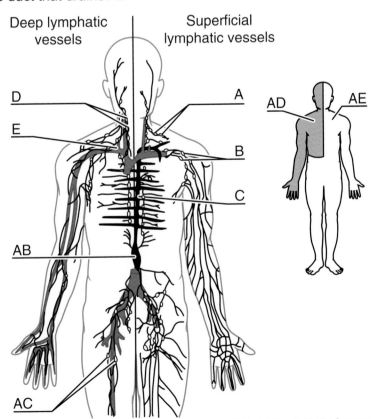

Deep lymphatic vessels   Superficial lymphatic vessels

D
E
A
B
C
AB
AC
AD
AE

© Kendall Hunt Publishing Company

Vasculature of the Body Practice Quiz

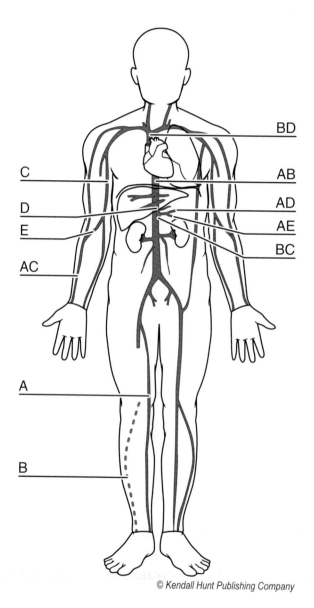

© Kendall Hunt Publishing Company

For questions 1–5, use the diagram above.

1. Choose the letter(s) that indicate the inferior vena cava.
2. Choose the letter(s) that indicate the lesser saphenous vein.
3. Choose 3 superficial veins that can be found in the upper limb.
4. Choose the letter(s) that indicate the 2 veins that make up the portal vein.
5. Choose the letter(s) that indicate the basilic vein.

6. This vessel can be used to feel a pulse at the tragus:
   a. Facial artery
   b. External carotid artery
   c. Internal carotid artery
   d. Superficial temporal artery
   e. Ophthalmic artery

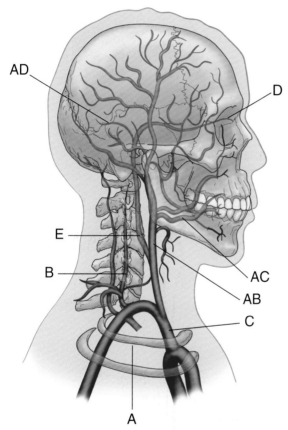

For questions 7–9, use the diagram above.

7. Choose the carotid artery that branches in the neck.

8. Choose the artery that causes decreased blood flow to the brain if pressure is applied by C6.

9. Choose the artery that goes through transverse foramen.

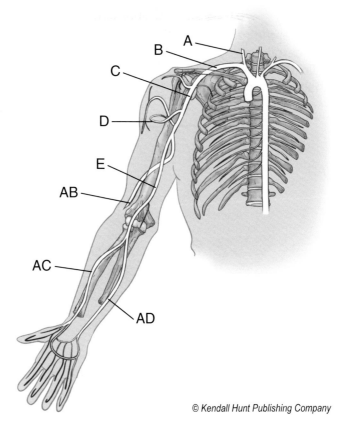

© Kendall Hunt Publishing Company

For questions 10–14, use the diagram above.

10. Choose the letter(s) that indicate(s) the radial artery.

11. Choose the letter(s) that indicate(s) the artery that supplies the humerus and shoulder joint.

12. Choose the artery that can be found after the inferior border of teres major.

13. Choose the letter(s) that indicate(s) the circumflex humeral artery.

14. Choose the letter(s) that indicate(s) the artery that supplies parts of the head and neck.

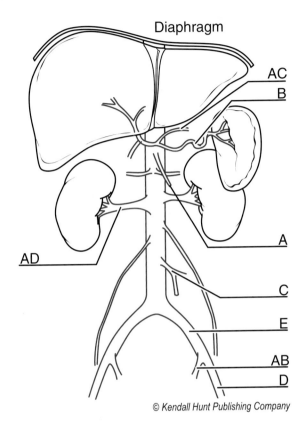

Diaphragm

© Kendall Hunt Publishing Company

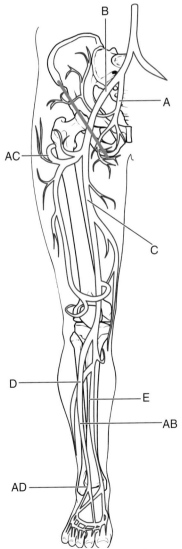

© Kendall Hunt Publishing Company

For questions 15–20, use the diagram above. If the artery does not have a letter indicating it, then exclude it from your answer.

15. Choose the artery/arteries that supply the pancreas.

16. Choose the artery/arteries that supply the large intestines.

17. Choose the artery/arteries that supply the urinary bladder.

18. Choose the artery/arteries that indicate the left gastric artery.

19. Choose the artery/arteries that supply the duodenum.

20. Choose the artery/arteries that supply the stomach.

For questions 21–25, use the diagram on the left. If the artery does not have a letter indicating it, then exclude it from your answer.

21. Choose the artery/arteries that supply the pelvis.

22. Choose the artery/arteries that indicate the peroneal artery.

23. What does an artery become after it passes the inguinal ligament/canal, branching from the external iliac artery?

24. Choose the letter(s) that indicate(s) the posterior tibial artery.

25. What artery is felt when trying to diagnose PAD?

Respiratory System Practice Quiz

1. The tertiary bronchi are attached to:
   a. The trachea
   b. The larynx
   c. Primary bronchi
   d. Bronchioles
   e. Alveoli

2. All of the following are true of the left lung EXCEPT: (Choose all that apply.)
   a. The hilus can be found on the medial surface of the lung
   b. The root of the lung contains the left primary bronchi
   c. It contains the oblique fissure
   d. It contains a middle lobe
   e. It contains a transverse fissure

3. Choose the false statement(s). (Choose all that apply.)
   a. The left primary bronchus is 2.5 cm long
   b. The trachea lies posterior to the esophagus
   c. In the hilum, a structure that allows passage for air can be found
   d. The trachea is 16–20 cm long
   e. The conductive phase consists of exchanging O_2 and CO_2 between blood and the air sacs of the lung

4. Choose the correct path.
   a. Larynx → trachea → bronchioles
   b. Tertiary bronchioles → respiratory bronchioles → alveolar ducts
   c. Respiratory bronchioles → alveolar ducts → alveoli
   d. Trachea → secondary bronchi → tertiary bronchi
   e. None of the above.

5. The key difference(s) between bronchi and bronchioles is/are: (Choose all that apply.)
   a. Bronchi are smaller
   b. Bronchioles are more numerous
   c. Bronchi do not contain cartilage
   d. Bronchi cannot be found in the lung
   e. None of the above

6. The surface that can be found adjacent to intercostal muscles is:
   a. Diaphragmatic
   b. Lateral
   c. Apex
   d. Medial
   e. Costal

7. All of the following forms the root of the lung EXCEPT:
   a. A structure that branches from the pulmonary trunk
   b. A structure that brings oxygenated blood from the heart → lung

    c. A structure that branches from the trachea
    d. A structure that brings deoxygenated blood from the heart → lung
    e. None of the above (all form the root of the lung)

8. The alveoli contains: (Choose all that apply.)

a. Cartilage	d. Connective tissue
b. Smooth muscle	e. Capillaries
c. Epithelium	

Digestive System Practice Quiz

1. The falciform ligament extends from:
    a. The liver to the obliterated umbilical vein
    b. The liver to the round ligament
    c. The greater curvature of the stomach to the transverse colon
    d. The lesser curvature of the stomach to the transverse colon
    e. None of the above

2. All of the following are functions of the tongue EXCEPT:
    a. Movement of food
    b. Chemical breakdown of food
    c. Mastication
    d. Taste

3. This structure is continuous with the esophagus:
    a. Larynx
    b. Nasal cavity
    c. Laryngopharynx
    d. Nasopharynx
    e. Oropharynx

4. This structure can be found posterior to the heart:
    a. Thoracic esophagus
    b. Larynx
    c. Pharynx
    d. Thyroid cartilage
    e. Abdominal esophagus

5. The greater curvature can be found in all of the following areas EXCEPT: (Choose all that apply.)
    a. Over the fundus
    b. Right side of stomach
    c. Left side of stomach
    d. Inferior side of pyloris
    e. Inferior side of cardiac opening

6. All of the following describe the duodenum EXCEPT: (Choose all that apply.)
    a. C-shaped organ
    b. Proximal two-fifths of small intestines
    c. Receives fluid from liver and pancreas
    d. Is adjacent to the appendix

7. The sigmoid colon: (Choose all that apply.)
    a. Extends from the left colic flexure inferiorly along abdominal wall
    b. Is continuous with the rectum
    c. Forms a loop
    d. Narrows inferiorly to form the anal canal
    e. Can be found adjacent to the cecum

8. The porta hepatis contains all of the following EXCEPT:
    a. Right hepatic duct
    b. Left hepatic duct
    c. Hepatic artery
    d. Hepatic vein
    e. Portal vein

9. The common hepatic duct, which drains the _____, and the cystic duct, which drains the _____, connect to become the _____.
    a. Spleen, cysts, bile duct
    b. Spleen, cytosol, mixed hepatic duct
    c. Liver, gall bladder, bile duct
    d. Kidneys, pancreas, pancreatic duct

Urinary System Practice Quiz

1. The urinary system: (Choose all that apply.)
   a. Includes the stomach.
   b. Contains the urethra, which conveys urine from the kidney to the bladder
   c. Contains the kidney
   d. Produces and eliminates urine
   e. Contains an organ that has a concave lateral border

2. All of the following are true of the kidney EXCEPT:
   a. The hilus marks the entrance into the renal sinus
   b. The hilus can be found on the medial border, which is convex
   c. The cortex can be found internally at the periphery
   d. The medulla contains pyramids
   e. None of the above

3. The suprarenal gland:
   a. Sits against the hilus
   b. Can be found near the medulla
   c. Is associated with the inferior pole
   d. Is found at the medial border
   e. None of the above

4. The ureter: (Choose all that apply.)
   a. Is a fibromuscular tube
   b. Extends from the renal pelvis to the urinary bladder
   c. Is found against the pubis
   d. Extends from the internal urethral orifice to the outside of the body
   e. Is 25 cm long

5. Choose the incorrect pair.
   a. The urinary bladder—musculomembranous sac
   b. Kidney—bean shaped
   c. Urethra—internal urethral orifice → external environment
   d. Ureter—fibromuscular tube
   e. Inferior pole—lower end of kidney

Reproductive Systems Practice Quiz

1. All of the following are true statements EXCEPT: (Choose all that apply.)
   a. Sperm courses through the testes → epididymis → ductus deferens → ejaculatory duct → seminal vesicle → prostate gland → urethra → penis
   b. Sperm leaves seminiferous tubules via efferent ducts
   c. The epididymis stores sperm and is C shaped
   d. The ejaculatory duct is formed by union of the seminal vesicle and the bulbourethral gland
   e. The vas deferens courses within the spermatic cord through the inguinal canal

2. All of the following are not accessory glands of the male reproductive system: (Choose all that apply.)
   a. Seminal vesicle
   b. Testes
   c. Ductus deferens
   d. Prostate gland
   e. Epididymis

3. Spermatogenesis:
   a. Is the production of the male sex cell
   b. Occurs in the epididymis
   c. Can only occur at a temperature slightly higher than body temperature
   d. Produces seminal fluid
   e. Involves the urinary bladder

4. All of the following are true regarding the prostate gland EXCEPT:
   a. Secretes seminal fluid
   b. Is found posterior to the pubis
   c. Contains 1 ejaculatory duct that joins the prostatic urethra
   d. Found below the urinary bladder
   e. Is an accessory gland

5. All of the following are false regarding the male reproductive system EXCEPT:
   a. There is 1 corpus cavernosum
   b. The corpus cavernosum contains venous sinuses and spongy urethra
   c. Venous sinuses filled with blood results in an erection
   d. There are 2 parts of the urethra

6. All of the following organs are used in ova production and transportation EXCEPT:
   a. Mons pubis
   b. Clitoris
   c. Greater vestibular glands
   d. Uterine tubes
   e. Uterus

7. The organ(s) that produces progesterone is/are: (Choose all that apply.)
   a. Fimbriae
   b. Uterine tube
   c. Uterus
   d. Ovary

8. Fertilization occurs:
   a. In the organ that produces the ovum
   b. In the organ that can be found at the lateral walls of the pelvis
   c. In the organ that possesses fingerlike processes
   d. In the organ that contains a thick muscular wall

9. All of the following are true regarding the female reproductive system EXCEPT: (Choose all that apply.)
   a. The vagina can be found anterior to the rectum
   b. The vagina can be found posterior to the urinary bladder
   c. The labia minora is 3 elongated folds of skin
   d. The clitoris can be found where 2 labia minora join posteriorly

UNIT 3 PRACTICE TEST

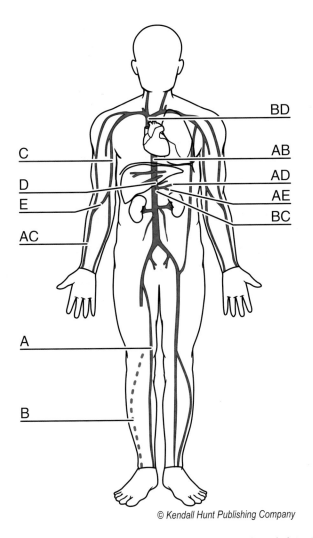

© Kendall Hunt Publishing Company

1. Choose the structure(s) that drain(s) blood into the right atrium.
2. Choose the structure(s) that make(s) up the portal vein.
3. This vessel is the longest vein in the body.
4. This vessel is where blood is drawn from.
5. This vessel drains blood into the popliteal fossa.

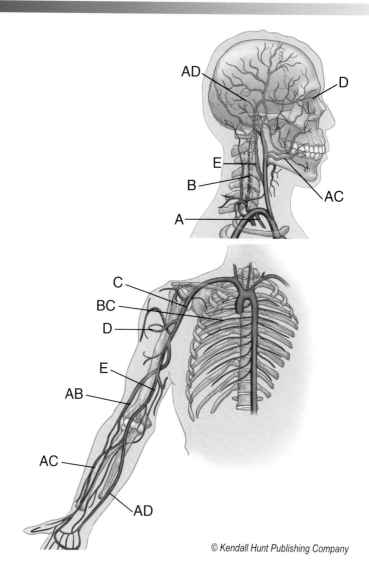

© Kendall Hunt Publishing Company

6. Choose the internal carotid artery.
7. Choose the artery that courses through the transverse foramen.
8. Choose the internal thoracic artery.

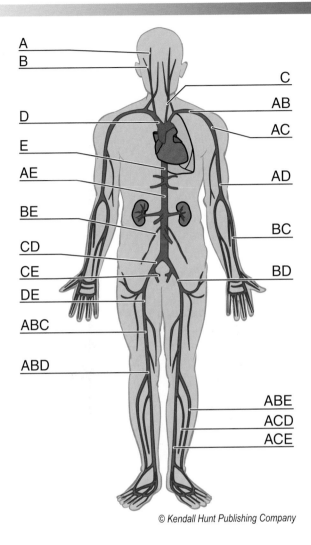

A
B
C
AB
AC
D
E
AE
AD
BE
BC
CD
CE
BD
DE
ABC
ABD
ABE
ACD
ACE

© Kendall Hunt Publishing Company

9. Choose the artery that changes its name once it reaches the inferior border of teres major muscle.
10. Choose the left subclavian artery.
11. Choose the radial artery.
12. Choose the common carotid artery.
13. Choose the brachial artery.
14. Choose the common iliac artery.
15. Choose the external iliac artery.
16. Choose the posterior tibial artery.
17. Choose the peroneal artery.
18. Choose the structure that branches into the right common carotid artery and the right subclavian artery.

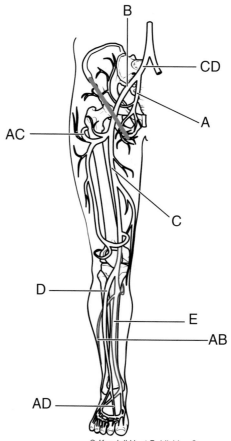

© Kendall Hunt Publishing Company

19. Name the femoral artery.

20. Choose the anterior tibial artery.

21. Choose the internal iliac artery.

22. Choose the dorsalis pedis artery.

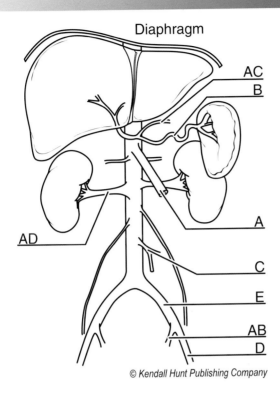

Diaphragm

AC
B

A

C

E

AB
D

AD

© Kendall Hunt Publishing Company

23. Choose the vessel(s) that supply(ies) the stomach.
24. Choose the vessel(s) that supply(ies) the pancreas.
25. Choose the vessel(s) that supply(ies) the urinary bladder and pelvis.
26. Choose the vessel(s) that supply(ies) the majority of the large intestine.
27. Choose the vessel(s) that supply(ies) the rectum.
28. Choose the vessel(s) that supply(ies) the lower limb.
29. Choose the correct statement. (Choose all that apply.)
    a. Tributaries form arteries
    b. Blood moves past the valve of a vein via contraction of surrounding muscles
    c. Oxygen and nutrients pass from the tissues to blood
    d. Lymphatic capillaries are capillaries that pick up lymph fluid
    e. All of the above are true
30. Choose the false statement regarding lymphatic ducts.
    a. The right lymphatic duct drains the right half of the chest
    b. The thoracic duct drains the left and right lower limb
    c. The lymph nodes are prevalent in the neck, chest, and groin
    d. The anterior axillary nodes can be found in the armpit
    e. The thoracic duct drains the left chest
31. All of the following is true regarding the right atrium EXCEPT:
    a. It lies posterior to the right ventricle
    b. It has 3 major venous openings
    c. The fossa ovalis can be found here on an adult on the interatrial septum

d. It contains an opening of a structure that drains the lower half of the body
e. All of the above are true statements

32. The pericardium:
a. Encloses the heart in tough muscular tissue
b. Attaches to the lungs as well
c. Blends in with the great vessels coming off the heart
d. Contains endocardium
e. None of the above

33. Choose the correct statement.
a. The pulmonary trunk contains deoxygenated blood
b. The coronary arteries drain the heart itself
c. The cardiac veins drain the pericardium
d. The right and left atrium contain musculi pectinati
e. All of the above statements are false

34. The apex: (Choose all that apply.)
a. Is the area where the great vessels attach
b. Contains the aorta, pulmonary trunk, and superior vena cava
c. Is where the left and right coronary arteries arise
d. Is the rounded projection of the heart
e. Points inferiorly and to the left

35. All of the following is true regarding the right atrioventricular valve EXCEPT: (Choose all that apply.)
a. It opens when the ventricles contract
b. It prevents retrograde flow
c. It is different than a semilunar valve because it has chordae tendinae and papillary muscles and does not have pocket like flaps
d. It is also known as the bicuspid valve
e. It allows oxygenated blood flow from the right atrium into the right ventricle

36. Choose the true statement(s). (Choose all that apply.)
a. The 2 pulmonary veins contain oxygenated blood flowing from the lungs back to the heart
b. The pulmonary veins empty blood into the right atrium
c. The cardiac veins drain into the coronary sinus, which drains into the right atrium
d. The right and left coronary arteries arise from the aortic semilunar valve
e. Blood leaving the left ventricle flows through the pulmonary semilunar valve to the rest of the body

37. Almost _____ die each year from heart disease in the United States.
a. 27% of the population
b. 7 million people
c. 29% of the population
d. 7000 people
e. None of the above

38. The condition characterized by plaque buildup and the narrowing and hardening of the arteries is called:
    a. Angina
    b. Atherosclerosis
    c. Arrhythmias
    d. Acute coronary syndrome
    e. None of the above

39. All of the following are symptoms of stable angina EXCEPT: (Choose all that apply.)
    a. Chest pain during physical exertion
    b. Chest pain during mental stress
    c. Chest pain during rest
    d. Chest pain during dinner
    e. Chest pain during sleep

40. Arrhythmias:
    a. Cause issues with timing or frequency of electrical impulses
    b. Cause irregular beating of the heart (slow or fast)
    c. Can cause ventricular or atrial fibrillation
    d. Can range from less severe to very severe
    e. All of the above are true

41. Causes of cardiomyopathy include which of the following? (Choose all that apply.)
    a. Prior myocardial infarctions
    b. Viral infection
    c. Bacterial infection
    d. Eating too much ice cream
    e. Getting your teeth cleaned at the dentist

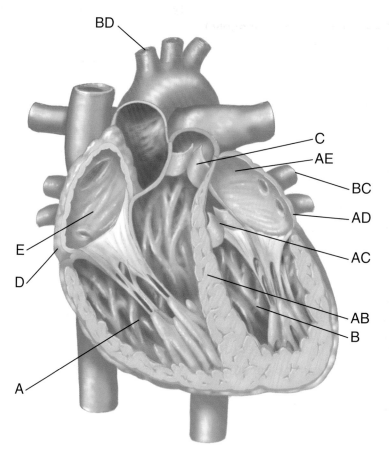

© Kendall Hunt Publishing Company

42. Choose the correct statement.
    a. AD contains trabeculae carneae
    b. A has a 2–3 times thicker wall than B
    c. C is the aortic semilunar valve
    d. BC contains oxygenated blood
    e. E contains the foramen ovale in an adult

43. Choose the false statement.
    a. AC and C contain 3 cusps each
    b. BD gives rise to the left subclavian and left common carotid arteries
    c. AE is the left atrium
    d. B contains trabeculae carneae
    e. B contains papillary muscles

44. The peritoneum involves the:
    a. Falciform ligament   d. Round ligament
    b. 7 million people   e. All of the above
    c. Mesentery

45. All of the following are salivary gland openings of the oral cavity EX-
    CEPT: (Choose all that apply.)
    a. Parathyroid gland
    b. Parotid gland
    c. Submaxillary gland
    d. Sublingual gland
    e. Subdental gland

46. Choose the correct statement.
    a. The nasopharynx sits superior to the oropharynx
    b. The laryngopharynx sits superior to the larynx
    c. The hypopharynx and the oropharynx refer to the same structure
    d. The oropharynx is continuous with the esophagus
    e. All of the above are true

47. The thoracic esophagus:
    a. Sits inferior to the abdominal esophagus
    b. Can also be found in the abdominal area
    c. Lies posterior to the trachea in the upper half
    d. All of the above are true
    e. 2 of the above are true

48. All of the following are false regarding the stomach EXCEPT:
    a. The greater curvature is located on the right side of the stomach
    b. The body lies between the fundus and the cardiac opening
    c. The fundus can be found above the level of entrance of the
       esophagus
    d. The cardiac opening is between the duodenum and the stomach
    e. The pyloric sphincter is a fold in the internal surface of the stom-
       ach

49. The small intestines:
    a. Contains the ileum, which is the distal three-fifths of the small intes-
       tine
    b. Contains an S-shaped organ
    c. Has a portion where it receives the openings of ducts draining the
       liver, stomach, gallbladder, and pancreas
    d. Extends from the pyloric sphincter to the duodenum
    e. Contains the cecum

50. The large intestines: (Choose all that apply.)
    a. Contain the vermiform appendix, which is a lymphatic organ
    b. Contain the hepatic flexure, which is also called the left colic flexure
    c. Have a structure that is continuous with the rectum
    d. Extend from the ileocecal junction to the anus
    e. All of the above are true regarding the large intestines

51. All of these structures are involved with the liver EXCEPT:
    a. Right lobe
    b. Hepatic artery
    c. Portal vein
    d. Gallbladder
    e. All of the above are involved with the liver

52. All of the following are true regarding the pancreas EXCEPT: (Choose all that apply.)
    a. The head points to the spleen
    b. The body is found in the concavity of the duodenum
    c. The tail courses across the vertebrae
    d. The produces digestive enzymes
    e. It is both an endocrine and an exocrine gland

53. Choose the correct statement(s).
    a. The right and left hepatic ducts form the common bile duct
    b. The cystic duct and the common bile duct form the common hepatic duct
    c. The cystic duct drains the liver
    d. The bile duct leads to the common hepatic duct
    e. All of the above are false statements

54. Choose the false statement(s). (Choose all that apply.)
    a. The kidney conveys urine to the bladder
    b. The urinary bladder conveys urine to the outside of the body
    c. The hilus marks the entrance into the renal sinus
    d. The medulla lies internal to the cortex
    e. The suprarenal gland lies upon the superior pole

55. The ureter: (Choose all that apply.)
    a. Is 28 cm long
    b. Is located in the pelvis, resting upon the pubis
    c. Drains the kidneys
    d. Is a fibromuscular tube
    e. Conveys urine from the renal pelvis to the urinary bladder

56. The trachea:
    a. Is a cartilaginous and membranous tube extending from the laryngopharynx
    b. Bifurcates into the left and right primary bronchioles
    c. Is 30 cm long
    d. Enters the lung
    e. None of the above

57. The alveoli: (Choose all that apply.)
    a. Are thin-walled tubes of connective tissue and smooth muscle
    b. Includes capillaries adjacent to them
    c. When combined with the capillary wall makes up the respiratory membrane
    d. Does not contain cartilage
    e. Rise from alveolar ducts

58. Choose the incorrect pair.
    a. Hilus—medial surface of lung
    b. Middle lobe—left lung
    c. Base—diaphragmatic surface
    d. Horizontal fissure—right lung
    e. Upper lobe—right and left lung

59. The hilus of the right lung contains:
    a. 1 vessel that comes off the pulmonary trunk
    b. 2 vessels that carry deoxygenated blood
    c. 2 branches off the trachea
    d. A structure for passage of food
    e. None of the above

60. All of the following are part of the male reproductive system EXCEPT:
    a. Urethra
    b. Seminal vesicle
    c. Epididymis
    d. Uterine tube
    e. Ductus deferens

61. The testes:
    a. Contain a structure that is necessary for the production of sperm and testosterone
    b. Allows sperm to leave seminiferous tubules to the efferent ducts to the epididymis
    c. Is located external to the abdominal cavity
    d. Is involved in the production of sperm, spermatogenesis
    e. All of the above

62. All of the following assist in producing seminal fluid EXCEPT: (Choose all that apply.)
    a. Ductus deferens
    b. Seminal vesicle
    c. Prostate gland
    d. Spongy urethra
    e. Bulbourethral gland

63. Choose the false statement. (Choose all that apply.)
    a. If fertilization occurs, it will occur within the cervix of the uterus
    b. The constricted portion of the uterus is the cervix
    c. Fimbriae are located along the wall of the uterus
    d. The ovary contains follicles
    e. The uterus has an extremely thick muscular wall

64. Choose the true statement. (Choose all that apply.)
    a. The vagina extends inferiorly from the vestibule of the vagina
    b. The labia minora are located anteriorly when the 2 labia majora join
    c. The labia minora are homologous to the penis
    d. The vagina is located anterior to the rectum and posterior to the urinary bladder
    e. The labia minora are located at either side of the vestibule of the vagina

65. How long is the right bronchus?
   a. 15 cm
   b. 30 cm
   c. 16–20 cm
   d. 5 cm
   e. 2.5 cm

66. The common hepatic artery supplies all of the following EXCEPT the:
   a. Liver
   b. Stomach
   c. Gallbladder
   d. Duodenum
   e. None of the above.

67. All of the following pertain to the stomach EXCEPT:
   a. The fundus is the part of the stomach below the level of entrance of the esophagus
   b. The body of the stomach is located between the fundus and the pyloric part of stomach
   c. The stomach presents 2 curvatures and 2 openings
   d. None of the above

Student Written Practice Test for Unit 3

1. Choose the statements that are correct regarding pulmonary circulation? (Choose all that apply.)
   a. Deoxygenated blood will flow through the pulmonary trunk into the pulmonary veins
   b. Deoxygenated blood will flow through the pulmonary trunk into the right and left pulmonary arteries
   c. All the 4 pulmonary veins will enter the left atrium
   d. Oxygenated blood will return to the heart via 3 right and left pulmonary veins

2. Choose the incorrect pair.
   a. Kidneys—renal artery
   b. Urinary bladder—external iliac artery
   c. Ovaries/testes—gonadal artery
   d. Rectum—inferior mesenteric artery

3. All the following is true regarding the lungs EXCEPT:
   a. Apex is the rounded superior end of the lung
   b. Base is the inferior end of the lung
   c. They have a medial surface that presents a locus known as the hilum
   d. They have a costal surface that includes the sternum, ribs, and trachea

4. Which statement(s) is/are true? (Choose all that apply.)
   a. Internal iliac artery supplies the bladder and pelvis
   b. External iliac artery supplies the upper limb
   c. The common hepatic artery supplies the liver, stomach, gallbladder, and duodenum
   d. The renal artery supplies the kidney and stomach

5. Arrhythmia is:
   a. A weakening of the heart muscle or a change in heart muscle structure
   b. Hardening of the arteries that supply blood to the arms and legs
   c. Irregular, or abnormally fast or slow, beating of the heart
   d. When the blood supply to the heart is severely reduced or completely blocked, and heart muscle cells begin to die

6. A large, highly folded, serous membrane located in the abdomen is the:
   a. Greater omentum
   b. Pyloric part
   c. Rugae
   d. Peritoneum

7. The right primary bronchus:
   a. Is more narrow then the left bronchus
   b. Is approximately 2.5 cm in length
   c. Makes more of an acute angle with the trachea then the left
   d. Enters the right lung and divides into 2 secondary bronchi

8. Lymph nodes are prevalent in the following regions except:
   a. Neck
   b. Axilla
   c. Abdomen
   d. Groin

9. Which of the following structures are involved in the urinary system? (choose all that apply).
   a. Ureters
   b. Urinary bladder
   c. Is convex
   d. Adrenal gland

10. The lateral border of the kidney:
    a. Contains the hilus
    b. Is concave
    c. Is convex
    d. Both a and b are correct

11. The medial border of the kidney:
    a. Contains the hilus
    b. Is concave
    c. Is convex
    d. Both a and b are correct

12. After sperm courses through the epididymis, it next courses through the:
    a. Ductus deferens
    b. Prostate gland
    c. Scrotum
    d. Urethra

13. Which glands make up those that are collectively known as accessory glands? (Choose all that apply.)
    a. Adrenal gland
    b. Seminal vesicle
    c. Prostate gland
    d. Ductus deferens
    e. Bulbourethral glands

14. The round ligament of the liver contains the:
    a. Falciform ligament
    b. Peritoneal fold
    c. Obliterated umbilical vein
    d. Mesentery

15. Regarding pulmonary circulation: (Choose all that apply.)
    a. Oxygenated blood will return to the heart via 2 pulmonary veins
    b. In the lungs, blood gives off CO_2
    c. In the lungs, blood receives O_2
    d. All 4 pulmonary veins will enter the right atrium

16. Choose the incorrect statement regarding the position of the heart.
    a. Atria lie posterior
    b. It causes blood to move vertically
    c. It rests on the diaphragm
    d. Ventricles lie anteriorly

17. The aortic arch has these branches coming off of it: (Choose all that apply.)
   a. Right subclavian artery
   b. Brachiocephalic artery
   c. Left subclavian artery
   d. Left common carotid artery
   e. Right common carotid artery

18. The subclavian artery changes to the axillary artery at:
   a. Inferior border of teres major
   b. Lateral border of 1st rib
   c. Popliteal fossa
   d. Femoral triangle
   e. None of the above

19. In which areas are the lymph nodes prevalent?
   a. Neck
   b. Axilla
   c. Groin
   d. Oral cavity
   e. Dorsum of the foot

20. Where does the descending aorta bifurcate?
   a. The L4 vertebrae
   b. The L2 vertebrae
   c. The iliac crest
   d. The aortic arch

21. What is another name for a heart attack?
   a. Congestive heart failure
   b. Cardiomyopathy
   c. Myocardial infarction
   d. Angina
   e. All of the above

22. How much longer is the esophagus than the trachea?
   a. 30 cm
   b. 15 cm
   c. 16–20 cm
   d. None of the above

23. How many lobes does the lung containing only 1 fissure have?
   a. Two
   b. Three
   c. Four
   d. One

24. Which of the following is correct, flowing from superior to inferior?
   a. Common iliac artery (a.) → internal iliac a. → femoral a
   b. External iliac a. → internal iliac a. → common iliac a
   c. Common iliac a. → external iliac a. → femoral a
   d. External iliac a. → common iliac a. → femoral a

25. The tricuspid valve connects what 2 chambers of the heart?
   a. Left atrium to right ventricle
   b. Left atrium to left ventricle
   c. Right atrium to right ventricle
   d. Right atrium to left ventricle

26. Which chamber of the heart has the thickest wall?
   a. Left atrium
   b. Right atrium
   c. Left ventricle
   d. Right ventricle

27. Which of the following is the correct path in which air flows from the inner respiratory system to the outer environment?
    a. Lungs → bronchi (left and right) → pharynx → larynx → trachea → nasal/oral cavity
    b. Lungs → bronchi (left and right) → trachea → larynx → pharynx → nasal/oral cavity
    c. Bronchi (left and right) → larynx → pharynx → trachea → nasal/oral cavity
    d. Lungs → bronchi (left and right) → pharynx → trachea → larynx → nasal/oral cavity

28. What part of the heart receives the cardiac veins that drain the heart itself?
    a. Opening of the coronary sinus
    b. Superior vena caval opening
    c. Inferior vena caval opening
    d. Fossa ovalis

29. Which artery supplies the esophagus?
    a. Splenic artery
    b. Superior mesenteric artery
    c. Common hepatic artery
    d. Left gastric artery

30. Between what 2 colons is the left colic flexure located?
    a. Ascending and transverse colon
    b. Descending and sigmoid colon
    c. Sigmoid and rectum
    d. None of the above

31. Which following statement is true?
    a. The esophagus is a muscular tube that lies anterior to the trachea
    b. The trachea is a cartilaginous and membranous tube extending from the pharynx
    c. The right and left auricles of the heart consist of irregular ridgelike projections of muscle called trabeculae carneae
    d. There are 5 types of blood vessels: artery, arterioles, capillaries, venules, and veins
    e. All of the above are false

32. Which lymphatic duct is responsible for draining the right half of the head, neck, chest, and the right upper limb:
    a. Thoracic duct   c. Common lymphatic duct
    b. Right lymphatic duct   d. Right thoracic duct

33. What are the 3 major venous openings of the right atrium?
    a. Superior vena cava, aortic artery, pulmonary artery
    b. Superior vena cava, inferior vena cava, coronary sinus
    c. Pulmonic semilunar valve, tricuspid valve, interatrial septum
    d. Superior vena cava, inferior vena cava, antrioventricular valve

34. Which statement is correct regarding coronary arteries?
    a. They bring oxygenated blood to the myocardium
    b. They bring deoxygenated blood to the myocardium
    c. They drain into the left ventricle
    d. They take deoxygenated blood away from the myocardium

35. What organs make up the urinary system?
    a. Urinary bladder, urethra, adrenal gland, kidney
    b. Urethra, urinary bladder, kidney, epididymis
    c. Adrenal gland, kidney, ureter, urinary bladder
    d. Kidney, ureter, urinary bladder, urethra

36. The venous sinuses lie in the:
    a. Corpus spongiosum   d. Testes
    b. Spongy urethra   e. 2 of these
    c. Corpus cavernosum

37. The pharynx has 3 parts, 1 being the _____, which is posterior to the

    _____.
    a. Hypopharynx, larynx
    b. Laryngopharynx, nasal cavity
    c. Oropharynx, nasal cavity
    d. Laryngopharynx, oral cavity
    e. Nasopharynx, oral cavity

38. The parts of the small intestine are arranged (from proximal to distal):
    a. Jejunum, ileum, duodenum
    b. Ileum, duodenum, jejunum
    c. Duodenum, ileum, jejunum
    d. Duodenum, jejunum, ileum
    e. Jejunum, duodenum, ileum

39. The ___ do(es) not exit at the porta hepatis:
    a. Hepatic veins   d. Left hepatic duct
    b. Portal vein   e. Right hepatic duct
    c. Hepatic artery

40. The cisterna chyli is a lymph node in the neck.
    a. True   b. False

41. Choose the false statement regarding the oral cavity.
    a. There are 32 teeth in adults
    b. Parotid, mandibular, and sublinginual are all salivary glands found
       here
    c. The tongue is skeletal muscle
    d. The 4 types of teeth are incisors, canines, premolars, and molars

42. Which is false regarding the left primary bronchus compared with the right primary bronchus?
    a. It is wider than the right primary bronchus
    b. It is longer than the right primary bronchus
    c. It enters the left lung at the hilus
    d. It makes a more acute angle with the trachea

43. Which of the following is not a lobe of the liver?
    a. Caudate lobe   c. Upper lobe
    b. Right lobe   d. Quadrate lobe

44. Choose the term(s) that describe(s) arteries. (Choose all that apply.)
    a. Smooth muscle
    b. Elastic fiber
    c. Cusps
    d. Thinner wall than corresponding vein

45. Blood capillaries are endothelial tubes that begin blindly.
    a. True   b. False

ANSWER KEY

For Unit 3 Practice Quizzes and Tests

3A Heart Practice Quiz
1. b
2. a, d
3. e
4. b
5. a, c, d
6. e
7. d, e
8. a and b
9. ac
10. ab
11. d
12. c
13. e, d, and ad
14. e
15. d
16. b
17. c

3B Heart Disease Practice Quiz
1. b, c
2. b, c
3. d
4. d
5. b
6. a, d
7. e

3C Blood Vessels/ Lymphatic System Practice Quiz
1. e
2. c, e
3. d
4. b, d
5. b, d
6. d

7. c, d
8. c
9. e
10. c

3D Vasculature of the Body Practice Quiz
1. ab
2. b
3. ac, e, c
4. ad, bc
5. c
6. d
7. ab
8. e
9. b
10. ac
11. ab
12. e
13. d
14. a, b
15. a, b
16. a, c
17. ab
18. ac
19. a
20. ac, b
21. a
22. ab
23. c
24. e
25. ad

3E Respiratory System Practice Quiz
1. d
2. d, e
3. a, b, d, e

4. c
5. b
6. e
7. b
8. c, d, e

3F Digestive System Practice Quiz
1. e
2. b
3. c
4. a
5. b, e
6. b, d
7. b, c
8. d
9. c

3G Urinary System Practice Quiz
1. c, d
2. b
3. e
4. b, e
5. d

3H&I Reproductive Systems Practice Quiz
1. a, d
2. b, c, e
3. a
4. c
5. c
6. a, b, c
7. d
8. c
9. c, d

3A–H Unit 3 Practice Test

1. bd, ab
2. ad, bc
3. a
4. e
5. b
6. e
7. b
8. a
9. ac
10. ab
11. bc
12. c
13. ad
14. cd
15. bd
16. ace
17. acd
18. d
19. c
20. d
21. a
22. ad
23. ac, b
24. a, b
25. ab
26. a
27. c
28. d
29. b, d
30. c
31. e
32. c
33. a
34. d, e
35. a, d, e
36. c, d
37. c
38. b
39. c, d, e
40. e
41. a, b, c
42. d
43. b
44. e
45. a, c, e
46. a
47. c
48. c
49. a
50. a, c, d
51. e
52. a, b, c
53. e
54. a, b
55. c, e
56. e
57. b, c, d, e
58. b
59. a
60. d
61. e
62. a, d
63. a, b, c
64. d, e
65. e
66. e
67. a

3A–H Student Written Practice Test for Unit 3

1. b, c
2. b
3. d
4. a, c
5. c
6. d
7. b
8. c
9. a, b, c
10. c
11. d
12. a
13. b, c, e
14. c
15. b, c
16. b
17. c, d
18. b
19. a, b, c
20. a
21. c
22. b
23. a
24. c
25. c
26. c
27. b
28. a
29. d
30. d
31. d
32. b
33. b
34. a
35. d
36. e
37. a
38. d
39. a
40. b
41. b
42. a
43. c
44. a, b
45. b